W9-BSQ-383

Weather Studies
Introduction to Atmospheric Science

Investigations Manual

2007 - 2008 and Summer 2008

Education Program

American Meteorological Society

The American Meteorological Society
Education Program

The American Meteorological Society (AMS), founded in 1919, is a **scientific and professional** society. Interdisciplinary in its scope, the Society actively promotes the development and dissemination of information on the atmospheric and related oceanic and hydrologic sciences. AMS has more than 10,000 professional members from more than 100 countries and over 135 corporate and institutional members representing 40 countries.

The Education Program is the initiative of the American Meteorological Society fostering the teaching of the atmospheric and related oceanic and hydrologic sciences at the precollege level and in community college, college and university programs. It is a unique partnership between scientists and educators at all levels with the ultimate goals of (1) attracting young people to further studies in science, mathematics and technology, and (2) promoting public scientific literacy. This is done via the development and dissemination of scientifically authentic, up-to-date, and instructionally sound learning and resource materials for teachers and students.

Online Weather Studies, a component of the AMS education initiative, is an introductory undergraduate meteorology course offered partially via the Internet in partnership with college and university faculty. **Online Weather Studies** provides students with a comprehensive study of the principles of meteorology while simultaneously providing classroom and laboratory applications focused on current weather situations. It provides real experiences demonstrating the value of computers and electronic access to time-sensitive data and information.

Developmental work for **Online Weather Studies** was supported by the Division of Undergraduate Education of the National Science Foundation under Grant No. DUE - 9752416.

This project was supported, in part, by the
National Science Foundation
Opinions expressed are those of the authors and
not necessarily those of the Foundation

Weather Studies: Investigations Manual 2007 - 2008 and Summer 2008
ISBN-10: 1-878220-81-0
ISBN-13: 978-1-878220-81-3
Copyright © 2007 by the American Meteorological Society

All rights reserved. No part of this publication may be reproduced, stored in a retrieval system, or transmitted, in any form or by any means, electronic, mechanical, photocopying, recording or otherwise. without the prior written permission of the publisher.

Published by the American Meteorological Society
45 Beacon Street, Boston, MA 02108

Cover photograph © 2003 Roger Edwards, www.skypix.ws

Welcome to *Weather Studies*

You are about to experience the excitement of real-world weather. This ***Weather Studies Investigations Manual*** is designed to introduce you to tools that enable you to explore, analyze, and interpret the workings of Earth's atmosphere.

This ***Investigations Manual*** is self-contained. Investigations draw from actual weather events to assist the learner in achieving their stated objectives. The investigations continually build on previous learning experiences to help the learner form a comprehensive understanding of the Earth system's atmospheric environment.

Additionally, case studies of current or recent atmospheric events are prepared in real time twice per week during fall and spring semesters in a schedule aligned with the ***Investigation Manual***'s table of contents (for Investigations 1A through 12B). These "Current Weather Studies" appear on the course website by noon, Eastern Time, on Monday and Wednesday for optional use by institutions operating on or near the AMS delivery timetable. They may be used as an alternative to the Manual's Applications portion of each activity or as a supplement to that printed section. Current Weather Studies accumulate each semester and remain available via a website archive. Studies expanding on ***Manual*** Investigations 13A through 15B are posted to the website at the beginning of each fall semester and available throughout the year.

Getting Started:

1. Your course instructor will provide you with the specific requirements of the course in which you are enrolled.

2. Your course instructor will provide you with the ***Weather Studies*** course website address. Record that address: ***http://***_____

3. When the page comes up, add this address to your list of bookmarks or favorites for future retrievals. Type the login ID and password provided by your instructor when prompted for full access to the contents of the page.

   Login ID: _____
   Password: _____

4. Explore the course website, noting its organization and the kinds of information provided. Throughout the year, 7 days a week, 24 hours a day, the meteorological products displayed are the latest available. You will learn to interpret and apply many of these products via the ***Weather Studies*** investigations.

5. Complete ***Investigation Manual*** activities and other course requirements, including use of Current Weather Studies, as directed by your instructor.

6. **Keep Current!** Keep up with the weather and your weather studies. Weather makes more sense if you watch it in action. Visit the ***Weather Studies*** website at least once a day if you can; more often when the weather is changing.

Weather Studies Investigations

1A   AIR PRESSURE AND WIND
    * Apply the hand-twist model to surface winds in highs and lows.

1B   SURFACE AIR PRESSURE PATTERNS
    * Draw isobars on a surface weather map and interpret isobar patterns.

2A   SURFACE WEATHER MAPS
    * Decode symbols on a surface weather map and interpret weather conditions.

2B   THE ATMOSPHERE IN THE VERTICAL
    * Plot a sounding on a Stüve diagram and compare to the U.S. Standard Atmosphere.

3A   WEATHER SATELLITE IMAGERY
    * Compare visible and infrared satellite images for weather interpretation.

3B   SUNLIGHT THROUGHOUT THE YEAR
    * Describe variations in solar radiation throughout the year by latitude.

4A   TEMPERATURE AND AIR MASS ADVECTION
    * Draw isotherms on a surface map and determine areas of warm and cold air advection.

4B   HEATING DEGREE-DAYS AND WIND CHILL
    * Calculate heating and cooling degree-days and determine wind chill.

5A   AIR PRESSURE CHANGE
    * Use a meteogram to describe changes in air pressure and other weather conditions with the passage of a warm front and a cold front.

5B   ATMOSPHERIC PRESSURE IN THE VERTICAL
    * Use the pressure block concept to demonstrate the influence of air density and air temperature on changes in air pressure with altitude.

6A   CLOUDS, TEMPERATURE, AND AIR PRESSURE
    * Use cloud-in-a-bottle demonstration and a sounding on a Stüve diagram to illustrate how temperature changes are related to pressure changes.

6B   RISING AND SINKING AIR
    * Use a Stüve diagram to illustrate dry and saturated adiabatic processes as air parcels ascend and descend in the atmosphere.

7A **PRECIPITATION PATTERNS**
* Locate and track areas of precipitation using weather radar operating in the reflectivity mode.

7B **DOPPLER RADAR**
* Describe the wind pattern detected by Doppler weather radar for a severe weather situation.

8A **SURFACE WEATHER MAPS AND FORCES**
* Examine the influence of forces on horizontal air motion near the Earth's surface.

8B **UPPER-AIR WEATHER MAPS**
* Describe the properties of a 500-mb map analysis and identify highs, lows, ridges, and troughs.

9A **WESTERLIES AND THE JET STREAM**
* Examine upper-air westerly wave patterns, the jet stream, and how these features influence midlatitude surface weather.

9B **¡EL NIÑO!**
* Describe atmospheric and oceanic conditions that accompany periodic warmings of the tropical Pacific Ocean.

10A **THE EXTRA-TROPICAL CYCLONE**
* Describe weather conditions surrounding the center of a typical extra-tropical cyclone in the midlatitudes.

10B **EXTRA-TROPICAL CYCLONE TRACK WEATHER**
* Compare weather conditions on either side of an extra-tropical cyclone in the midlatitudes.

11A **THUNDERSTORMS**
* Examine thunderstorms as they appear on visible, infrared, and water vapor satellite images.

11B **TORNADOES**
* Determine some of the characteristics of two intense tornadoes.

12A **HURRICANES**
* Plot a hurricane as it approaches a coastal area and assess the potential threats to life and property.

12B **HURRICANE WIND SPEEDS AND PRESSURE CHANGES**
* Explore the relationships between central sea-level pressures and wind speeds throughout the life of Hurricane Wilma.

13A WEATHER INSTRUMENTS AND OBSERVATIONS

      * Explore the data provided by the Automated Surface Observing System (ASOS) and access weather observations for the U.S. and the world via the Internet.

13B WEATHER FORECASTS

      * Describe the general elements of a weather forecast and explore the NWS office forecast made available for the public.

14A OPTICAL PHENOMENA

      * Describe interactions of light with atmospheric water droplets and ice crystals and the resulting optical phenomena.

14B ATMOSPHERIC REFRACTION

      * Describe how refraction of light varies with solar altitude and how it affects periods of daylight.

15A VISUALIZING CLIMATE

      * Portray statistical climate values on a climograph and compare climographs from various locations to explore climate controls.

15B LOCAL CLIMATIC DATA

      * Interpret data appearing in the *Local Climate Data, Annual Summary With Comparative Data* and determine how to access archived data.

Investigation 1A: AIR PRESSURE AND WIND

Objectives:

Air pressure is determined by the weight of the overlying air, and it varies from place to place and over time. Air moves in response to horizontal differences in air pressure, setting the stage for much of the weather we experience. Wind (air in motion) tends to blow from where the air pressure is relatively high to where the air pressure is relatively low. Once air is in motion, its speed and direction may be influenced by the rotation of the Earth on its axis (the Coriolis Effect) and/or contact with the Earth's surface (friction). The Coriolis Effect is important in large-scale weather systems (highs and lows of weather maps, for example) and friction affects winds blowing close to the Earth's surface below an altitude of about 1000 meters.

After completing this investigation, you should be able to:

- Describe the relationship between the pattern of relatively high and low air pressure areas (Highs or **H**s and Lows or **L**s) on a surface weather map and the direction of surface winds.
- Apply the "hand-twist" model of wind direction to the circulation in actual highs and lows.

Introduction:

Turn to Figure 1: High. Lightly draw a circle an inch or so in diameter around the large "H" appearing on the map. The "H" represents the location of highest pressure in a high-pressure area.

Place the map flat on your desk. If possible, stand up. (This exercise works better standing up.) Using your left hand (if you are right-handed) or your right hand (if you are left-handed), bring the thumb and fingertips of your hand close together and place them on the circle you drew as in the sketch to the right.

Rotate your hand slowly <u>clockwise</u>, as seen from above, and gradually spread out your thumb and fingertips as your hand turns. Be sure the map does not move. Practice this motion until you achieve as full a twist as you can comfortably. Place your thumb and fingertips back in the starting position on the circle. Mark and label the positions of your thumb and fingertips 1, 2, 3, 4, and 5, respectively.

Slowly rotate your hand <u>clockwise</u> while gradually spreading your thumb and fingertips. Go through about a quarter of your twisting motion. Stop, mark, and label (1 through 5) the positions of your thumb and fingertips on the map. Follow the same procedure in quarter steps until you complete a full twist.

Connect the successive numbered positions for each finger and your thumb using a smooth curved line. Place arrowheads on the ends of the lines to show the directions your thumb and fingertips moved. **The spirals represent the general flow of surface winds that occurs in a typical high-pressure system**.

Now turn to Figure 2: Low. Lightly draw a circle an inch or so in diameter around the large "L" shown on the map. The "L" marks the location of lowest pressure in a low-pressure area. Again, if possible, stand up. Place your non-writing hand flat on the map with your palm covering the circle as shown to the right.

Practice rotating your hand <u>counterclockwise</u> as seen from above while gradually pulling in your thumb and fingertips as your hand turns until they touch the circle. Be sure the map does not move. Practice until you achieve a maximum twist with ease.

Place your hand back in the spread position on the map. Mark and label the positions of your thumb and fingertips 1, 2, 3, 4, and 5, respectively.

Slowly rotate your hand <u>counterclockwise</u> while gradually drawing in your thumb and fingertips. Stopping after quarter turns, mark and label (1 through 5) the positions of your thumb and fingertips. Continue the twist until your thumb and fingertips are on the circle.

Connect the successive numbered positions for each finger and your thumb using a smooth curved line. Place arrowheads on the end of the lines to show the directions your fingertips and thumb moved. **The spirals represent the general flow of surface air that occurs in a typical low-pressure system**.

1. Which of the following best describes the surface wind circulation around the center of a high-pressure system (as seen from above)?
    a)   a counterclockwise and outward spiral
    b)   a counterclockwise and inward spiral
    c)   a clockwise and outward spiral
    d)   a clockwise and inward spiral

2. Which of the following best describes the surface wind circulation around the center of a low-pressure system (as seen from above)?
    a)   a counterclockwise and outward spiral
    b)   a counterclockwise and inward spiral
    c)   a clockwise and outward spiral
    d)   a clockwise and inward spiral

3. On your desk, repeat the hand twists for the high- and low-pressure system models. Note the vertical motions of the palm of your hand. For the high, the palm of your hand [(***rises***) (***falls***)] during the rotating motion.

4. In the case of the Low, the palm of your hand [(***rises***) (***falls***)] during the rotating motion.

5. The motions of your palms during these rotations represent the directions of vertical air motions in highs and lows. Vertical air motion in a High is therefore [(*__upward__*) (*__downward__*)].

6. In the case of the Low, vertical air motion is [(*__upward__*) (*__downward__*)].

7. Considering the complete air motions then, for the high-pressure system, air flows
    a) downward and outward in a clockwise spiral.
    b) downward and inward in a counterclockwise spiral.
    c) upward and outward in a clockwise spiral.
    d) upward and inward in a counterclockwise spiral.

8. In a low-pressure system, air flows
    a) downward and outward in a clockwise spiral.
    b) downward and inward in a counterclockwise spiral.
    c) upward and outward in a clockwise spiral.
    d) upward and inward in a counterclockwise spiral.

As directed by your course instructor, complete this investigation by either:

1. *Going to the Current Weather Studies link on the course website, or*
2. *Continuing to the Applications section for this investigation that immediately follows in this Investigations Manual.*

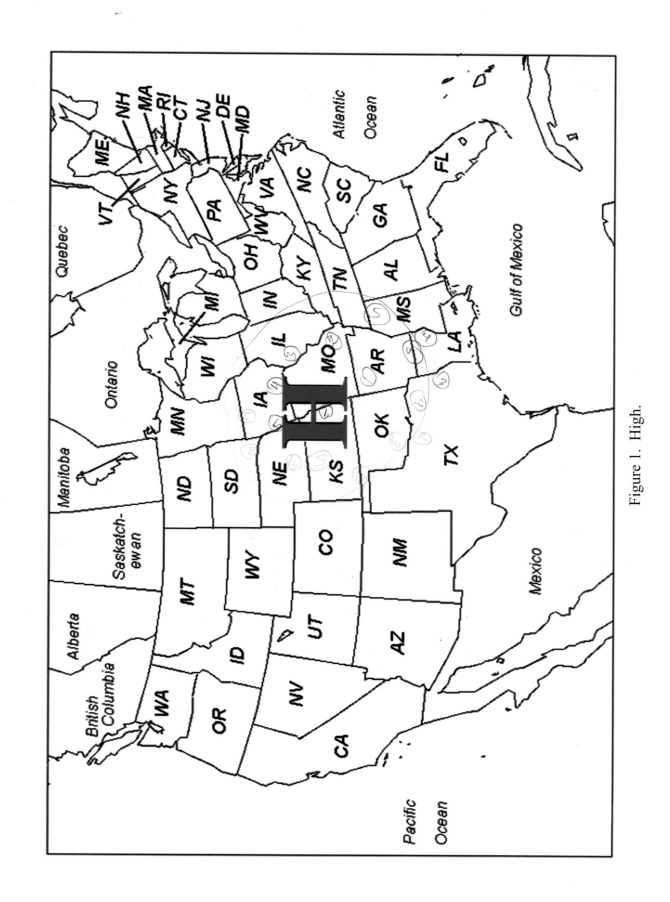

Figure 1. High.

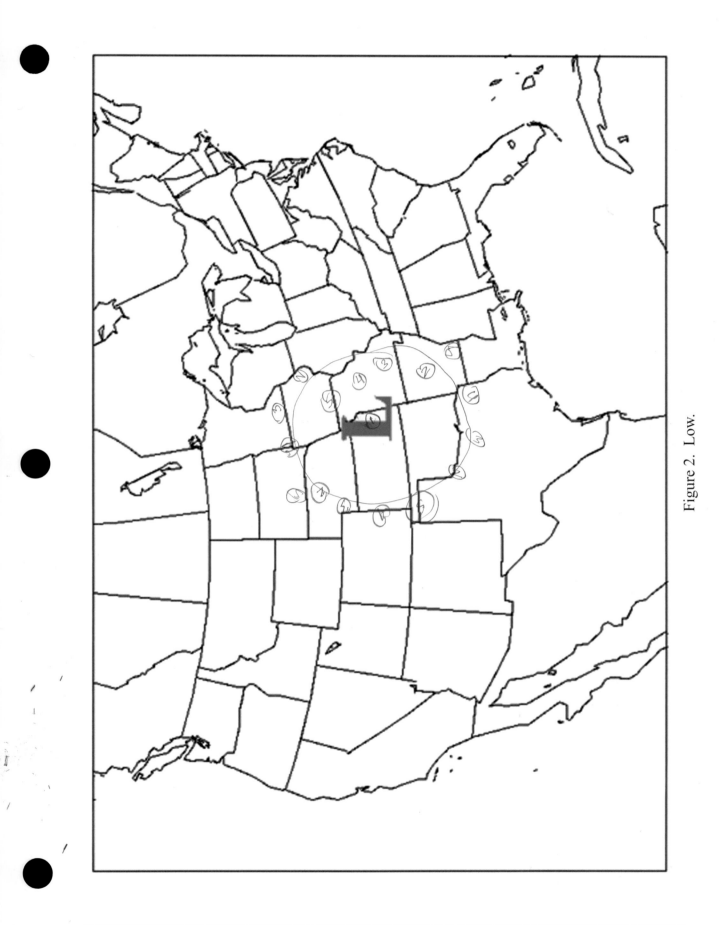

Figure 2. Low.

Investigation 1A: AIR PRESSURE AND WIND
Applications

In this portion of the investigation, we examine the patterns of winds exhibited on actual weather maps and compare them to the models.

The Figure 3 "U.S. - Data" map acquired from the course website depicts weather conditions at stations across the contiguous U.S. at 00Z 16 JAN 2006. [00Z is 5 hours ahead of Eastern Standard Time (EST), so the map portrays conditions on the evening of January 15th at 7 PM EST (6 PM CST, 5 PM MST and 4 PM PST).]

9.   Weather data at individual locations are plotted in a coded format called the "station model". The wind directions at reporting stations on the map are shown by the line (which can be thought of as an arrow shaft) which depicts the air flow <u>into</u> circles representing station locations. Wind at a station is named for the direction <u>from</u> which the air flows, *i.e.*, air coming towards the station from the south is a ***south*** wind. The wind direction at Amarillo, Texas, in the northern Texas "panhandle", was blowing <u>from</u> the [(***south***) (***west***)].

   (All reporting surface weather stations can be identified from the "Available Surface Stations" link on the course website and identities given in the "User's Guide". Also a map of National Weather Service offices can be found at: *http://www.wrh.noaa.gov/wrh/ forecastoffice_tab.php*)

10. Given the direction the wind at Amarillo was <u>from</u>, it was reported as a [(***south***) (***west***)] wind.

   The wind speed is given by a combination of long and short "feathers" on the direction shaft. [The station model will be explained in Investigation 2A. Further details for deciphering station data can be found in your User's Guide (linked from the course website).] At map time, Amarillo had a 10-knot wind (single, long feather). [A double circle without a direction shaft signifies calm conditions, such as Charleston, SC, and a shaft without feathers denotes 1-2 knots. A knot is a nautical mile per hour. One nautical mile is about 1.2 land miles.]

11. Mark a bold "**L**" about 1 cm in height centered on the station circle (without plotted data) in eastern South Dakota, representing Huron, SD. Compare the *hand-twist* model of a Low to the wind directions in the several-state area about this low-pressure center. Wind directions at stations across this region of the north-central U.S. show that, as viewed from above, the air spiraled generally [(***clockwise***) (***counterclockwise***)] around this low-pressure center, denoted by your **L**.

12. The wind directions around the low-pressure center also indicated that the air generally spiraled [(***inward toward***) (***outward from***)] the low-pressure center.

---

13. This wind flow pattern about the Low is [(*consistent with*) (*contrary to*)] the *hand-twist* model of a Low.

14. Mark a bold "**H**" about 1 cm in height centered in western Oregon near the coast. Compare the *hand-twist* model of a High to the wind directions reported by stations in the arc from Washington State through Idaho to western Nevada and northern California. Wind directions at these stations show that, as seen from above, the air spiraled generally [(*clockwise*) (*counterclockwise*)] around this high-pressure center, denoted by your **H**.

15. The wind directions around the high-pressure center also generally spiraled [(*inward toward*) (*outward from*)] the **H**.

16. This pattern is [(*consistent with*) (*contrary to*)] the *hand-twist* model of a High.

Note: the hand-twist model must be applied cautiously. Mountainous terrain in the western US and coastal influences can be predominant factors affecting wind directions as can low wind speeds.

Suggestions for further activities: Try your own detective game. You can call up the **Weather Studies** "U.S. Data" map on the course website and apply the hand-twist model to find High or Low centers. Then verify their positions by looking at the "Isobars, Fronts, Radar & Data" map.

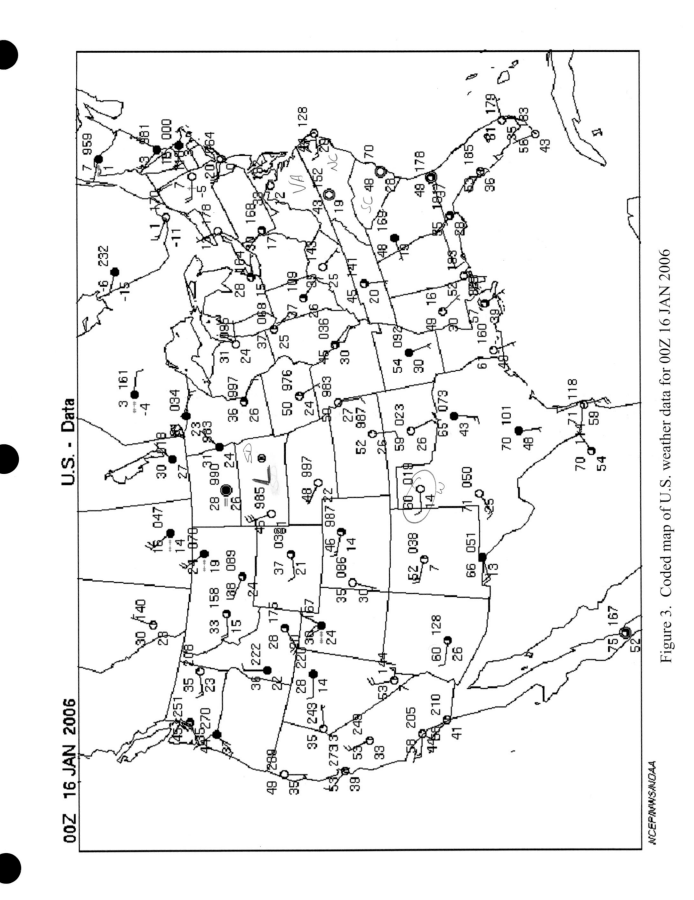

Figure 3. Coded map of U.S. weather data for 00Z 16 JAN 2006

Investigation 1B: SURFACE AIR PRESSURE PATTERNS

Objectives:

Whenever and wherever the air pressure changes from one place to another (producing an *air pressure gradient*, i.e., a change in air pressure over distance), the wind tends to blow from where the air pressure is relatively high to where the air pressure is relatively low. Knowing the patterns of pressure across the country is basic to understanding what the weather is and what it is likely to be wherever you live. By analyzing the reported values of air pressure across the country, the locations of weather map highs and lows can be found.

After completing this investigation, you should be able to:

- Draw lines of equal pressure (isobars) to show the pattern of surface air pressures across the nation at map time.
- Locate regions of relatively high and low air pressures on the same surface map.

Introduction:

Air pressure at any point on Earth's surface or in the atmosphere is equal to the weight per unit area of the atmosphere above that point. This means that air pressure decreases with increasing altitude. Hence, the higher the elevation of Earth's surface, the lower the air pressure.

Air pressures routinely reported on surface weather maps are values "corrected" to sea-level. That is, air pressure readings are adjusted to what they would be if the reporting station were actually located at sea-level. Adjustment of air pressure readings to the same elevation (sea-level) removes the influence of Earth's relief (topography) on air pressure readings. This adjustment allows comparisons of horizontal pressure differences that can lead to the recognition of pressure patterns. These patterns reveal existing broad-scale pressure areas that have a major influence on the weather.

Horizontal air pressure patterns on a weather map are revealed by drawing lines representing equal pressure. These lines are called *isobars* because every point on the same line has the same air pressure value. Each isobar separates stations reporting pressure values higher than that of the isobar from stations reporting pressure values lower than that of the isobar.

The Figure 1 surface map segment which follows shows air pressure in millibar (mb) units at various locations. [One millibar is equal to one hectopascal (hPa).] (Average midlatitude, sea-level air pressure is 1013.25 mb.) Consider each pressure value to be located at the center of the plotted number. The 1000-mb isobar has been drawn in two locations. Also, the 1004-mb isobar has been drawn. **Complete the pressure analysis by drawing the 996-,**

1008-, 1012-, 1016-, 1020-, 1024- and 1028-mb isobars. Label each isobar by writing the appropriate pressure value at its ends as shown.

1. By U.S. convention, isobars on surface weather maps are usually drawn using the same interval (the difference in air pressure value from one isobar to the next) as that used on the map segment. The isobar interval is __4__ mb. The isobar interval is selected so as to provide what is generally the most useful resolution of the field of data; too small an interval would clutter the map with too many lines and too great an interval would mean too few lines to adequately define the pattern.

2. On the Figure 1 map, all of the numbers on the map segment between the 1000-mb isobars are [(*less than*) (*equal to*) (*greater than*)] 1000 mb.

3. Also by U.S. convention, isobars drawn on surface weather maps follow a sequence of values which produce whole numbers when divided by 4 (e.g., 1000 ÷ 4 = 250). The sequence can be found by adding or subtracting 4 from 1000, then adding or subtracting another 4 from the resulting numbers, and so on. Which of the following numbers do not fit such a sequence of isobar values: 992, 994, 996, 1000, 1002, 1004, 1008, 1010, 1012? 992,996, 994, 1010, 1012

4. On surface weather maps, the strongest pressure gradients are oriented perpendicular to the isobars. And, the closer the isobars appear on a map, the stronger the pressure gradients. In Figure 1, the horizontal pressure gradient is stronger, *i.e.* pressure changes more rapidly with distance, across [(*Vermont to Maine*) (*central Wisconsin to central Michigan*)].

Tips on Drawing Isobars:

a. Always draw an isobar so that air pressure readings greater than the isobar's value are consistently on one side of the isobar and lower values are on the other side.

b. When positioning isobars, assume a steady pressure change between neighboring stations. For example, a 1012-mb isobar would be drawn between 1013 and 1010 about one-third the way from 1013.

c. Adjacent isobars tend to look alike. The isobar you are drawing will generally parallel the curves of its neighbors because horizontal changes in air pressure from place to place are usually gradual.

d. Continue drawing an isobar until it reaches the boundary of the plotted data or "closes" to form a loop by making its way to its starting point.

e. Isobars never stop or end within a data field, and they never fork, touch or cross one another.

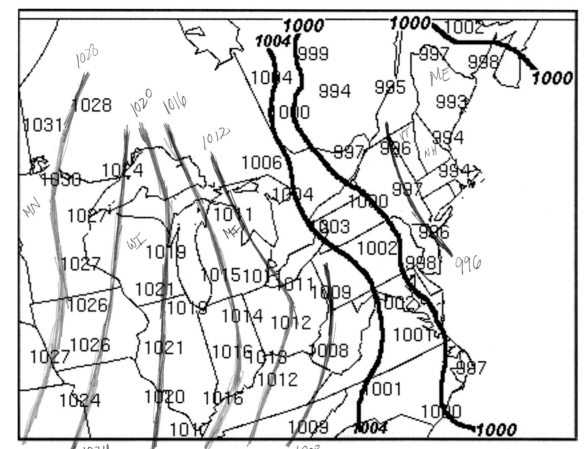

Figure 1. Map segment of sea-level air pressures. The 1000- and 1004-mb isobars have already been drawn.

f. Isobars cannot be skipped if their values fall within the range of air pressures reported on the map. Isobars must always appear in sequence; for example, there must always be a 1000-mb isobar between the 996-mb and 1004-mb isobars.

g. Always label all isobars.

As directed by your course instructor, complete this investigation by either:

1. ***Going to the Current Weather Studies link on the course website, or***
2. ***Continuing to the Applications section for this investigation that immediately follows in this Investigations Manual.***

Investigation 1B: SURFACE AIR PRESSURE PATTERNS
Applications

In this portion of the investigation, we analyze the pressure pattern existing over the coterminous U.S. at a particular time.

Investigation 1A dealt with the hand-twist model for relating wind directions to centers of high or low air pressure. This investigation demonstrates how those air pressure patterns can be determined and the high and low pressure centers found.

5.   The Figure 2 map, originating from the course website and labeled at the top center as "Pressures", displays atmospheric pressure values in whole millibars at the time of __00__ Z on __16 JAN 2006__ (date).

6.   The lowest reported air pressure on the map at St. Johns, New Brunswick, in eastern Canada, is [(**977**) (**988**) (**995**)] mb.

7.   The highest reported pressure is __1029__ mb at Arcata in northern California.

8.   The isobars in the conventional series that will be needed to complete the pressure analysis <u>between</u> those lowest and highest values on this map are: 992, __996__, __1000__, __1004__, __1012__, __1016__, __1020__, __1012__, __1024__, and __1028__. More than one isobar of the same value may need to be drawn if pressure values located in separate sections of the map area require it.

<u>Using a pencil</u>, **follow the steps below to draw the indicated isobars on this map to determine the pressure pattern that existed at the time the observations were made.** Consider each pressure value to be located at the center of the reported number. The 1016-mb and 1020-mb isobars have already been drawn in the eastern portion of the map.

Let us arbitrarily choose to complete the analysis of pressures by first drawing the 1012-mb isobar adjacent to the western 1016-mb isobar already on the map. The 1012-mb isobar enters the map data region between "1007" and "1016" in central Canada and across Lake Superior. It passes through the center of "1012" in Lower Michigan, between numbers heading southward to finally pass through the 1012s along the south Texas Gulf coast. Label the isobar value by printing *1012* at both ends of the isobar line you drew. Note, this isobar generally follows the curve of its neighboring 1016-mb isobar.

Moving westward from the 1012-mb isobar towards lower pressures, next draw the 1008-mb isobar. Arbitrarily starting in Canada near the 1012-mb isobar, the 1008-mb isobar curves southeastward and around to central Texas before heading back northward along the AZ-NM border, finally ending at the data edge back in central Canada. Label the isobar at the ends with its value, *1008*. (It is customary to end an isobar at the edge of the plotted values unless the plotted data indicate otherwise. Connecting the nearby ends of the 1008-mb isobar could be done and labeled in a break of the line.)

Complete the pattern of lower-valued isobars in the central U.S. These isobars, 1004 and 1000, will circle around to meet within the data field. Label each isobar line with its value at a break along the line rather than at the end. (Although it is an isobar value, 996 is represented at a single point, so no line needs to be drawn as separation of values below that.) Place a bold *L* in South Dakota where the lowest pressure value is plotted.

Complete the pressure analysis over the western quarter of the map for the appropriate isobar values listed in the sequence above (item 8). Beginning with 1012, the isobars increase in value westward. Add the isobars across the northeastern U.S. and Canada, to the east of the eastern 1016-mb isobar where the pressure values decrease from 1012 to 992 mb. (Again, 988 represents only a single point; hence, no line is needed.) Be sure to label each isobar with its value.

9. Figure 3 is the "Isobars, Fronts, Radar & Data" map for 00Z 16 JAN 2006. This map [(*does*) (*does not*)] represent the same time and date as the Figure 2 map of pressures you have just analyzed.

10. The time/date of the Figure 3 map [(*is*) (*is not*)] the same time/date as the U.S. Data map of national weather conditions you used for the hand-twist patterns in Investigation 1A.

11. Compare your hand-drawn pressure analysis on the Figure 2 map with the analysis made by computer on the Figure 3 map. Some of the differences between your analysis and that shown can be explained by the fact that the computer analysis is based on data from a larger number of stations. Note the position of the **L** in east-central South Dakota and the **H** near the California-Oregon border on the Figure 3 "Isobars, Fronts, Radar & Data" map. These positions [(*are*) (*are not*)] near the approximate locations of the **L** and **H** you positioned in the Investigation 1A map used for the hand twist model.

12. These **L** and **H** positions [(*are*) (*are not*)] also the approximate locations of locally lowest and highest plotted air pressure values you showed with your isobar analysis of the Figure 2 "Pressures" map.

The map you have just analyzed represents atmospheric conditions across the country at the time of those observations. Meteorologists (or their computer systems) analyze pressure patterns as you have done to locate centers of storminess and fair weather. In Investigation 2A we will look at the more complete set of weather conditions reported in the station models.

Suggestions for further activities: The course website routinely delivers unanalyzed ("Pressures") and analyzed ("Isobars & Pressures") surface pressure maps (under the **Surface** section on the website). Practice drawing isobars by calling up and printing out the unanalyzed version. Use the analyzed map as your "answer key". You might try this "detective scheme" of analyzing surface air pressures to find storms or broad-scale air masses that are mentioned in the news.

To practice more on drawing isopleths (lines of a constant value) in fields of numbers beginning with simple patterns, go to: *http://cimss.ssec.wisc.edu/wxwise/contour/*. This page also examines the set of isolines in addition to isobars that are used in weather map analysis.

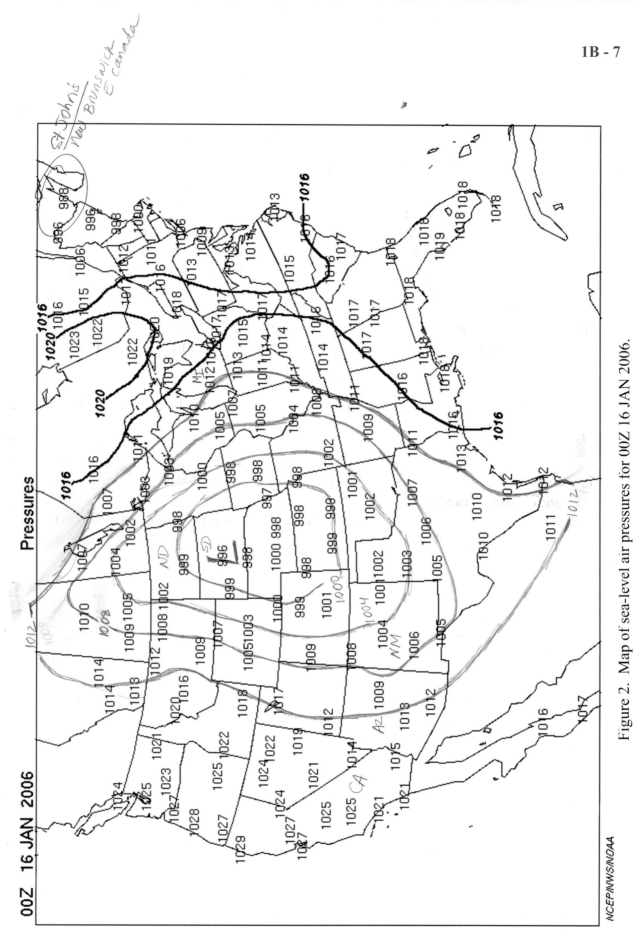

Figure 2. Map of sea-level air pressures for 00Z 16 JAN 2006.

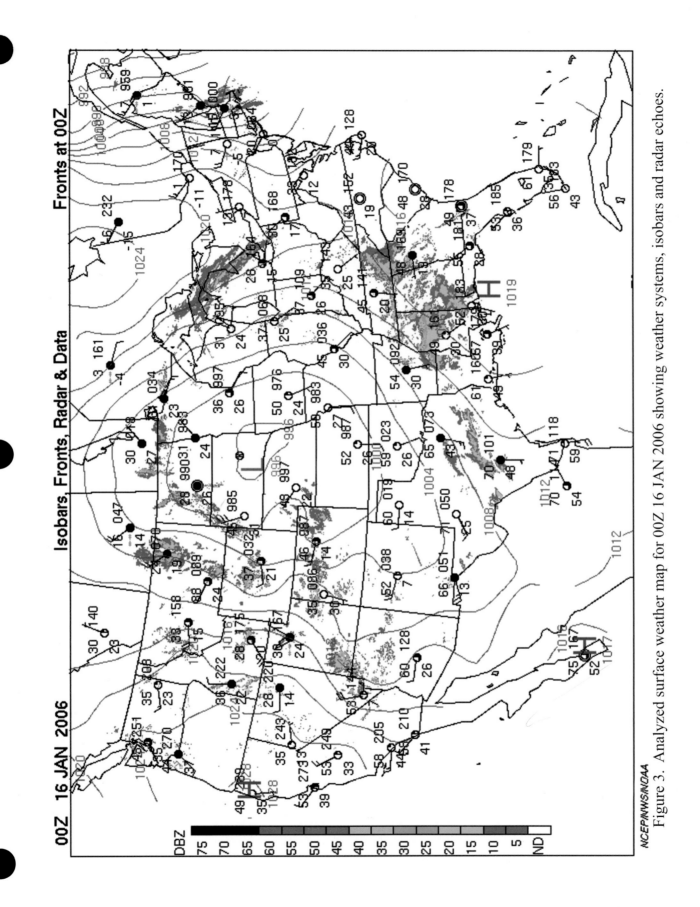

Figure 3. Analyzed surface weather map for 00Z 16 JAN 2006 showing weather systems, isobars and radar echoes.

Investigation 2A: SURFACE WEATHER MAPS

Objectives:

Weather is the state of the atmosphere at a particular time and place, mainly with respect to its impact upon life and human activity. It is defined by various elements including air temperature, humidity, cloudiness, precipitation, visibility, air pressure, and wind speed and direction. The surface weather map is a useful tool for depicting weather conditions over broad areas.

After completing this investigation, you should be able to:

- Decode the symbols appearing on a surface weather map and describe weather conditions at various locations on the map.
- Identify fronts appearing on the map, the weather likely to be occurring on either side of a front, and the motion of fronts.
- Describe general relationships between wind patterns and the high and low air pressure centers shown on weather maps.

Introduction:

1. Examine the surface weather map presented in Figure 1 of this investigation. The weather map symbols shown are those commonly seen on television and in newspapers. The H's and L's identify centers of relatively high or low air pressure compared to their surroundings. Moving outward horizontally in any direction from the red L located in Lower Michigan, air pressure would [(*increase*) (*decrease*)].

2. Moving outward horizontally from the blue H positioned in Texas, air pressure would [(*increase*) (*decrease*)].   (from H to L?)

3. The thick curved lines with triangles (spikes) and/or semi-circles on the map are air mass boundaries. In the atmosphere, broad expanses of air with generally uniform temperature, humidity, and density come in contact with other masses of air having different temperature, humidity, and density characteristics. Because air masses of different densities do not readily mix, the boundaries separating air masses tend to remain distinct. These boundaries, called *fronts*, typically separate warm and cold air. The leading edge of advancing cold air is a cold front and, as shown in the lower part of Figure 1, is signified by blue spike symbols which are pointing in the direction toward which the cold front is moving. The leading edge of advancing warm air is a warm front and is signified by red semi-circles on the side of the front's movement. The front plotted in the Southeastern U.S. is a [(*cold*) (*warm*)] front.

4. According to the map, persons living in South Carolina can expect [(*colder*) (*warmer*)] weather after the front passes.

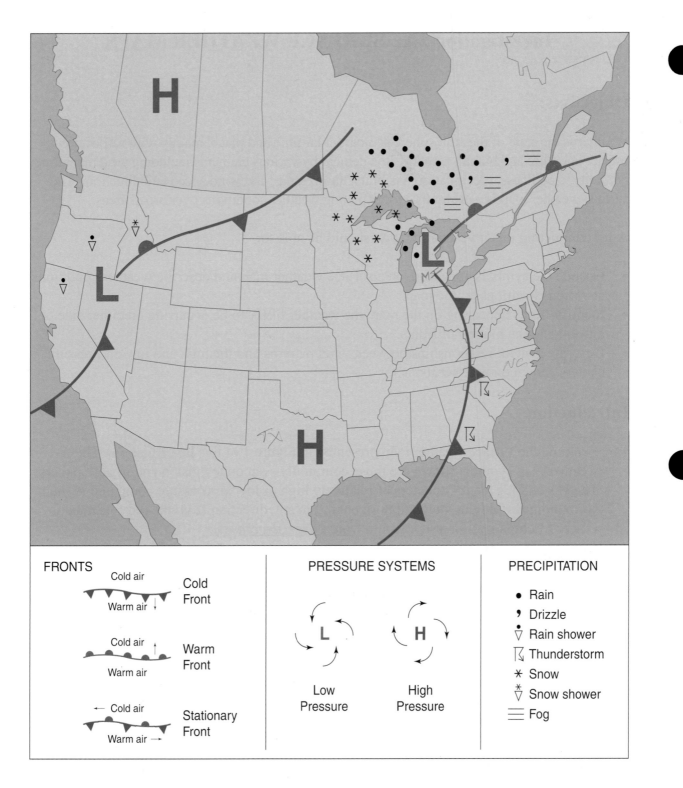

Figure 1. Idealized surface weather map showing some common map symbols.

5. Precipitation is depicted on maps by a variety of symbols including dots or periods to represent [(*rain*) (*snow*)].

6. Two or three, whole or broken, horizontal lines symbolize [(*hail*) (*fog*) (*blowing snow*)]. Some weather maps display weather conditions at individual weather stations by the use of a station model. One such model is shown in the course website User's Guide, available on the website under User's Guide, Extras, *Map Symbols*. Refer to the model legends to interpret the plotted weather data in the red box of the map segment below:

7. Temperature: ___15___ °F.

8. Dewpoint: ___11___ °F.

9. Wind direction is shown by the "arrow" shaft drawn into the circle representing the station. North is to the top on the map and east is to the right. Wind is always named for the direction *from which* it blows. In the above depiction, the wind direction is from the

    ___North___ .

10. Wind speed is rounded off to the nearest 5 knots (1 knot equals 1.2 miles per hour) and is symbolized by "feathers" drawn on the clockwise side of the wind-direction shaft. A full feather represents 10 knots and half feather indicates 5 knots. A pennant flag indicates 50 knots and a circle drawn around the station circle signifies calm conditions. In this case, the reported wind speed is ___10___ knots.

11. Air pressure (adjusted to sea level) is reported as a coded number to the nearest tenth of a millibar (mb). To decipher the plotted pressure value, first place a decimal point between the second and third numbers from the left. Then add either a "9" or "10" to the left so that the resulting number falls within the range of air pressures that could

occur at sea level (usually between 960 mb and 1050 mb). For example, a plotted value of 126 represents 1012.6 mb and 863 denotes 986.3 mb. The air pressure reported above is __1000__ mb. *nearest 10th?*

12. Sky cover is reported inside the station circle and is expressed as a number of eighths or other descriptors (scattered, broken, overcast, obscured). As examples, an empty circle indicates no clouds, and a half-shaded circle means four-eighths of the sky is cloud-covered. According to the User's Guide, <u>Extras</u>, *Map Symbols*, the reported cloud cover is _____.

13. Current weather is plotted at the "9 o'clock" position on the station model (to the left of the station circle) using a variety of symbols representing the particular weather conditions. The reported current weather is ____*15*____. *?*

As directed by your course instructor, complete this investigation by either:

1. *Going to the Current Weather Studies link on the course website, or*
2. *Continuing to the Applications section for this investigation that immediately follows in this Investigations Manual.*

Weather Studies: Investigations Manual 2007-2008

Investigation 2A: SURFACE WEATHER MAPS
Applications

The weather maps used in this course and available from the course website typically have greater detail than those seen on television or printed in newspapers. The Figure 2 "Isobars, Fronts, Radar, & Data" 12Z 29 JAN 2006 (7 AM EST, 6 AM CST, 5 AM MST, 4 AM PST, etc.) surface weather map has plotted station models as well as locations of centers of high and low pressure from a computer analyzed pressure pattern, fronts, and radar reports of precipitation.

14. The station models depict weather conditions across the country at that time. The center of the storm system, denoted by the lowest pressure, is marked by an "**L**" shown along the Wisconsin-Illinois border. The winds in the several-state area surrounding the Low center were generally [(***clockwise***) (***counterclockwise***)].

15. The pattern of winds around the Low center were also generally directed [(***inward***) (***outward***)] relative to the center, consistent with the hand-twist model of a Low presented in Investigation 1A.

16. The heavy line with triangles from the Wisconsin-Illinois Low extending southward to Louisiana marked the position of a [(***cold***) (***warm***) (***stationary***)] front. This front was the leading edge of a cooler air mass.

17. The triangle symbols along the front show that the cooler air was moving generally toward the [(***east and southeast***) (***west and northwest***)].   Triangles = direction from which wind blows

18. The heavy line with half-circles from the Low eastward along Lake Erie's northern shore marked the position of a [(***cold***) (***warm***) (***stationary***)] front. Another such front is shown in west-central Canada extending from another developing low-pressure system.

The heavy line with half-circles and triangle symbols on opposite sides of the line that weaves its way from the Canadian Low northwestward to the map boundary marked the position of a stationary front indicating little or no movement of the front.   Heavy dashed orange lines, including those in Texas and in the northern Plains states, mark "troughs" or extensions of lower pressure.

19. Observe the station model for Little Rock, in central Arkansas, on the Figure 2 map. The station model showed an air temperature of [(***63***) (***50***)] degrees F, and a dewpoint of 47 degrees F.

20. At Little Rock, surface winds were generally from the [(***north-northwest***) (***west-southwest***)] at 10 knots.

(10 + 11₀1)

21. The coded pressure value at Little Rock was plotted as "*111*", meaning that the actual air pressure corrected to sea level was [(***111.0***) (***1111.0***) (***1011.1***)] mb.

22. The sky cover was shown as [(***clear***) (***partly cloudy***) (***overcast***)].

23. The weather symbol for current conditions at a station, two short, horizontal lines, (in the 9 o'clock position of the station model) as shown at Los Angeles and San Diego, California and also at Fargo, ND, Huron, SD, and Des Moines, IA, indicated that those stations were experiencing [(***rain***) (***snow***) (***fog***)].

24. The temperature at Los Angeles was 49 °F and the dewpoint was __50__ °F. Equivalent temperature and dewpoint values mean that the air at Los Angeles was saturated with water vapor (100% relative humidity) producing this weather condition. The air was also very close to saturation at the other stations noted in item 23 reporting the same weather condition.

25. The weather symbol for the current conditions at Atlanta, Georgia (composed of dots) signified _____Rain_____.

26. The 12Z map has shaded areas indicating where NOAA's National Weather Service radar sites have detected signal returns (*radar echoes*) primarily from precipitation. Radar can survey the sky for a more complete picture than may be sensed at individual stations. On surface maps, the intensity of the radar echoes, which is related to the intensity of the precipitation, is shown by shadings using the scale near the left border of the map (with intensity increasing upward). Assuming the shaded areas do represent precipitation, precipitation probably was occurring:

    a) (***in a broad arc over the eastern U.S. from Lake Superior to the Gulf of Mexico***)
    b) (***from southwestern Washington State to northern California***)
    c) (***widely scattered over the western states and the East Coast***)
    d) (***in all these locations***).

The on-screen purple shadings are often "false" radar echoes produced by early morning atmospheric conditions, common on 12Z maps such as this, and are not really detecting precipitation. Also, patches of dots with shadings on the lower end of the intensity scale may signify light precipitation that evaporates before reaching the ground.

Suggestions for further activities: The course website also delivers maps with just the station models plotted, "U.S. Data" (as used in Investigation 1A), or regional maps such as "Southeast US - Data" (under the **Surface** section on the website). You might call up the "State Surface Data - Text" and plot the station models for your state to compare with the regional plot drawn by computer.

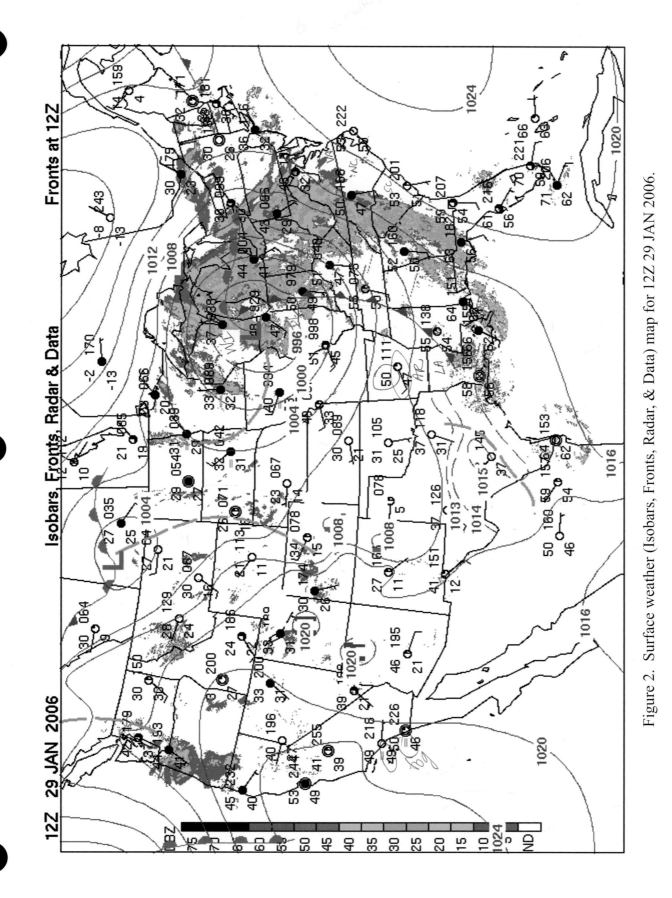

Figure 2. Surface weather (Isobars, Fronts, Radar, & Data) map for 12Z 29 JAN 2006.

The National Weather Service provides information of current weather conditions, especially highlighting threatening and/or severe weather. Go to the course website under **Watches, Warnings, Advisories, and Forecasts** section and click on "Current NWS Weather Watches and Warnings". Click on a state to find its reporting sites, which may be useful to locate the stations, as well as to obtain the current observations and forecast conditions. You may wish to note or "bookmark/favorite places" this site for future reference.

One can also find an explanation of frontal symbols and the station model information by clicking on "NWS Surface Analyses" on the Surface section of the website. Below the blue area containing the latest map, are links: *Description of Station Plot Data* and *Description of Surface Front Types*.

Investigation 2B: THE ATMOSPHERE IN THE VERTICAL

Objectives:

The atmosphere has a vertical as well as horizontal dimensions. For a more complete understanding of weather, knowledge of atmospheric conditions in the vertical is necessary. Air, a highly compressible fluid, held to the planet by gravity, thins rapidly with increasing altitude. The atmosphere is heated primarily from below, is almost always in motion, and contains a substance (water) that continually undergoes changes in phase.

After completing this investigation, you should be able to:

- Describe the vertical temperature of the atmosphere in the troposphere (the "weather" layer) and in the lower stratosphere.
- Compare the temperature profile specified by the U.S. Standard Atmosphere with actual soundings of the lower atmosphere.

Introduction:

The diagram below shows the average vertical temperature profile of essentially the entire atmosphere as a function of the altitude above Earth's surface. Figure 1 is a Stüve diagram, a temperature/pressure graph of the lower portion of the atmosphere. Figure 1 focuses on the lowest 16 km of the figure below (that is, the troposphere plus the lower stratosphere).

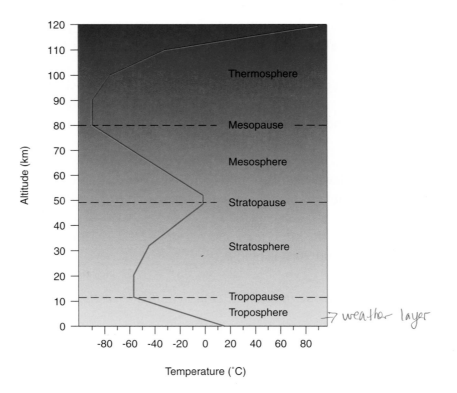

1. **Plot the data points given below on Figure 1 and connect adjacent points with solid straight lines.** Note: altitude is plotted along the right vertical axis increasing from bottom to top, and temperature is plotted along the horizontal axis increasing from left to right.

Altitude (km)	Temperature (°C)
0	+ 15.0
11	− 56.5
16	− 56.5

You have drawn the temperature profile of the lower portion of the "U.S. Standard Atmosphere". The Standard Atmosphere describes representative or average conditions of the atmosphere in the vertical. According to the the vertical temperature profile diagram, the temperature profile from the surface to 11 km depicts the lowest layer of the atmosphere, called the ___Troposphere___.

2. The lower portion of the ___Stratosphere___ is evident above 11 km in Figure 1 where temperatures remain steady with increasing altitude.

3. The troposphere is characterized generally by decreasing temperature with altitude, significant vertical motion, appreciable water vapor, and weather. According to the Standard Atmosphere data provided in item 1 above, the temperature within the troposphere decreases with altitude at the rate of __−41.5__ C degrees per km.
   −56.5 −15 = −41.5

4. Air pressure is plotted along the left vertical axis of the figure in millibars (mb), with pressure decreasing upward as it does in the atmosphere. Air pressure, which is very close to 1000 mb at sea level in the Standard Atmosphere, decreases most rapidly with altitude in the lowest part of the atmosphere. The diagram shows that an air pressure of 500 mb (about half that at sea level) occurs at an altitude of about __4.75__ km.

5. Because air pressure is determined by the weight of the overlying air, half of the atmosphere by weight or mass is above the altitude at which the air pressure is 500 mb and half of it is below that altitude. In other words, half of the atmosphere by weight or mass is within __2__ km of sea level.

6. Other pressure levels can be found similarly. For example, 10% of the atmosphere is located above the altitude where the pressure is [(___100___) (___900___)] mb.

7. In other words, at the altitude of approximately _____ km, 10% of the atmosphere by weight is above and 90% is below.

As directed by your course instructor, complete this investigation by either:

1. *Going to the Current Weather Studies link on the course website, or*
2. *Continuing to the Applications section for this investigation that immediately follows in this Investigations Manual.*

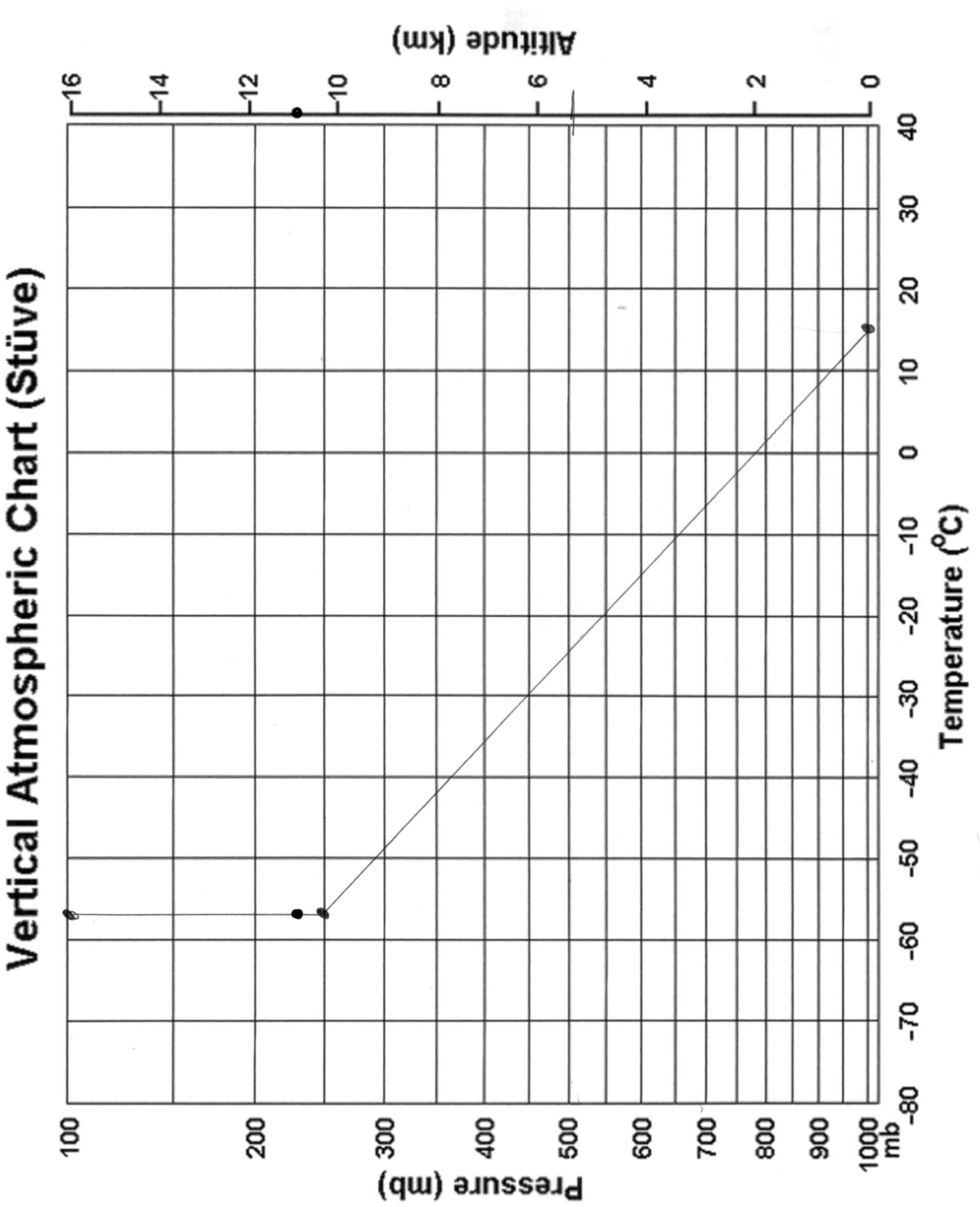

Figure 1. Vertical atmospheric chart (Stüve diagram).

Investigation 2B: THE ATMOSPHERE IN THE VERTICAL
Applications

8. Upper air observational data are collected twice a day at nearly 70 U.S. stations. The data from selected stations can be viewed via the course website's "Upper Air" section in tabular, chart, and map form. The following data are from a morning rawinsonde observation at Green Bay, Wisconsin (GRB), at 12Z 31 January 2006, two days later than Investigation 2A's Figure 2 map.

Pressure (mb)	Temperature (°C)	Altitude (m)
100	−59.1	15970
200	−55.9	11560
263	−55.5	9808
300	−48.7	8960
500	−23.3	5420
700	−10.7	2883
850	−8.7	1379
986	−6.1	214

The station pressure (computed for the level of the station elevation) at Green Bay, Wisconsin (GRB) at 12Z 31 January 2006 was 986 mb and the surface temperature was −6.1 °C, equivalent to 21 °F. This temperature was [(*4*) (*10*) (*16*)] Fahrenheit degrees cooler than the 37 °F temperature at the same time of day 48 hours earlier at Green Bay (see Green Bay station model on the Investigation 2A Figure 2 map). Green Bay was experiencing cooler air following the passage of a storm system and cold front plotted on the Investigation 2A map.

On the Figure 1 atmospheric chart, plot the reported temperatures at the pressure levels given in the table above from 986 mb at Earth's surface at the Green Bay weather station, upwards to 100 mb. [*Note:* The pressure scale given on the left side of the graph decreases upward as does pressure in the open atmosphere!] Connect the adjacent plotted points with <u>dashed</u> straight lines.

9. The tropopause, the boundary separating the troposphere from the stratosphere, is located where the temperature begins to be either nearly steady with altitude (*isothermal*) or to increase with altitude (a *temperature inversion*). The Green Bay sounding you plotted shows an essentially isothermal layer from 263 mb upward to 100 mb. Consequently, the Green Bay (GRB) temperature/pressure values at the time of observation indicated the tropopause was located at 263 mb. Compared to the Standard Atmosphere temperature profile you drew in Item 1, the vertical depth ("thickness") of the troposphere from the surface to the tropopause over GRB at 12Z 31 January 2006 was [(***greater than***) (***equal to***) (***less than***)] standard conditions.

10. Compare the Standard Atmosphere and the actual GRB temperature profiles you just plotted. The troposphere over GRB when the actual observation ("sounding") was made was generally [(**_warmer_**) (**_colder_**)] than Standard Atmosphere conditions.

Figure 2 is the plotted Stüve diagram for Green Bay (GRB) at 1200Z 31 January 2006 from the course website (**Upper Air**, "Stüves for Selected Cities in the U.S."). The Stüve diagram is one of a variety of vertical diagrams used in meteorology to display atmospheric soundings acquired by rawinsondes. The temperature and pressure scales are the same as those in the chart on which you drew part of the Standard Atmosphere and the Green Bay sounding. (You have already plotted data on a Stüve diagram!) In addition to the temperature and pressure lines that are used in this investigation, other sets of lines appear; these will be referred to in later investigations. Soundings for temperature and dewpoint for GRB are plotted as "curves" on the Figure 3 diagram. The plotted curve to the right with higher values is the temperature profile. It is plotted by computer using all the data points reported from the radiosonde observation. Note that temperatures over Green Bay on this day decrease going upward through much, but not all, of the troposphere. You can compare the Figure 3 Stüve temperature profile for GRB with the profile you drew for the same time using fewer data points.

11. The temperature profile plotted on the Figure 2 Green Bay Stüve shows a pattern where the temperature [(**_decreased_**) (**_remained the same_**) (**_increased_**)] from 986 mb at the surface up to about 945 mb. A similar pattern of air temperature change with increasing altitude within layers of the atmosphere is referred to as a temperature inversion.

12. From about 945 to 850 mb, the temperature [(**_decreased_**) (**_remained the same_**) (**_increased_**)] as generally expected in the troposphere. Layers from 850 to about 770 mb and again from 700 to about 670 mb are characterized by temperature inversions.

13. From the data listed in the table above for the GRB rawinsonde observation at 12Z 31 January 2006, the pressure of 500 mb occurred at an altitude of ___5574___ m.

14. In the Standard Atmosphere 500 mb is found at 5574 m (18,289 ft.) The 500-mb pressure level over GRB at the time of observation occurred at a [(**_lower_**) (**_higher_**)] altitude than it does in the Standard Atmosphere. This typically occurs whenever the troposphere below a pressure level is generally colder than the Standard Atmosphere model.

Note: Several additional items of information from the sounding are listed across the top margin of the Stüve diagram for each station. They will not be addressed in this Investigation. Wind observations at various levels are plotted to the right of the diagram. In this Figure 3 GRB sounding, the surface wind was from the west at about 5 knots. At 263 mb, the wind is shown as 100 knots (2 pennants) from the northwest.

Suggestions for further activities: Try plotting Stüve diagrams from the blank Stüve form in the Extras section of the website using text data from the "Upper Air Data – Text" for the station nearest you. Then associate the atmospheric temperature patterns with the surface weather map for same time.

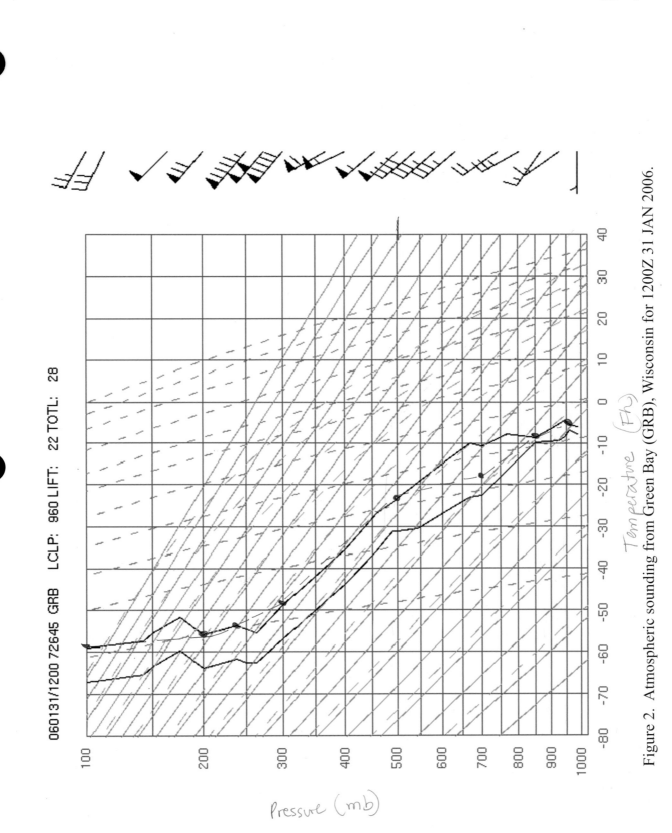

060131/1200 72645 GRB   LCLP: 960 LIFT: 22 TOTL: 28

Temperature (F°)

Pressure (mb)

Figure 2. Atmospheric sounding from Green Bay (GRB), Wisconsin for 1200Z 31 JAN 2006.

You can obtain Stüve diagrams for locations in the U.S. and around the world not provided by the course website by going to a Plymouth State University (PSU) website. Following the table of cities on the "Stüves for Selected Cities." page, use the link ("click here" near bottom of page) for additional Stüve diagrams. Once at the PSU site, click on "map" and select a region to find a station identifier. For example, try Antarctica and compare a station sounding there to Green Bay or Anchorage.

Investigation 3A: WEATHER SATELLITE IMAGERY

Objectives:

Orbiting satellites are platforms carrying sensors that make it possible for us to "look" down on the atmosphere and underlying Earth surfaces. It is obvious from the broad expanses seen from their vantage points that fair and stormy weather are somehow related. Clear areas and giant swirls of clouds fit together as part of the canopy of air that thinly envelops the planet. Over time, weather systems can be observed as they evolve, swirl, and voyage across Earth's surface. With the satellite views, areas showing signs of potential or actual hazardous weather conditions can be carefully monitored.

Satellite images are produced by sunlight that is reflected (and scattered) by the Earth-atmosphere system and by radiation that is emitted by that same system.

After completing this investigation, you should be able to:

- Distinguish among the different types of weather-satellite imagery and describe the information they can provide.
- Interpret probable atmospheric conditions from weather-satellite imagery.

Introduction:

The accompanying images in Figure 1 were acquired simultaneously from sensors aboard an Earth geostationary satellite in orbit about 36,000 km (22,300 mi) above a spot on the equator at 75 degrees West Longitude. A geostationary (or more correctly geosynchronous) satellite orbits toward the east at the same rate as the Earth rotates eastward so that the satellite appears to be hovering above the same place on the Earth's surface.

1. Continental outlines are superimposed on the satellite images for orientation. A small "+" is marked in the center of each image approximately where the horizontal equator intersects the vertical 75°W longitude line. This marks the location of the sub-satellite point, that is, the spot on the Earth's surface directly under the satellite. The sub-satellite point is located in [(**_South_**) (**_North_**)] America.

One satellite image was produced by reflected sunlight and the other by infrared radiation. **Keeping in mind that the Earth radiates infrared radiation continually (day and night), label the appropriate images as "visible" or "infrared".**

2. On the visible satellite image, the Sun's rays are from the general direction of [(**_east_**) (**_west_**)].

3.   Because the Earth rotates eastward, local time at the sub-satellite point is in the [(***morning***) (***afternoon***)].

4.   Using reflected visible light the satellite sensor "sees" clouds and surface features as we do. In the visible image, the general appearance of all the clouds in the illuminated portion of the image is [(***white***) (***dark***)].

5.   The broad expanse of clouds across most of northern South America illustrates this point. Compared to the land and ocean, clouds have a [(***lower***) (***higher***)] albedo.

6.   The broad-scale organization of clouds provides clues as to the types and locations of various weather systems. On the visible satellite image, a large swirl of clouds characterized a large storm system that is evident over [(***the North Atlantic Ocean***) (***the Caribbean Sea***)]. Another swirl (of opposite rotation) is located over the southern Atlantic Ocean.

7.   An important advantage of infrared imagery is that it can be used to observe the planet both day and night. The image produced by infrared radiation emitted by the Earth-atmosphere system demonstrates that there are clouds in [(***only the daylight portion***) (***both the daylight and night portions***)] of the Earth view shown.

8.   In the infrared image, relatively warm land and sea surfaces appear dark, cooler low cloud tops are gray, and cold high cloud tops are shown as bright white. Therefore, the contrast in the appearance of blobs of clouds across northern and central South America versus those over the middle latitude ocean west of South America indicates that the oceanic cloud tops are at relatively [(***low***) (***high***)] level.

9.   In the infrared image, we can infer that the swirl of clouds associated with the storm system north of the Gulf of Mexico Coast has relatively [(***high***) (***low***)] tops.

As directed by your course instructor, complete this investigation by either:

   1. Going to the Current Weather Studies link on the course website, or
   2. Continuing to the Applications section for this investigation that immediately follows in this Investigations Manual.

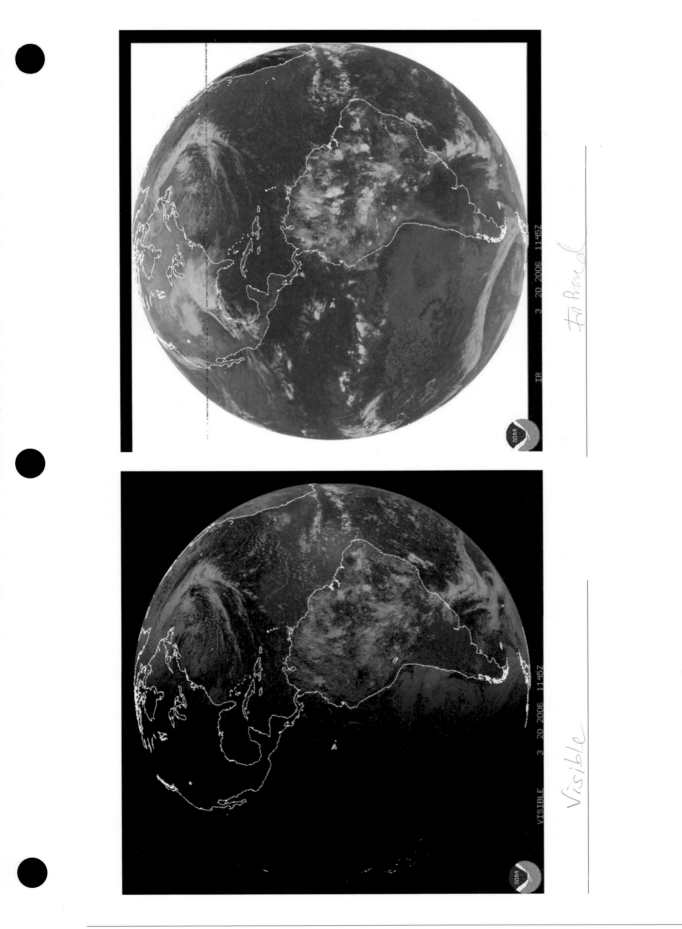

Figure 1. Geostationary satellite images from 1145Z 20 MAR 2006.

Investigation 3A: WEATHER SATELLITE IMAGERY
Applications

As you have undoubtedly noticed, from the winter solstice (about Dec. 21st) to the summer solstice (about Jun. 21st), the days get longer (and vice versa for the other half of the year). That is, the period of daylight increases in the Northern Hemisphere during the winter and spring seasons. At the same time, the daily path of the sun moves progressively higher in the sky so that the rays of the mid-day sun reach the surface with increasing intensity. Greater solar heating, due to both the changing elevation of the sun's path in the sky and the increase in the duration of the daylight period, overcomes winter cooling and produces a general warming of the Northern Hemisphere and its atmosphere as we progress from one month to the next.

Figure 2 is the *visible* satellite display for the evening, 0015Z on 06 FEB 2006 (6:15 PM Central Standard Time on 5 February), labeled across the upper margin "Visible Image" (listed as "Visible - Latest" on the course website). The image is for the time when sunset was occurring along a line stretching from southern Texas to eastern Montana on that Sunday evening.

10. The visible satellite image shows the cloud patterns over the western US. Major expanses of cloud cover the regions of the Pacific Ocean and the Northwest states and also occur across southern California and northern Mexico. At the time of the visible satellite image, sunlight was reaching the U.S. from the general direction of [(*southeast*) (*southwest*)].

11. Cloud conditions, if any existed at this time, are not seen across the eastern half of the image because [(*of nighttime conditions*) (*the satellite is beyond the horizon*)].

At the Figure 2 time of 0015Z it was approximately sunset time at Jordan, Montana (5:16 PM MST at longitude 106.9 degrees W, in east-central Montana) and at Brownsville, Texas (6:16 PM CST at longitude 97.4 degrees W, at the southernmost tip of Texas). Mark these approximate locations with dots on the map. **Draw a straight line between these two cities and extend it beyond the borders of the satellite image.** The line you drew represents the "terminator" or line separating day and night at the time of Figure 2. Label this line **"terminator"**.

12. The north-south western borders of the Dakotas and Nebraska represent an approximate north-south longitude line. **Draw a straight line superimposed on these borders and extend to the edges of the image.** Label this line at the map edge in Canada "**N**" and at the southern edge "**S**". The terminator line you drew is [(*approximately parallel*) (*at an angle*)] to the north-south border longitude line. The terminator's orientation relative to north-south longitude lines changes throughout the year and will be discussed in Investigation 3B.

13. Figure 3 is the *infrared* satellite image (from "Infrared - Latest") for the same time (0015Z on 06 FEB 2006) as the visible image. This image shows much [(***less***) (***more***)] extensive cloudiness, particularly the eastern portion of the US, than was seen in the visible image.

14. Infrared images are basically temperature maps of the surfaces "seen" by the satellite sensor. Warm surfaces (land during most of the year, water surfaces and low clouds) would appear relatively [(***bright white***) (***dark***)].

15. Cold surfaces emitting little infrared radiation would appear [(***bright white***) (***dark***)]. Surfaces with intermediate temperatures appear in gray shadings.

At 0015Z 06 FEB 2006 one storm system had exited the U.S. in the east with its frontal system's curve of cloud cover shown along the satellite image border in the Atlantic while another storm was forming in the south-central states.

16. The brightness of clouds in the infrared image shown in broad streaks along the southwest U.S.-Mexican border and from western Texas across Arkansas, for example, showed the cloud tops to be generally [(***"warm"***) (***"cold"***)].

17. These cloud tops, associated with jet stream-level winds and some rain showers in northeast Arkansas, were generally [(***low***) (***high***)] in altitude.

18. Comparatively, the cloud tops located in "blotches" from eastern Montana southward to Colorado were generally [(***"warmer"***) (***"colder"***)] than the southwestern cloud streaks.

19. The tops of these more northerly clouds were at [(***lower***) (***higher***)] altitudes.

The moderate gray shade of clouds located over the eastern Great Lakes indicated these were relatively low-level clouds although at the time it was reported they were producing heavy lake-effect snows from lower Michigan to New York state and West Virginia. The darker shading of western Lakes Superior and Michigan indicate the water surfaces (skies were clear over those areas) were warmer than the surrounding land and provided ingredients (heat and moisture) in the snow-making process.

20. If you wished to create a 24-hour time-lapse animation of the cloud patterns across the U.S. using the satellite images from each hour, you should choose the [(***visible***) (***infrared***)] images. (Most satellite images seen on television are this type of image.)

21. Continuous loops using [(***visible***) (***infrared***)] images would be undesirable because they would appear with black gaps during nighttime hours.

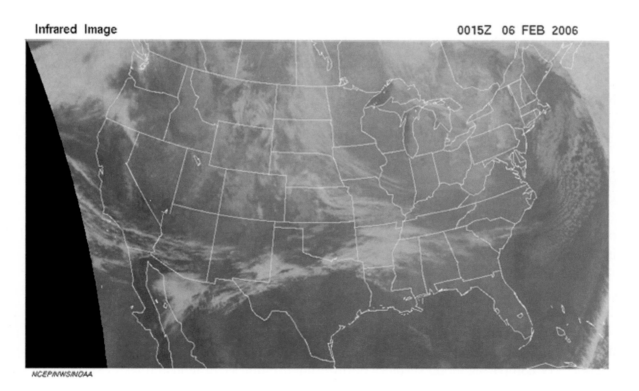

Figure 2. Visible satellite image for evening, 0015Z on 06 FEB 2006.

Figure 3. Infrared satellite image for 0015Z on 06 FEB 2006.

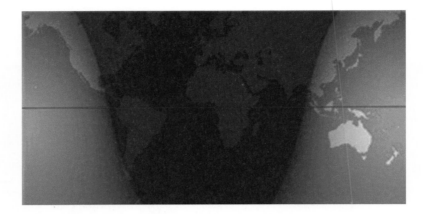

Figure 4. Model depiction of portions of Earth's surface in sunlight and darkness at 6:15 PM CST 06 FEB 2006. (From http://www.time.gov)

22. Figure 4 is an enlarged image from the web site, *http://www.time.gov*, at 6:15 PM CST 06 FEB 2006, the same time as the satellite images. The depiction in Figure 4 is from a model showing the positions of the sunrise and sunset terminators and the portions of the entire Earth's surface in sunlight and darkness at that time. The Figure 4 sunset terminator line across the U.S. [(***did***) (***did not***)] generally coincide with the sunset line you drew where sunsets were about 6:15 PM CST/5:15 PM MST.

23. The sunlit portions of horizontal zones (latitude) at comparable distances north and south of the Equator (denoted by the dark horizontal line bisecting the map view) are proportional to the lengths of daylight at those latitudes. These widths show that, at this time of the year, 6 February, the daylight periods are [(***longer in the Northern Hemisphere***) (***longer in the Southern Hemisphere***) (***equal in both hemispheres***)].

Routinely compare the latest satellite views with the latest analyzed surface map available via the course website. Compare what you see on-screen with your local weather. You can ask yourself such questions as: Are your skies clear or cloudy? Do the satellite views show the same?

Suggestions for further activities: The GOES Satellite Server link (*http://www.goes.noaa. gov/*) is a source for more detailed satellite images from various perspectives and other geostationary satellite images. This website also highlights specific dramatic weather and other events that are shown in satellite images. (Sunrise times, along with other astronomical information, can be obtained from the U. S. Naval Observatory site, *http://aa.usno.navy.mil/ AA/data/docs/RS_OneDay.html*.)

The course website contains the link, "Infrared Surface Temperature Determination", under the Satellite section. Calling up this Java applet allows one to determine the temperature in degrees Celsius of cloud and ground surfaces related to their amounts of emitted infrared energy. Try comparing cloud surfaces of differing brightness, or land and water surfaces in clear areas. Another comparison may be the same land surface between early morning and late afternoon as the surface responds to diurnal solar heating.

Investigation 3B: SUNLIGHT THROUGHOUT THE YEAR

Objectives:

Ultimately, all weather and climate begins with the sun. That is because solar radiation is the only significant source of energy that determines conditions at and above the Earth's surface.

The average rate at which solar radiation is received outside Earth's atmosphere on a surface oriented perpendicular to the sun's rays is about 2 calories per square centimeter per minute (1370 W m^{-2}). The amount of solar radiation that actually reaches the Earth's surface is quite different.

The nearly-spherical Earth, rotating once a day on an axis inclined to the plane of its orbit, presents a constantly changing face to the Sun. Wherever there is daylight, the path of the Sun through the local sky changes through the course of a year. Everywhere on Earth, except at the equator, the number of hours of daylight also changes through the year. In addition, the atmosphere absorbs and scatters the solar radiation passing through it. Clouds, especially, can block much of the incoming radiation.

The purpose of this investigation is to consider the variability of sunlight received at different latitudes over the period of a year.

After completing this investigation, you should be able to:

- Describe the variation of solar radiation received at equatorial, mid-latitude, and polar locations over the period of a year.
- Estimate and compare the amounts of sunlight received at equatorial, mid-latitude, and polar locations during the different seasons of the year.

Introduction:

Examine the accompanying graph of Figure 1. Data points plotted on the graph represent monthly averages of measurements of actual solar radiation received daily on a horizontal plane at Earth's surface at near equatorial (Singapore), midlatitude (Brockport, NY), and polar (Antarctica) locations. On Figure 1, month of the year is plotted along the horizontal axis and average daily incident radiant energy in calories per square centimeter per day is plotted vertically. On the horizontal axis, the longer marks represent the first day of each month and the shorter marks represent mid-month.

Construct an annual solar radiation curve for __each__ of the three locations. Do this by drawing a smooth curved line connecting the radiation values already plotted for each location. Note that at the South Pole (90 degrees S latitude) the sun rises on or about September 23 and sets on or about March 21. Draw each curve to the ends of the plotted values. December values are plotted twice to more clearly illustrate the annually repeating radiation cycles.

1. According to the curves you have drawn, at which latitude shown does average daily solar radiation vary the least over the period of a year? _Singapore 1.5°N_

2. The variation in average daily solar radiation that does occur at the latitude identified in item 1 is primarily due to changes in the daily [(***period of sunlight***) (***path of sunlight through the atmosphere***)]. (Refer to Figures 2 through 6 when answering this and the following questions 3 through 7.)

3. The pattern of sunlight received at the equator over the course of a year indicates that the seasonal contrast there is [(***similar to***) (***much less than***)] the seasonal contrast experienced in midlatitudes.

4. The graph shows that there is a six-month period during which there is no sunlight at the [(***equatorial***) (***midlatitude***) (***polar***)] location.

5. According to the graph, there are months when both the midlatitude and polar locations receive more solar radiation than the equator. For both midlatitude and polar locations, the major factor that causes this difference is the greater [(***local noon solar altitude***) (***length of daylight each day***)].

6. Comparison of the three annual radiation curves indicates that the annual range (that is, the difference between the curve's maximum and minimum) of solar radiation received daily [(***increases***) (***decreases***)] as latitude increases.

7. Based on how solar radiation received varies with latitude, it can be inferred that the seasonal temperature contrast [(***increases***) (***decreases***)] as latitude increases.

Mark the equinoxes and solstices on Figure 1 by drawing vertical lines at approximately March 21, June 22, September 23, and December 22. On the equinoxes the noon sun is directly above the equator, whereas on the solstices the noon sun is directly above 23.5 degrees N or 23.5 degrees S latitude. **Label the intervals between the lines as the Northern Hemisphere's winter, spring, summer, and fall seasons.**

8. Two maxima and two minima appear in the annual solar radiation curve for the equatorial location. Maxima occur near the [(***solstices***) (***equinoxes***)].

9. Because the rate of radiation received at Earth's surface is plotted over time in Figure 1, the area enclosed under the curve in each of the seasonal segments is directly proportional to the total solar radiation received during that season. According to the "seasonal" areas under each curve, all seasons at the [(***equatorial***) (***midlatitude***) (***polar***)] location receive about the same total amount of solar radiation.

Variation of Solar Radiation Received on Horizontal Surfaces at Different Latitudes

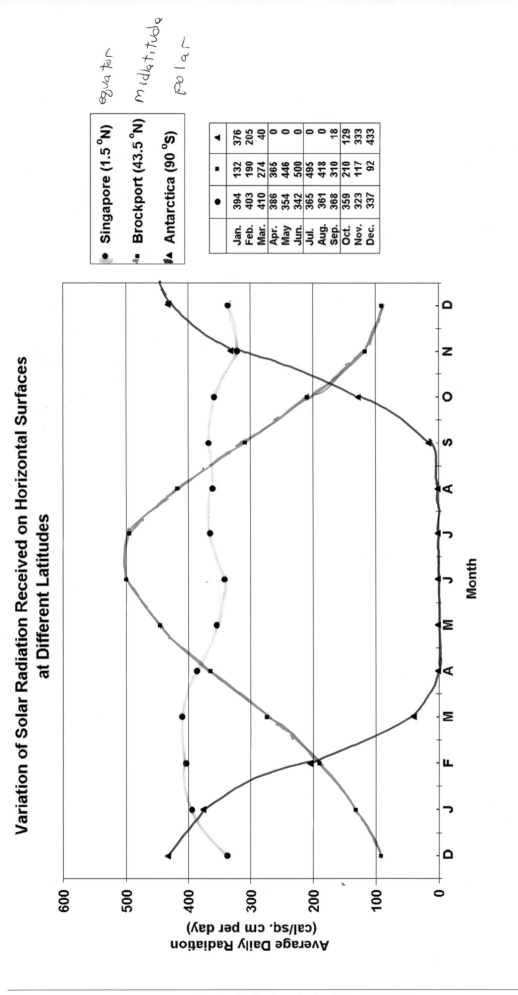

	●	■	▲
Jan.	394	132	376
Feb.	403	190	205
Mar.	410	274	40
Apr.	386	365	0
May	354	446	0
Jun.	342	500	0
Jul.	365	495	0
Aug.	361	418	0
Sep.	368	310	18
Oct.	359	210	129
Nov.	323	117	333
Dec.	337	92	433

● Singapore (1.5 °N)
■ Brockport (43.5 °N)
▲ Antarctica (90 °S)

equator
midlatitude
polar

Figure 1. Variation of solar radiation received on horizontal surfaces at different latitudes.

10. At the midlatitude location, the seasons of _____ receive(s) the most solar radiation.

11. For that same midlatitude location, the seasons of _____ receive(s) the least solar radiation.

12. During spring and summer in the Northern Hemisphere, the South Pole receives [(***its maximum***) (***zero***)] solar radiation.

13. In the Southern Hemisphere, these are the seasons of _____ and _____.

As directed by your course instructor, complete this investigation by either:

1. *Going to the Current Weather Studies link on the course website, or*
2. *Continuing to the Applications section for this investigation that immediately follows in this Investigations Manual.*

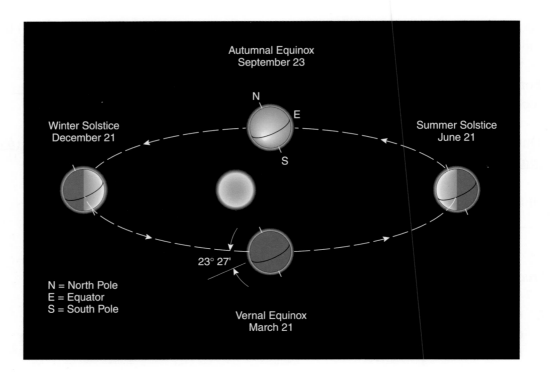

Figure 2. Earth's orbital relationship to the sun on the solstices and equinoxes.

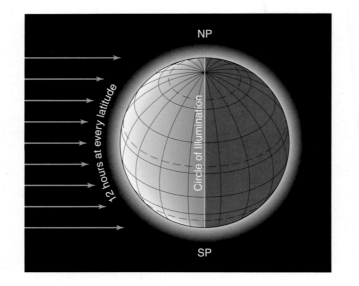

Figure 3. Solar radiation received at Earth on the equinox.

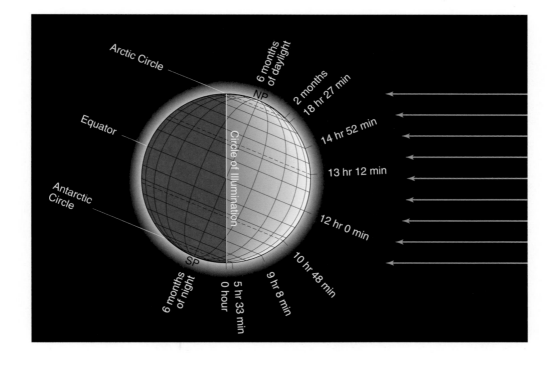

Figure 4. Solar radiation received at Earth on Northern Hemisphere's summer solstice.

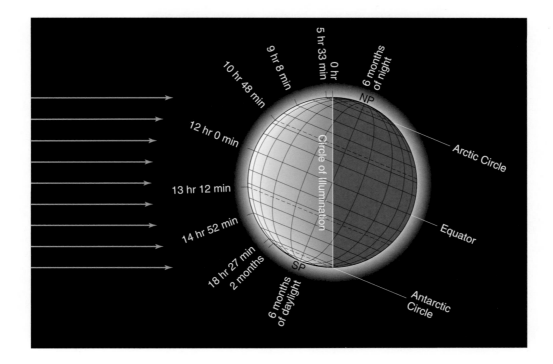

Figure 5. Solar radiation received at Earth on Northern Hemisphere's winter solstice.

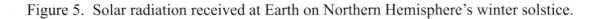

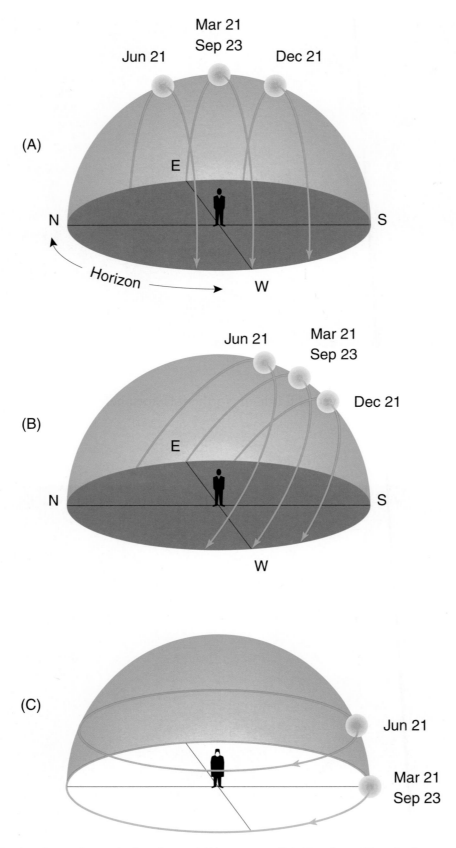

Figure 6. Path of sun through the sky at (A) equator, (B) Northern Hemisphere midlatitudes, and (C) North Pole.

Investigation 3B: SUNLIGHT THROUGHOUT THE YEAR
Applications

Examine the three visible satellite images in Figures 7, 8 and 9. These are actual images which were obtained on or near the first days of the Northern Hemisphere's fall, winter and summer seasons. Next, examine the small drawing to the right of each Earth image. The drawing shows the relative positions of Earth, the satellite, and rays of sunlight at the time each image was recorded. (In the small drawing, the view is from above Earth's Northern Hemisphere.) If you were located on the satellite, you would have seen the same view of Earth as shown in each accompanying satellite image.

The Earth images in Figures 7 to 9 were acquired when sunset was occurring at the point on the equator directly below the viewing satellite (in the center of the Earth's disk). Sunset was occurring along the dashed line passing through the sub-satellite point. The arrows to the left in each image represent incoming rays of sunlight at different latitudes. When answering the following questions, ignore the effects of Earth's atmosphere on the sun's rays.

14. Look at Figure 7, the 23 September image. Note that the Earth's axis is perpendicular to the sun's rays, so the sunset line and Earth's axis line up together. Because the Earth rotates once in 24 hours, the period of daylight is _____ hours everywhere except right at the poles.

15. Now look at Figure 8, the 21 December satellite image. On the Northern Hemisphere's winter solstice, the Earth's North Pole is tilted the farthest away from the sun it ever gets during the year. Consequently, poleward from the Arctic circle, the daily period of daylight is ____ hours.

16. Poleward from the Antarctic Circle on 21 December, the daily period of daylight is ____ hours.

17. Now look at Figure 9, the 21 June satellite image. On the Northern Hemisphere's summer solstice, Earth's North Pole is tilted towards the sun as far as it ever gets during the year. Consequently, poleward from the Arctic Circle, the period of daylight is ____ hours.

18. Poleward from the Antarctic Circle on 21 June, the period of daylight is _____ hours.

Along with these variations in the length of daylight at various latitudes as shown in the satellite views, the intensity of incoming sunlight varies with the angle of incidence of the sun's rays striking Earth's surface. (A latitude line on Earth's disk and sun's rays could also be added at your latitude.) Thus, the solar energy received at a location over the course of the year depends on the varying **solar altitude** (angle of the sun above the horizon) <u>and</u> the **period of daylight** at that location.

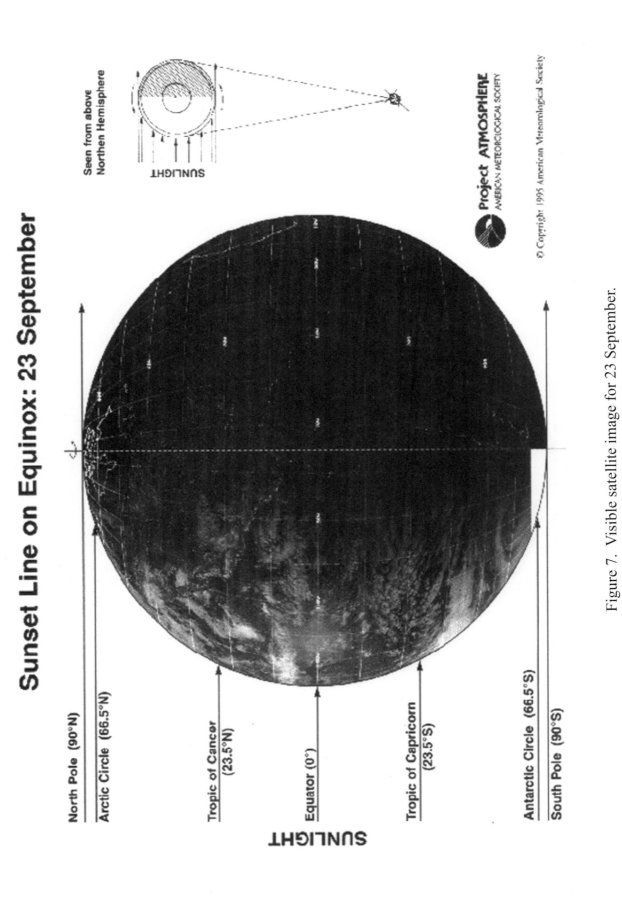

Figure 7.   Visible satellite image for 23 September.

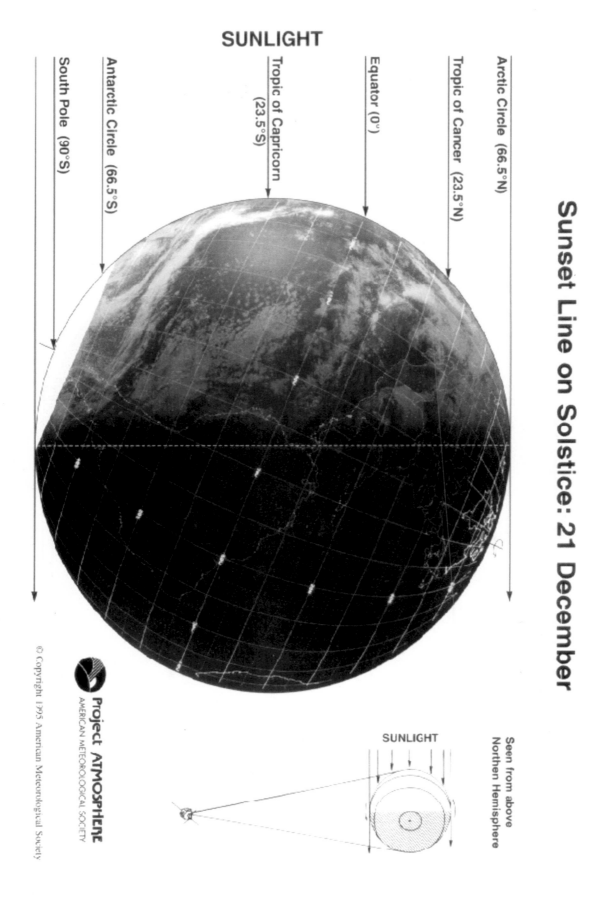

Figure 8. Visible satellite image for 21 December.

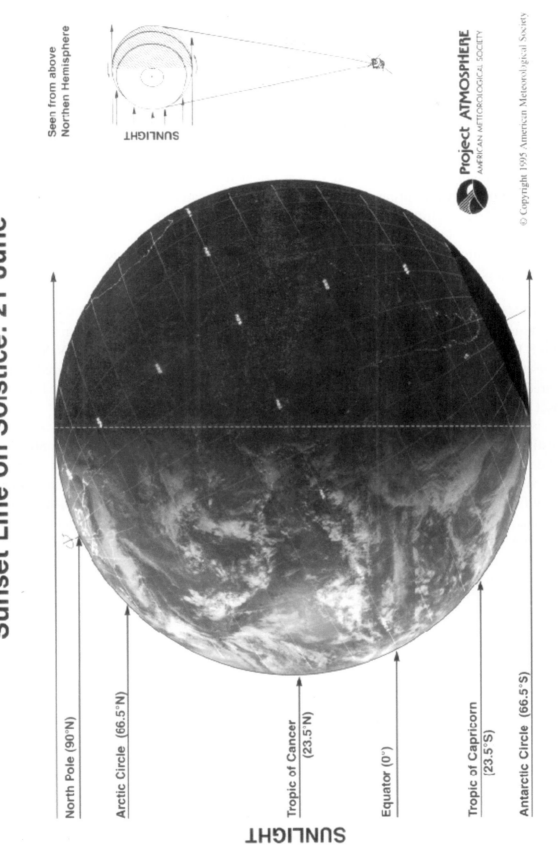

Sunset Line on Solstice: 21 June

Seen from above Northern Hemisphere

SUNLIGHT

Project ATMOSPHERE
AMERICAN METEOROLOGICAL SOCIETY

© Copyright 1995 American Meteorological Society

North Pole (90°N)

Arctic Circle (66.5°N)

Tropic of Cancer (23.5°N)

Equator (0°)

Tropic of Capricorn (23.5°S)

Antarctic Circle (66.5°S)

SUNLIGHT

Figure 9. Visible satellite image for 21 June.

19. **Return to Investigation 3A's Figure 1a.** This view is a satellite image for the first day of the Northern Hemisphere's spring season. Approximate the position of the terminator. It's orientation (the sunrise line in this view) most nearly looks like the orientation of the terminator line in the image for the first day of [(***winter***) (***fall***) (***summer***)] that you have just examined in this activity.

Suggestions for further activities: As time progresses through the seasons, call up visible satellite images near times of local sunrise or sunset every week or so, and observe changes in the orientation of the terminator. For example, the Investigation 3A terminator line that you drew on Figure 2 in Investigation 3A was oriented slightly southeast – northwest (on 06 February 2006). By the spring equinox, the terminator became south-north in orientation. Also, relate these satellite views to the path of the sun through your local sky and the length of daylight at your location. And, note the general trend of temperatures relative to these changing conditions. Finally, you might call up *http://www.time.gov* to keep track of the changing length of daylight at various locations on the Earth.

Full disk satellite views like those of Figure 7 through 9 can be obtained from the course website under the **Satellite** section by clicking on "GOES Satellite Server", then selecting "GOES Full Disk" from the left side menu. Then click on one of the full disk "VIS"s or images to view an enlarged visible display. The visible image can also be compared with the infrared image for the same time. Check on these visible images for sunrise (near 12Z) or sunset (near 00Z) times to compare to this Investigation.

To estimate amounts of solar radiation received at your location for the various months of the year similar to that given in Figure 1 of Investigation 3B, you can call up *http://rredc. nrel.gov/solar/old_data/nsrdb/redbook/atlas/*. Because this site is designed to display the energy from solar collectors, you need to choose the options of: (a) type of data, such as "average", (b) month of year or annual, and (c) collector orientation - "horizontal flat-plate". Then click on "View The Map". Finally, the energy units of kilowatt hours per square meter per day estimated from the map need to be multiplied by 86.04 to obtain calories per square centimeter per day as used in this Investigation.

Investigation 4A: TEMPERATURE AND AIR MASS ADVECTION

Objectives:

The Earth-atmosphere system is heated unevenly by solar radiation. Low latitudes receive more energy from the sun than they lose to space as outgoing infrared radiation. Averaged over a year, high latitudes experience more outgoing than incoming radiation and low latitudes experience more incoming than outgoing radiation. These energy deficits and excesses are balanced by horizontal movements (called advection) of heat energy poleward by migrating air masses, storm circulations, and ocean currents. The horizontal transport of air from a region of relatively high temperatures to a region of relatively low temperatures by air in motion (the wind) is referred to as *warm air advection*. Conversely, the transport of air from a region of relatively low temperatures to a region of relatively high temperatures by the wind is called *cold air advection*. Identification of areas of warm and cold air advection requires, in addition to information about winds, determination of the air temperature pattern made possible through the drawing of isotherms.

After completing this investigation, you should be able to:

- Draw lines of equal temperature (isotherms) to reveal the pattern of air temperatures across the nation at map time.
- Locate regions on a weather map where cold and warm air advection is likely to be occurring.
- Relate warm and cold air advection patterns to circulations of weather systems.

Introduction:

Temperature patterns are found on weather maps by drawing lines representing specific temperatures. These lines are called *isotherms* because every point on the same line has the same temperature value. Each isotherm separates temperatures having values higher than the isotherm from temperatures having lower values.

The Figure 1 map segment shows temperatures in degrees Fahrenheit (°F) at various weather stations. Consider each temperature value to be located at the center of the plotted number. The 70 °F isotherm has been drawn and labeled. **Draw the 10, 20, 30, 40, 50 and 60 °F isotherms. Be sure to label each isotherm at both ends.**

1.   Isotherms are drawn at regular intervals; on this map, the interval between successive isotherms is __10__ Fahrenheit degrees.

Tips on Drawing Isotherms:

    a. Always draw an isotherm so that temperatures higher than its value are consistently to one side and lower temperatures are to the other side.

    b. Assume a steady temperature change between neighboring stations when positioning isotherms; that is, use interpolation to place isotherms.

    c. Adjacent isotherms tend to look alike. The isotherm you are drawing will often parallel in a general way the curves of its neighbor because changes in air temperature from place to place are usually (but not always) gradual.

    d. Continue drawing an isotherm until it reaches the boundary of plotted data or "closes" within the data field by making its way to its other end and completing a loop.

    e. Isotherms can never be open ended within a data field and they never fork or touch or cross one another.

    f. Isotherms cannot be skipped if their values fall within the range of temperatures reported on the map. Isotherms must always appear in sequence; for example, when the isothermal interval is 10 degrees, there must be a 50 °F isotherm between the 40 °F and the 60 °F isotherms.

    g. Always label isotherms.

2.   The Figure 2 weather map is an adaptation of the weather map appearing in Investigation 2A. Wind observations taken at several weather stations and three isotherms are shown on the Figure 2 map. The isotherm values are _50_ °F, _60_ °F, and _70_ °F.

3.   Hence, the interval between isotherms is _10_ Fahrenheit degrees.

Warm air advection occurs where the wind blows across the isotherms from the higher (warmer) values to the lower (colder) values. That is, warmer air is being transported to a weather station by the horizontal winds. Based on this factor alone, one would expect temperatures at that station to rise in the near future. Cold air advection occurs where the wind blows across the isotherms from the lower (colder) values to the higher (warmer) values. Then, colder air is being transported to the station by horizontal winds.

Based on wind directions and the isotherm pattern on the map, determine the type of air advection (warm or cold) that would be occurring at each station.

4.   Warm air advection was occurring at stations (circle those that apply): [(*A*) (*B*) (*C*) (*D*)]

5.   Cold air advection was occurring at stations: [(*A*) (*B*) (*C*) (*D*)]

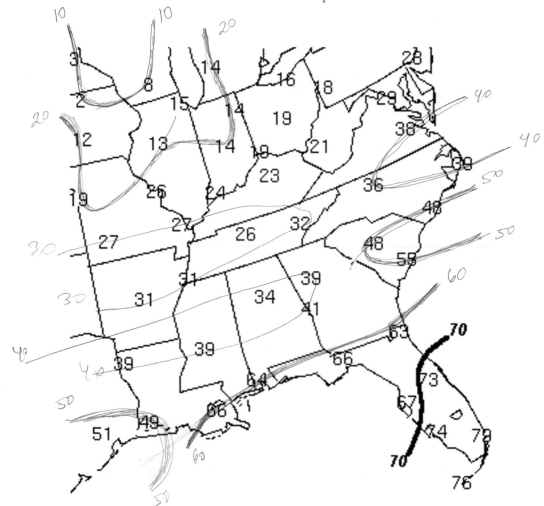

Figure 1. Southeastern U.S. map of temperatures.

Surface Weather Map Showing Storm System in the Eastern United States

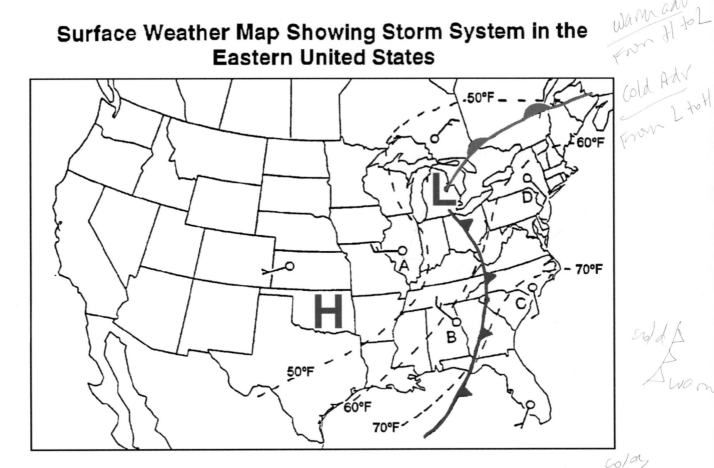

Figure 2. Simplified surface weather map.

6. Generalizing from this map depiction of wind and temperature patterns associated with weather systems, areas southeast of Lows can be expected to have [(**warm**) (**cold**)] air advection.

7. Meanwhile, areas to the west of Lows can be expected to have [(**warm**) (**cold**)] air advection.

8. Areas to the east of Highs would be expected to have [(**warm**) (**cold**)] air advection.

9. And while not shown here, areas to the west of Highs should have [(**warm**) (**cold**)] air advection.

On actual weather maps, the patterns of isotherms and winds vary greatly. The intensity of warm and cold air advection will depend on the wind speeds, the angle at which the wind crosses the isotherms, and the closeness of neighboring isotherms. In general, the faster the wind, the more perpendicular the angle, and the closer the isotherm lines, the stronger the advection.

10. Not surprisingly, behind cold fronts one can expect [(**warm**) (**cold**)] air advection.

11. And behind warm fronts one can expect [(**_warm_**) (**_cold_**)] air advection.

12. Where the horizontal wind blows parallel to isotherms, there is [(**_warm_**) (**_cold_**) (**_no_**)] air advection.

13. Air temperatures are governed by a combination of warm or cold air advection and radiational controls. With no advection, the lowest temperature of the day is likely to occur around [(**_sunrise_**) (**_sunset_**)].

14. If a day's lowest temperature actually occurs just before midnight, then [(**_warm_**) (**_cold_**)] air advection likely occurred during the afternoon and evening hours.

__As directed by your course instructor, complete this investigation by either:__

1. *__Going to the Current Weather Studies link on the course website, or__*
2. *__Continuing to the Applications section for this investigation that immediately follows in this Investigations Manual.__*

Investigation 4A: TEMPERATURE AND AIR MASS ADVECTION

Applications

15. The Figure 3 weather map shows a major **nor'easter**, a strong East Coastal low pressure system, whose passage brought heavy rains and some record-setting snowfalls to the Northeast U.S. at the time. The map displays plotted station models with reported surface weather conditions, "Isotherms, Fronts, & Data", for 20Z Saturday, 11 FEB 2006 (3 PM EST, 2 PM CST, etc.). ***Note that on the Figure 3 map, the isopleths are isotherms (not isobars).*** At map time, the storm system's center was shown marked by the **L** in South Carolina. The station model for Greensboro, North Carolina, showed the temperature to be _____ °F with a dewpoint of 34 °F.

16. The wind at Greensboro was reported as 10 knots from the [(***north***) (***east***)].

17. The Greensboro's sky condition was [(***clear***) (***mostly cloudy***) (***overcast***)].

18. The weather symbol (2 dots) in the "9 o'clock" position of the station model signified that Greensboro reported _____ occurring at map time.

19. To determine warm and cold air advection patterns, compare the wind flow with the temperature pattern. The curved lines drawn on the map are isotherms. As noted at the lower right border of the map, the isotherms are drawn at intervals of ___ Fahrenheit degrees.

20. The isotherm shown from the Del-Mar-Va (Delaware, Maryland, Virginia) Peninsula, across North Carolina and the northern portions of the Gulf states to northern Texas onward, north and west of the storm system with its fronts, is the [(***20***) (***40***) (***60***)] °F isotherm. Highlight or otherwise mark this isotherm for reference. Also, note that the neighboring isotherms roughly parallel it.

21. Generally, station models from the north-central states south to Texas and eastward to Virginia and North Carolina exhibit winds that were directed across the isotherms at relatively large angles (such as Greensboro), from [(***higher to lower***) (***lower to higher***)] temperature regions.

22. [(***Cold***) (***Warm***)] air advection was occurring at these locations. **Lightly shade around those stations (in blue if possible) where you noted that cold air advection was occurring.**

23. This advection pattern shows that along the Gulf coast, [(***warm***) (***cold***)] air advection followed the passage of the cold front. The isotherm spacing northwest of the cold front shows a relatively moderate temperature *gradient*, or change of temperature over distance, indicating moderate cold air advection.

24. Note the station model at Jacksonville, in northeast Florida. Conditions at Jacksonville represented the remnants of warm air that had covered the eastern U.S. prior to the storm's development. Winds at Jacksonville were from the southwest and blowing across the isotherm drawn on the map, generally from regions of [(***higher to lower***) (***lower to higher***)] temperatures.

25. Weak [(***cold***) (***warm***)] air advection was occurring at Jacksonville. **Lightly hatch or otherwise denote the area around Jacksonville (in red) where you noted warm air advection occurring.**

26. Typically, warm air advection would occur [(***ahead of***) (***behind***)] a cold front.

27. Figure 4 is the "Isobars, Fronts, Radar & Data" map for 20Z Saturday, 11 FEB 2006, the same time as the Figure 3 map. Isopleths on the Figure 4 map are *isobars* showing pressure patterns across the country and beyond. The Figure 4 map also shows the South Carolina storm center. The wind directions around the low-pressure center indicated that the air generally spiraled [(***inward toward***) (***outward from***)] the low-pressure center consistent with the *hand-twist* model of a Low.

Suggestions for further activities: As weather systems cross your region in the coming weeks and months, you might call up the "Isotherms, Fronts, & Data" map on the course website and identify patterns of cold or warm air advection associated with these passing systems. You can shade regions of warm (red) and cold (blue) air advection on the map and relate them to the weather systems and to your daily temperature patterns.

Because solar radiation changes little from day to day, large temperature changes at the same time from one day to the next may be the result of air mass advection. One source for pinpointing these advection regions is the map of 24-hour temperature change provided by The Weather Channel (*http://www.weather.com/maps/activity/achesandpains /us24hourtemperaturechange_large.html*).

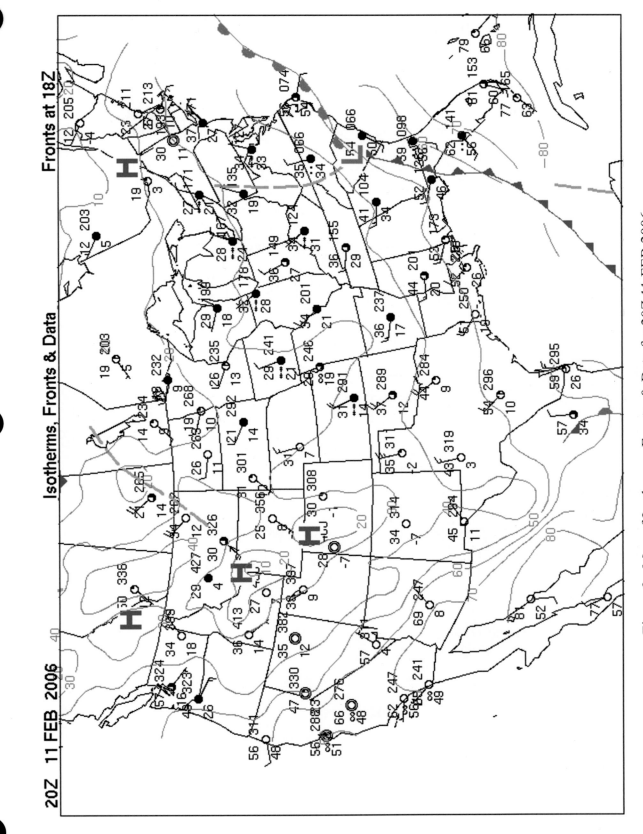

Figure 3. Map of Isotherms, Fronts, & Data for 20Z 11 FEB 2006.

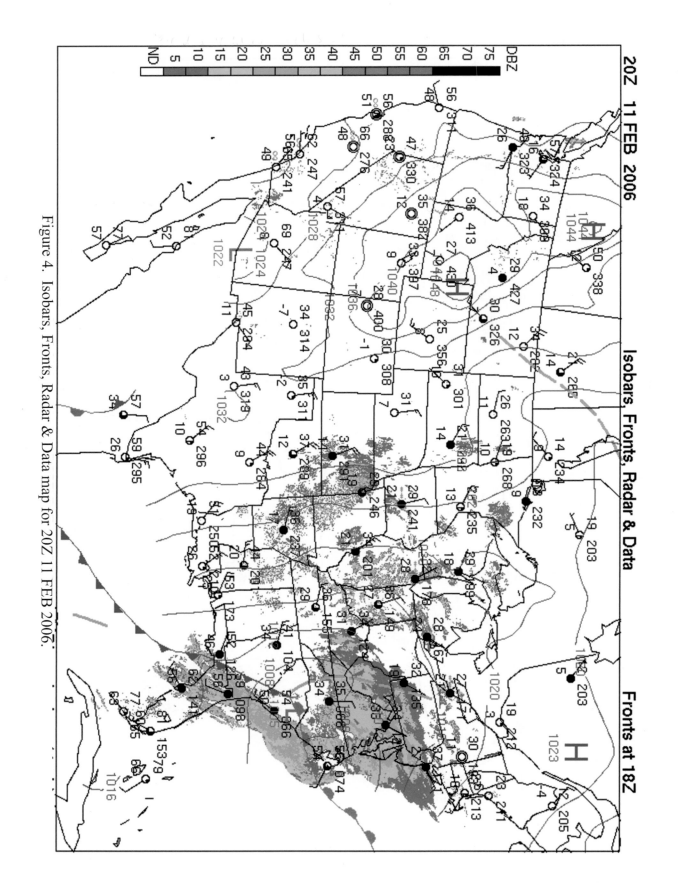

Figure 4. Isobars, Fronts, Radar & Data map for 20Z 11 FEB 2006.

Investigation 4B: HEATING DEGREE-DAYS AND WIND CHILL

Objectives:

Weather, by definition, refers to the state of the atmosphere mainly in terms of its effect upon life and human activities. Perhaps the most noticeable aspect of weather to individuals is air temperature. Outside air temperatures can require energy useage to make interior living spaces comfortable. The chilling effects of temperature combined with wind on exposed flesh is another aspect of weather that people in colder climates must guard against.

After completing this investigation, you should be able to:

- Calculate the number of heating or cooling degree-days accumulated on a given day, and demonstrate the use of current data to determine the number of heating or cooling degree-days in selected locations.
- Describe the pattern of average annual heating-degree totals over the coterminous United States.
- Determine the wind chill temperature based on temperature and wind observations.

Introduction:

1. During cool or cold weather episodes, fuel is consumed to make buildings comfortable living spaces. A useful indicator of fuel consumption for heating purposes is the determination of heating degree-days. They are calculated by accumulating one unit for each Fahrenheit degree the daily **mean temperature** is <u>below</u> the base value of 65 °F (18 °C). For example, a day with a maximum temperature of 70 °F and a minimum of 50 °F has a mean temperature of 60 °F. Subtracting 60 from 65 yields 5 heating degree-days for that day. Hence, a day with a high temperature of 40 °F and a low of 20 °F produces _____35_____ heating degree-days (HDD).

The accompanying Figure 1 map displays the <u>average annual total</u> number of heating degree-days accumulated at various locations around the country. Assume that each location is at the center of the number plotted on the map. **Determine the pattern of degree-days accumulated yearly by drawing on the map contour lines representing 2000, 4000, 6000, 8000, and 10,000 heating degree-days.** Be sure to label each contour.

2. Compare your map analysis to the map appearing in Figure 2, which is based on data from many additional locations. According to that map, Southern [(**_California_**) (**_Texas_**) (**_Florida_**)] has the lowest annual heating degree-day totals among the lower-48 states.

3. Latitude, elevation, and nearness to large bodies of water are factors that influence the annual heating degree-day pattern appearing on the map you analyzed. Of these three

Elevation ?

factors, ~~Nearness to large bodies of H₂o~~ is generally the most important for the coterminous U.S.

4. Examine Figure 3. Figure 3 shows the annual temperature curves for (A) San Francisco, CA, a maritime station and (B) St. Louis, MO, a continental location. Although both are at about the same latitude, the city that typically accumulates heating degree-days <u>during fewer months</u> of the year is [(***St. Louis***) (***San Francisco***)].

5. The city that records more heating degree-days <u>annually</u> is [(***San Francisco***) (***St. Louis***)]. (We suggest you locate San Francisco and St. Louis on the Figure 2 map to confirm your response. This result is typical for West coast maritime locations compared to continental locations at the same latitude. Even though heating degree days may be accumulated at continental locations over a shorter part of the year, much lower temperatures during the cold part of the year cause more heating degree-days to be accumulated annually.)

6. When the weather is too hot for human comfort, there is a need to condition air in living spaces. Cooling degree-days are calculated to estimate fuel needs for air conditioning when the day's mean temperature is <u>above</u> 65 °F. The calculation is made by subtracting 65 °F from the day's mean temperature. On a day when the maximum temperature is 95 °F and the minimum temperature is 75 °F, the number of cooling degree-days is ____20____.

$$\frac{\begin{array}{r}95\\75\end{array}}{170}/2 = 85 \quad \begin{array}{r}85\\-65\\\hline 20\end{array}$$

7. It takes only a short time outdoors in cool or cold weather for a person to realize that temperature and wind both play major roles in the rate at which the human body loses heat to the environment. The National Weather Service Windchill Chart (Figure 4) enables us to determine the windchill equivalent temperature (WET) based on combined effects of air temperature and wind speed. The WET is an attempt to approximate the rate of sensible heat loss from exposed skin caused by the combined effect of low air temperature and wind. However, when the air is calm and there is no additional heat-loss effect from wind, one should expect the WET to be [(***higher than***) (***the same as***) (***lower than***)] the actual air temperature.

8. According to the Windchill Chart, the WET is ___-19___ °F when the temperature is 5 °F and the wind speed is 30 miles per hour (mph).

9. It can be seen from the Windchill Chart that above 35 mph, changes in wind speed have relatively little effect on WET values. At 25 °F, an increase in wind speed from 5 to 10 mph causes a 4-degree drop in the WET value. At the same temperature, an increase in wind speed from 40 to 45 mph reduces the WET by ___1___ Fahrenheit degree(s).

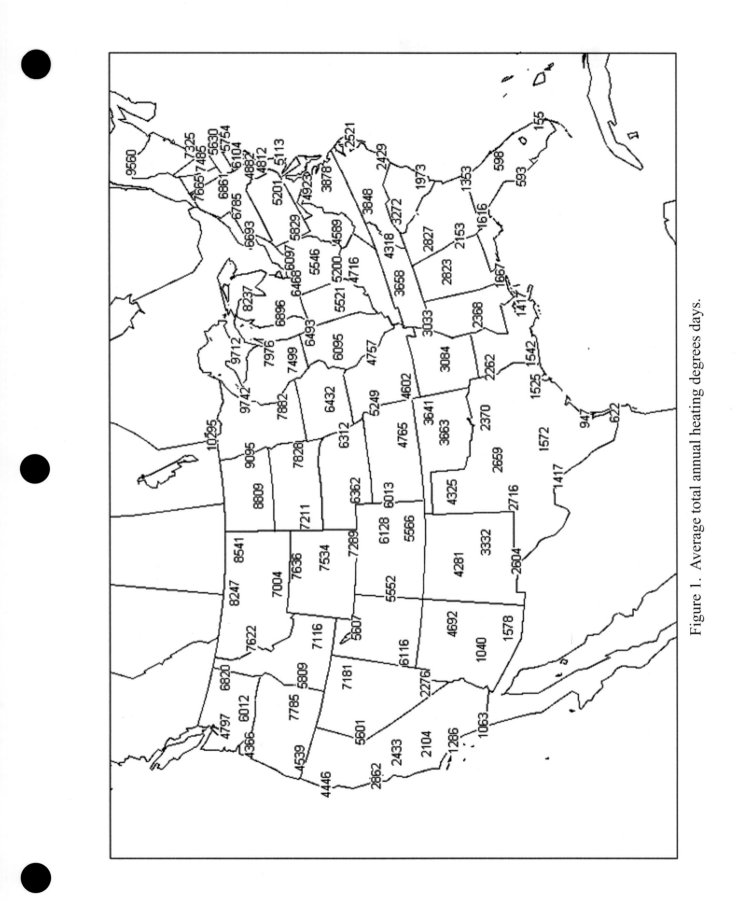

Figure 1. Average total annual heating degrees days.

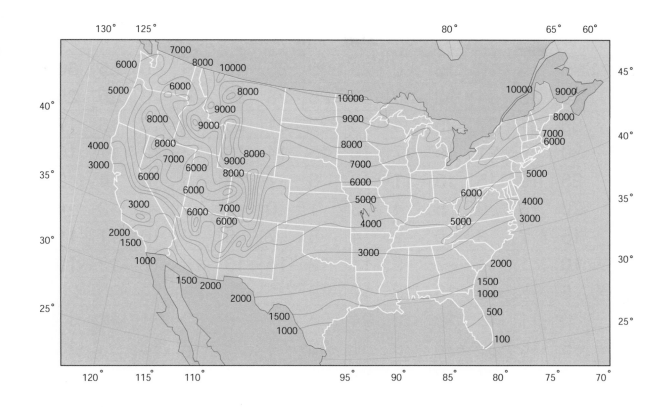

Figure 2. Average annual heating degree-day totals over the lower 48 states using a base of 65 °F.

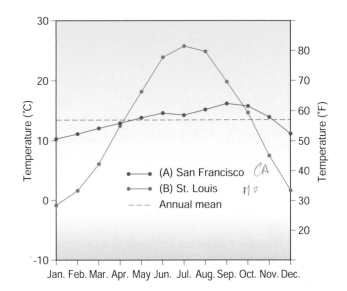

Figure 3. Monthly mean temperatures for San Francisco and St. Louis.

Wind (mph)

Calm	5	10	15	20	25	30	35	40	45	50	55	60
40	36	34	32	30	29	28	28	27	26	26	25	25
35	31	27	25	24	23	22	21	20	19	19	18	17
30	25	21	19	17	16	15	14	13	12	12	11	10
25	19	15	13	11	9	8	7	6	5	4	4	3
20	13	9	6	4	3	1	0	-1	-2	-3	-3	-4
15	7	3	0	-2	-4	-5	-7	-8	-9	-10	-11	-11
10	1	-4	-7	-9	-11	-12	-14	-15	-16	-17	-18	-19
5	-5	-10	-13	-15	-17	-19	-21	-22	-23	-24	-25	-26
0	-11	-16	-19	-22	-24	-26	-27	-29	-30	-31	-32	-33
-5	-16	-22	-26	-29	-31	-33	-34	-36	-37	-38	-39	-40
-10	-22	-28	-32	-35	-37	-39	-41	-43	-44	-45	-46	-48
-15	-28	-35	-39	-42	-44	-46	-48	-50	-51	-52	-54	-55
-20	-34	-41	-45	-48	-51	-53	-55	-57	-58	-60	-61	-62
-25	-40	-47	-51	-55	-58	-60	-62	-64	-65	-67	-68	-69
-30	-46	-53	-58	-61	-64	-67	-69	-71	-72	-74	-75	-76
-35	-52	-59	-64	-68	-71	-73	-76	-78	-79	-81	-82	-84
-40	-57	-66	-71	-74	-78	-80	-82	-84	-86	-88	-89	-91
-45	-63	-72	-77	-81	-84	-87	-89	-91	-93	-95	-97	-98

Temperature (°F)

Frostbite times (minutes)   30   10   5

Figure 4. NWS Windchill Chart.

As directed by your course instructor, complete this investigation by either:

1. *Going to the Current Weather Studies link on the course website, or*
2. *Continuing to the Applications section for this investigation that immediately follows in this Investigations Manual.*

Investigation 4B: HEATING DEGREE-DAYS AND WIND CHILL
Applications

Heating and Cooling Degree Days and wind chill values are calculated with the use of observational data collected at weather stations. Annual totals of Heating Degree Days are accumulated beginning 1 July while Cooling Degree Days begin with 1 January.

10. The course website delivers 24-Hour Maximum and Minimum Temperature maps which can be used to calculate these heating and cooling unit values. Figure 5 is an NWS map showing both maximum and minimum temperatures, in degrees Fahrenheit, at selected stations across the U. S. during the preceding 24-hour period, ending at 12Z on 13 FEB 2007. The upper red number is the period's maximum temperature and the lower blue number the minimum at the station denoted by the green dot. Consider only the contiguous 48 states for the following questions. The highest <u>maximum</u> temperature reported on the map in the "lower 48" was _____ °F.

11. This highest maximum temperature occurred at [(***Miami, FL***) (***Brownsville, TX***)].

12. The lowest <u>maximum</u> temperature plotted on Figure 5 was 3 °F at [(***Caribou, ME***) (***Fargo, ND***)].

13. The lowest <u>minimum</u> temperature reported on the map was _____ °F at Bismarck and Fargo, ND.

14. The highest minimum temperature in Figure 6 was 71 °F at [(***Phoenix, AZ***) (***Key West, FL***)].

The following table lists some selected cities from Figure 5 with their temperature maxima or minima. **For each, list the maximum or minimum value needed, then calculate the average daily temperature and, using the base of 65 °F, determine whether Heating Degree Day units or Cooling Degree Day units were produced and how many.** (Following NOAA/NWS practices, the mean daily temperature is rounded <u>up</u> to the nearest whole degree, if necessary, before calculating HDD or CDD. Report the rounded mean in the table.)

Degree Day Units

City	Max. T (°F)	Min. T (°F)	Mean T (°F)	HDD/CDD Units	Circle which
15. Bismarck, ND	8	_____	_____	_____	HDD / CDD
16. San Francisco, CA	____	47	_____	_____	HDD / CDD
17. Brownsville, TX	____	60	_____	_____	HDD / CDD
18. Wilmington, NC	61	_____	_____	_____	HDD / CDD

19. Scanning the map's maximum and minimum temperatures, it can be inferred that utility energy usage in the U. S. during this daily period was probably most needed for **heating** across the [(***southwestern***) (***south-central***) (***north-central***) (***southeastern***)] U. S.

20. The NWS map of highest and lowest temperatures can be accessed from the course website. Go to the website, scroll down to **Climate** and click on the "National Temps/ Precip." link. When viewing the NWS page with the latest map, go to the "Max/Min Temperatures" option bar to the upper left of the map and click on the down arrow. The list of temperature dates displayed shows that, including the current day's map, you can access max/min temperature maps for a total of _____ days. Similarly, there are station precipitation values given. The option bar to the upper right provides future climate outlooks.

    The station located at the green dot can be verified on some browsers by pausing your cursor over the station dot on the website map. (On some browsers you will need to click on the dot to take you to the station's NWS website. Then you need to click on the return arrow to come back to the map.) By clicking on an individual station dot on the website map, the page opens for that local National Weather Service Office's climate information. Here you can link to the daily data showing the calculated heating and cooling degree days for cities in that NWS Office's area for the day, month to date and year to date along with other interesting data.

21. Heating and Cooling Degree Day units reflect energy needs to attain indoor human comfort. Outdoors the cooling effect of wind along with temperature on an individual is reflected using the windchill equivalent temperature. The Figure 5 map shows that the minimum temperature across the North Dakota area on February 13th was about –15 °F. Assume that this area was experiencing a wind speed of 10 miles per hour when the temperature was –15 °F. Using the windchill equivalent temperature (WET) Table in Figure 4, the WET for this combination of temperature and wind speed would have been _____ °F.

Suggestions for further activities: The HDD values you determined in this investigation are reasonably consistent in pattern with the national annual HDD map of the first part of the investigation. Tables of HDD for selected cities can be found at: *http://www.cpc.ncep.noaa .gov/products/analysis_monitoring/cdus/degree_days/mctyhddy.txt* and tables of CDD at: *http://www.cpc.ncep.noaa.gov/products/analysis_monitoring/cdus/degree_days/mctycddy.txt* You can compare your area for the winter or summer through the latest month with other regions of the country for the impact on utility bills.

The National Weather Service Internet site provides current meteorological data for any selected station (by state and city) for the U.S. These data also include a station's daily maximum and minimum temperatures. The Web address is: *http://weather.noaa.gov/ weather/ccus.html*. Also, the NOAA Climate Prediction Center has a webpage of *Degree Day Assessment* information at: *http://www.cpc.ncep.noaa.gov/products/predictions/ experimental/ddtest/weekass.html*.

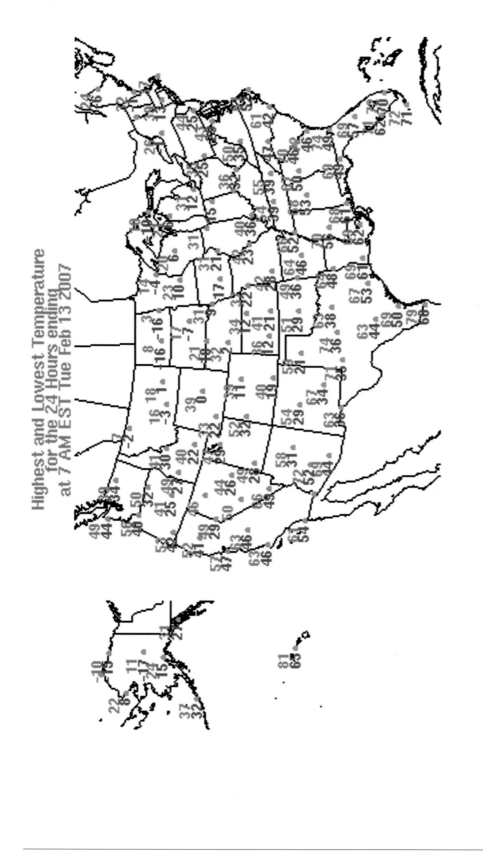

Figure 5. Map of selected U.S. maximum and minimum temperatures ending at 7 AM EST on 13 FEB 2007 (from NOAA/NCEP/ HPC).

Investigation 5A: AIR PRESSURE CHANGE

Objectives:

Atmospheric pressure at any place on the Earth's surface changes over time. In midlatitudes, these changes are often related to the migration of air masses. An air mass is a huge volume of air covering thousands of square kilometers that is relatively uniform horizontally in temperature and water vapor concentration. Neighboring air masses with contrasting characteristics tend not to mix so that distinct boundaries (fronts) form between them. Fronts occupy troughs of low pressure. As an air mass travels over the Earth's surface, there are changes in the air pressure and weather at places in its path. Those changes are particularly dramatic at or near the leading edge of the air mass.

After completing this investigation, you should be able to:

- Identify air pressure changes and other local weather conditions that indicate the passage of a cold front.
- Relate local air pressure changes and weather conditions to the presence of different air masses before and after the passage of a cold front.
- Estimate the speed of movement of a strong, well-defined cold front.

Introduction:

Highs (*H*s) and Lows (*L*s), the centers of pressure systems routinely plotted on surface weather maps, identify local values of atmospheric pressure that are relatively the highest or lowest in a region. These systems generally move from west to east across our midlatitude portion of the globe. Pressure values at locations in the paths of these migrating systems fall as a Low approaches or a High departs, and pressures rise with approaching Highs or departing Lows. Fronts mark the boundaries of these Highs and generally show the transition from one air mass to another. Fronts frequently anchor at low-pressure centers.

Figure 1 is a cross-section schematic of a cold front moving towards the right across the surface. The warm air mass is being replaced by the cold air mass. Each air mass would have a high-pressure center as shown. For someone initially located at the red *H*, the weather parameters of temperature and pressure would vary as the front approaches and moves past the location. (For a map view, see Figure 2 of Investigation 4A.)

1.   As the cold front passes your location, the temperature would [(***rise***) (***remain steady***) (***fall***)].

2.   As the cold front moves toward and passes your location, the air pressure would [(***rise then fall***) (***fall then rise***)].   falls because air is dryer (more dense)

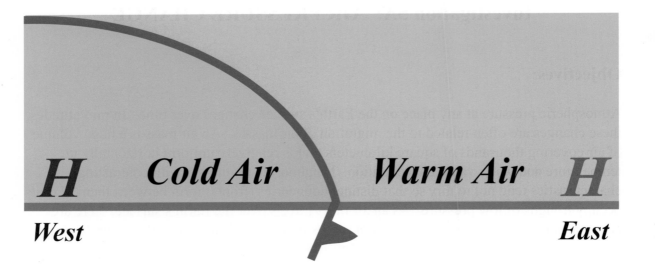

Figure 1. Cross-section of idealized cold front.

As directed by your course instructor, complete this investigation by either:

1. *Going to the Current Weather Studies link on the course website, or*
2. *Continuing to the Applications section for this investigation that immediately follows in this Investigations Manual.*

Investigation 5A: AIR PRESSURE CHANGE
Applications

3. As shown on the accompanying Figure 2 surface weather map for 00Z 17 FEB 2006 (7 PM EST 16 February), relatively warm air covered the Eastern and Southeastern U.S. while very cold air plunged southeastward across the Central U.S. At map time the major low-pressure center was located in southern Michigan. A [(*__cold__*) (*__warm__*) (*__stationary__*)] front curved from the Low center southwestward to across Texas and back northward to Washington State.

Also, a front shown generally as stationary was oriented west-east from western New York State into the Atlantic. (The northward bulge of the front just east of the Michigan low-pressure center was a short warm front.)

4. The wind directions at stations over the large area dominated by the low-pressure system centered in Michigan were generally [(*__clockwise and outward__*) (*__counterclockwise and inward__*)], consistent with the *hand-twist model* of a Low.

5. Compare wind conditions as shown by the station models ahead of (to the east of) the frontal system from Louisiana and Arkansas to the Carolinas and New York City, with those behind (west of) the front from Chicago to north Texas. Wind directions to the east of the front were generally from the [(*__south__*) (*__northwest__*)].

6. Meanwhile, wind directions at stations to the west, behind the front, were generally from the [(*__south__*) (*__northwest__*)].

7. At 00Z 17 FEB 2006, at Detroit, MI (the station model was partially obscured under the "1004" isobar label), the warm/stationary front [(*__had already__*) (*__had not yet__*)] passed its location. The cold front remained to the west of Detroit.

Examine the accompanying Figure 3 meteogram for Detroit (DTW). A meteogram provides a continuous time record of air temperature, dewpoint, precipitation, wind speed and direction, sky coverage, visibility, weather conditions, and air pressure. (A complete explanation of the meteogram is in the course website User's Guide.) The meteogram covers the 24-hour period from 1200Z 16 FEB 2006 (060216/1200 as *YYMMDD/XXXX hrs*) to 1200Z 17 FEB 2006. **On the Figure 3 meteogram, draw a vertical line at 00Z 17 FEB 2006, the time of the Figure 2 surface weather map.**

8. From 1200Z through 2000Z on the 16th, the wind direction at Detroit (second panel) was generally from the [(*__east or northeast__*) (*__south or southwest__*)].

9. The sky coverage during the same time period was _____.

10. Weather conditions (bottom of third panel) were variously reported as [(***rain and fog***) (***snow and freezing rain***)].

11. The air pressure (fourth panel) was [(***steady or falling gradually***) (***rising gradually***)]. Temperatures and dewpoints were generally steady.

12. Next consider the period from 2100Z on the 16th to 0500Z on the 17th. Wind directions were generally from the [(***east or northeast***) (***south or southwest***)].

13. The air pressure was [(***falling gradually***) (***rising gradually***)].

14. Temperatures and dewpoints [(***rose rapidly and then became steady***) (***fell rapidly***)]. During the last four hours of this period, moderate to heavy rain fell.

15. Finally, from 0500Z to about 1100Z on the 17th, the temperatures and dewpoints [(***rose gradually***) (***fell steadily***)].

16. Beginning with 0600Z on the 17th the wind direction was generally from the [(***west or northwest***) (***south or southwest***)].

17. The air pressure was [(***falling gradually***) (***rising rapidly***)].

18. In the 17-hour period from 1200Z on the 16th to 0500Z on the 17th, the air pressure fell by about [(***4***) (***8***) (***16***)] mb.

19. From 0500Z to 1200Z on the 17th, the air pressure [(***rose***) (***fell***)] by about 21 mb.

20. Based on the patterns of temperature, dewpoint and wind direction, one can conclude that the [(***warm***) (***cold***)] front passed over Detroit between 20Z and 21Z on the 16th.

21. Also the patterns indicate that the [(***warm***) (***cold***)] front passed between 05Z and 06Z on the 17th.

22. The directional change (from falling to rising) in the pressure pattern was associated with the passage of the [(***warm***) (***cold***)] front.

Figure 4 is the surface weather map for 12Z 17 FEB 2006, 7 AM EST, 12 hours following the Figure 2 map. Compare the Figure 3 map's atmospheric conditions at Detroit to those reported on the Figure 2 meteogram at 12Z on the 17th. They are the same.

23. Compared to the air at 00Z on the 17th, the air over Detroit a half-day later at 12Z was [(***warmer and more humid***) (***colder and less humid***)].

24. As noted on the meteogram for weather conditions occurring at 0900 and 1000Z on the 17th, _____ fell at Detroit.

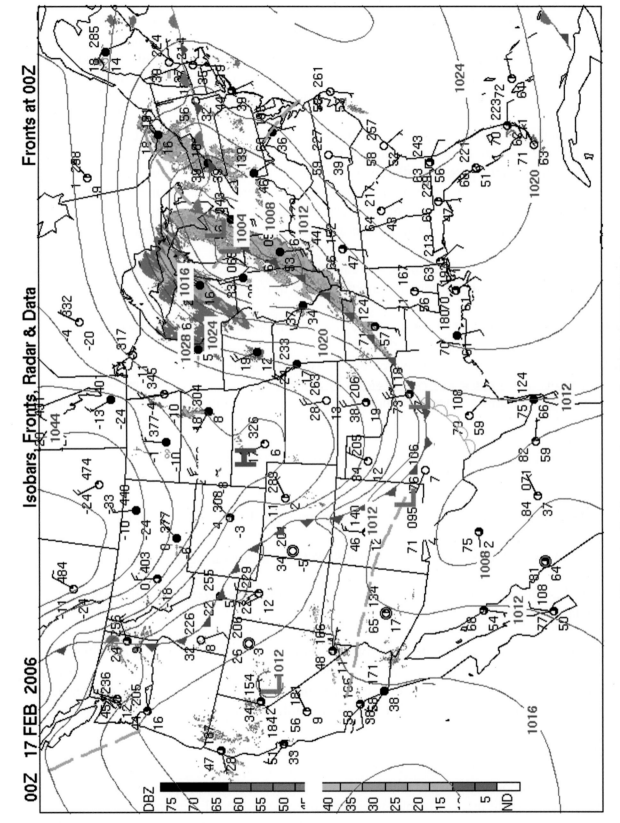

Figure 2. Surface weather map for 00Z 17 FEB 2006.

25. On the Figure 2 surface weather map, the cold front was located across the Indiana-Illinois border at 00Z. The Figure 4 map included a segment of the front along the West Virginia-Virginia border at 12Z indicating that the front traveled almost due east about 780 km in the 12 hours. Therefore, the cold front was moving at about _____ km per hr. This speed of travel, approximately 40 mph, often characterizes strong cold fronts that bring about rapidly changing weather conditions.

26. On the Figure 4 map, the pressure at the station nearest the center of the Low was "943" while the pressure nearest the center of the Montana High was "511". These decoded pressures meant a pressure difference over that distance of _____ mb. This change was concentrated near the center of the Low, leading to strong and damaging winds that were reported with this system. Also, note the temperatures reported at stations near the U.S.-Canadian border. This cold air moved over the central US during the ensuing weekend.

27. Using these fronts as examples, one can conclude that when a warm front passes a station, typically the air temperature will begin to [(***rise***) (***fall***)].

28. With the passage of a warm front, the dewpoint typically begins to [(***rise***) (***fall***)].

29. Also with a warm front passage, the wind typically shifts from [(***south to west or northwest***) (***northeast or east to south or southwest***)]. As noted here, pressure changes with warm fronts are generally not great and may only be in rate of change, not shift of direction.

30. When a cold front passes a station, typically the air temperature will begin to [(***rise***) (***fall***)].

31. With the passage of a cold front, the dewpoint typically will begin to [(***rise***) (***fall***)].

32. The wind typically shifts from [(***south to west or northwest***) (***northeast to northwest***)].

33. And finally with the cold front's passing, the air pressure [(***rises***) (***falls***)], perhaps relatively rapidly.

In traditional weather forecasting, a barometer showing falling pressure would predict approaching stormy weather while a rising barometer presages clearing and/or continued fair weather. This simple relationship between pressure tendency and weather was demonstrated on this particular meteogram with the passing frontal system.

Suggestions for further activities: You might follow weather changes where you live. Weather observations from the course website, local media, local recording instruments (if any), or those reported hourly by NOAA Weather Radio, can be plotted on a meteogram for convenient archiving. (A blank meteogram or metgram for plotting purposes may be printed from the course website.) You might also relate the view of weather conditions from meteograms with those of a sequence of weather maps or surface text data.

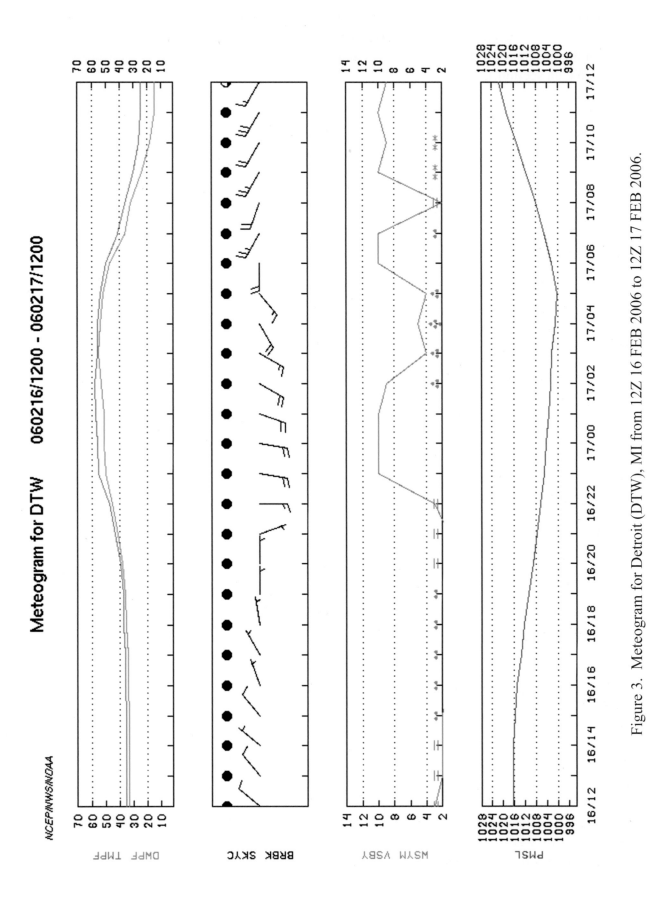

Figure 3. Meteogram for Detroit (DTW), MI from 12Z 16 FEB 2006 to 12Z 17 FEB 2006.

You can acquire meteograms for the NWS station closest to you (or to locations around the US and world) by going to: *http://vortex.plymouth.edu/statlog.html*. [This is the "click here" link on the bottom of the *Metgrams for Selected Cities in the U.S.* page from the website **Surface** data section.]

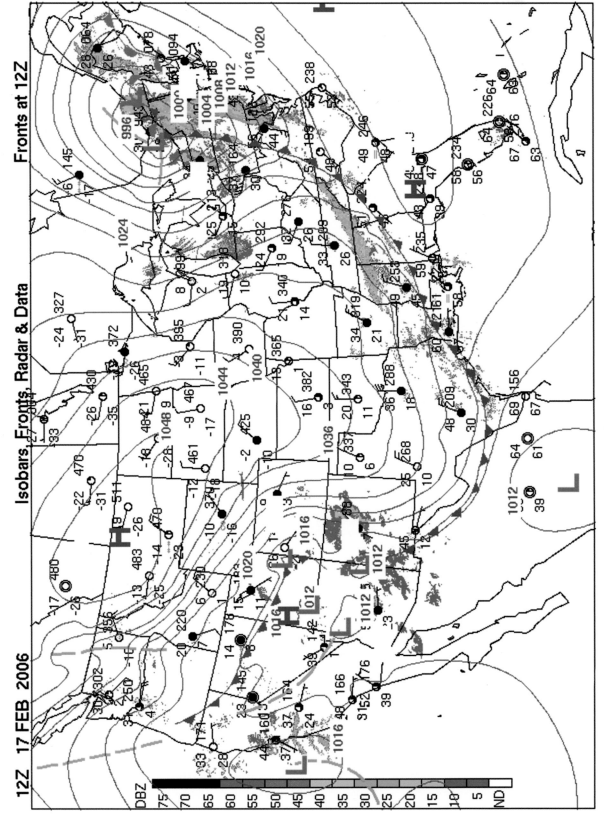

Figure 4. Isobars, Fronts, Radar & Data map for 20Z 11 FEB 2006.

Investigation 5B: ATMOSPHERIC PRESSURE IN THE VERTICAL

Objectives:

One of the most important properties of the atmosphere is air pressure. After barometer readings at the Earth's surface are "reduced" or "corrected" to sea level, air pressure still varies from place to place and with time. The principal reason for this variability in air pressure is the variability of air temperature. With otherwise similar conditions warm air is less dense than cold air. Density variations produced by temperature differences can lead to pressure differences in the horizontal throughout the atmosphere.

This investigation simulates special "blocks" to study basic understandings about pressure and pressure differences produced by density variations.

After completing this investigation, you should be able to:

- Explain what air pressure is.
- Explain how variations in air temperature cause differences in air pressure.
- Describe how density contrasts between warm and cold air produce horizontal variations in air pressure at different altitudes in the atmosphere.

Introduction:

To study pressure, we must first define it. Pressure is a force acting on a unit area of surface (*e.g.*, pounds per square inch is a pressure measurement). Air pressure is described as the weight (a force) of an overlying column of air acting on a unit area of horizontal surface. To investigate the concept of pressure we will simulate the use of tall and short "blocks". One tall block and one short block are shown in Figure 1. Tall blocks are cube-shaped and short blocks have the same size base as the tall blocks and are half as high.

> Whether tall or short, the blocks employed in this investigation have the following common characteristics:
>
> a. All blocks have the same weight regardless of the volume they occupy.
> b. All blocks have the same size square base.
> c. All individual blocks exert the same downward pressure on the surface beneath them (because the equivalent weights are acting on the same size bases).

1. Figure 1 shows one tall red block and one short blue block side-by-side on their square bases on the flat surface of a table (*T*). Because both blocks weigh the same (despite

their different volumes) and their bases are the same size, the blocks exert [(***equal***) (***unequal***)] pressure on the surface of the table.

2. The shorter blocks occupy half of the volume of the taller blocks while containing the same mass. (We know this because they weigh the same.) Because density is mass per unit volume, the smaller blocks are [(***twice***) (***half***)] as dense as the larger blocks.

3. In Figure 2, another identical block was placed on top of each block already on the table. Each stack is now exerting [(***the same***) (***twice the***)] amount of pressure on the table as the single blocks did initially.

4. The pressure exerted on the table by the tall stack is [(***equal***) (***not equal***)] to the pressure exerted on the table by the short stack.

5. As shown in Figure 3, the two stacks are side-by-side with another identical block added to each stack (for a total of 3 blocks in each stack). An imaginary surface (*1*) has been inserted horizontally through the two stacks so that two shorter blocks and one taller block are positioned beneath the surface. Compare the pressure exerted on the imaginary surface by the overlying blocks. The taller-block stack exerts [(***greater***) (***equal***) (***less***)] pressure on this imaginary surface than does the shorter-block stack.

6. Figure 4 shows two more blocks added for a total of five in each stack. A second imaginary horizontal surface (*2*) is added beneath the top short block and beneath the three top tall blocks. The pressure exerted on the table by the tall stack remains [(***equal***) (***unequal***)] to the pressure exerted on the table by the short stack.

Each block exerts one unit of pressure (1 *UP*) on the surface beneath it due to its own weight. In the table below, indicate the total pressure in *UP* units each stack of blocks exerts on each surface. For each surface, compute and record the pressure difference between the two stacks.

	Tall-Block Pressure (UP)	Short-Block Pressure (UP)	Pressure Difference (UP)
7. On Top Surface (*2*)	_____	_____	_____
8. On Lower Surface (*1*)	_____	_____	_____
9. On Table Top (*T*)	_____	_____	_____

10. Starting at the table top and moving upward, the difference in downward pressure exerted by the overlying portions of the two stacks [(***increases***) (***decreases***)].

11. In the [(***taller, less dense***) (***shorter, more dense***)] stack, the pressure decreases more rapidly with height.

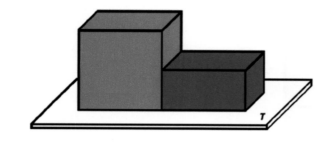

Figure 1. One tall and one short block.

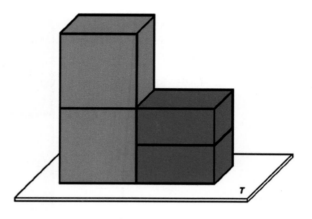

Figure 2. Two tall and two short blocks.

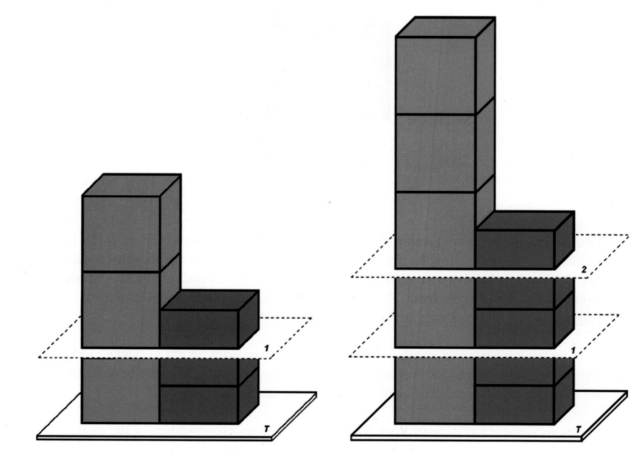

Figure 3. Three tall and three short blocks with surface 1 inserted.

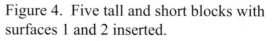

Figure 4. Five tall and short blocks with surfaces 1 and 2 inserted.

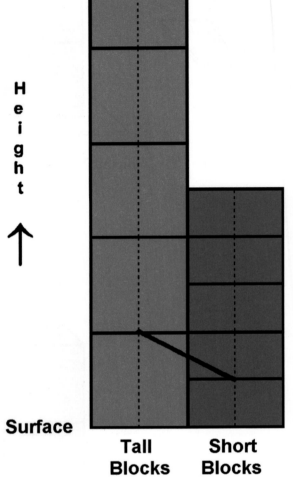

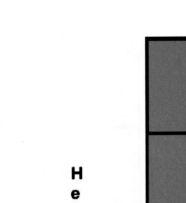

Figure 5. Pressure Blocks, Side View.

12. Look at Figure 5 showing a side view of the two stacks of pressure blocks. It is a view of the same blocks seen in the previous figure. **Following the example shown with the bottom blocks, draw straight lines connecting the mid-points of bases of blocks exerting the same pressures.** These lines connecting equal pressure dots become [(*more*) (*less*)] inclined with an increase in height.

To this point we have been examining the change in pressure with height in stacks of blocks of different density (short blocks versus tall blocks). Now we apply what we have learned to the rate at which air pressure drops with altitude in the atmosphere.

13. Figure 6: Vertical Cross-Section of Air Pressure, shows a cross-section of the atmosphere based on upper-air soundings obtained by radiosondes simultaneously at Miami, Florida and at Long Island, New York, approximately 1150 mi. (1850 km) apart. Air pressure values in millibars (mb) are plotted as marks at the altitudes where they were

observed, starting with identical values (1000 mb) at the Earth's surface. At Florida, the air pressure at approximately 12,400 m above sea level was [(***200***) (***250***) (***300***)] mb.

14. Air above the New York weather station was colder and therefore denser than the air above the more southern and warmer Florida location. Following the examples shown at the surface and at 925 mb, draw straight lines connecting equal air-pressure dots on the graph. Above the Earth's surface these lines representing equal air pressures are [(***horizontal***) (***inclined***)].

15. Compare the lines of equal pressure you drew on the two figures. They appear quite different because one deals with rigid blocks whereas the other deals with air, and their scales are much different. However, both reveal the effect of density on pressure. The lines of equal pressure slope [(***upward***) (***downward***)] from the lower-density tall blocks or warm air column above Florida to the higher-density short blocks or cold air column above New York, respectively.

16. Because of the slope of the equal-pressure lines in Figure 6, it is evident that at 12,400 m above sea level the air pressure in the warmer air over Florida is [(***higher than***) (***the same as***) (***lower than***)] the air pressure in the colder New York air at the same altitude.

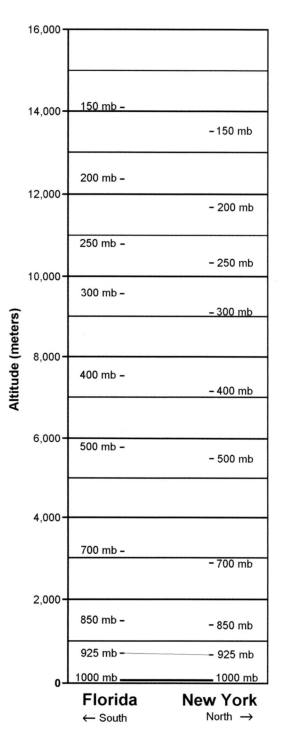

Figure 6. Vertical Cross-Section of Air Pressure.

17. The influence of air temperature on the rate of pressure drop with altitude has important implications for pilots of aircraft that are equipped with air pressure altimeters. An air pressure altimeter is actually a barometer in which altitude is calibrated against air pressure.

A little before 12Z on 21 March 2006, an aircraft starts its flight from Miami to New York. At 12Z over southern Florida, the onboard pressure altimeter indicates that the aircraft is at about 3200 meters above sea level. From Figure 6, the air pressure is about [(**_700_**) (**_800_**)] mb at an altitude of 3200 meters over Florida.

18. Relying on the pressure altimeter, the pilot continues to fly toward New York along a constant pressure level with an indicated altitude of 3200 meters. En route, the air temperature outside the aircraft gradually falls but the pilot does not alter the calibration between air pressure and altitude. Over New York, the pressure altimeter still reads 3200 meters, the *indicated altitude* of the aircraft. From Figure 6, however, it is evident that the *true altitude* of the aircraft over New York is [(**_lower than_**) (**_the same as_**) (**_higher than_**)] the altitude indicated by the altimeter.

19. The *true altitude* of the aircraft over New York is about [(**_2900_**) (**_3100_**) (**_3300_**)] meters.

20. In this example, the aircraft flies along a constant pressure surface (the 700-mb surface) which is at a [(**_higher_**) (**_lower_**)] altitude in cold air than in warm air. In actual practice, a pilot must adjust the aircraft's pressure altimeter to correct for changes in the altitude of pressure surfaces due to changes in air temperature en route. This correction ensures a more accurate calibration between air pressure and altitude.

As directed by your course instructor, complete this investigation by either:

1. *Going to the Current Weather Studies link on the course website, or*
2. *Continuing to the Applications section for this investigation that immediately follows in this Investigations Manual.*

Investigation 5B: ATMOSPHERIC PRESSURE IN THE VERTICAL

Applications

We will now consider another real-world comparison of southern and northern U.S. data. Radiosonde observations at 0000Z 22 FEB 2006 (*060222/0000*) from Miami (MFL), Florida, and Caribou (CAR), Maine, depicting the tropospheric conditions over those stations are plotted on Stüve diagrams shown in Figures 7 and 8, respectively. At the surface, Miami was reporting a temperature of 75 °F (23.8 °C) while Caribou was 22 °F (–5.7 °C).

21. Compare the temperature curves (plotted curves to the right on the Stüve diagrams) for the two stations. Comparing the two temperature curves, the atmosphere was generally warmer above [(***Caribou***) (***Miami***)]. (Note: This can be seen by laying one Stüve over the other and holding up to the light.)

The following table lists a portion of the text data from the two radiosonde observations. (Complete data for the most recent soundings are available from the course website section, **Upper Air**, "Upper Air Data - Text"). Pressure levels given are the so-called "mandatory" levels reported in each sounding plus the surface. The surface pressures were different and are listed separately. The data are presented with the highest pressures at the bottom as is the case in the open atmosphere.

Pressure (mb)	Miami		Caribou	
	Temp (°C)	Altitude (m)	Temp (°C)	Altitude (m)
100	–77.1	16540	–55.7	15630
200	–51.1	12340	–50.3	11140
300	–36.7	9640	–53.5	8500
400	–20.5	7580	–48.9	6640
500	–8.3	5880	–40.1	5150
700	8.0	3188	–24.7	2778
850	14.8	1567	–14.3	1337
925	18.2	845	–9.1	690
986 (sfc)	---	---	–5.7	190
1019 (sfc)	23.8	5	---	---

22. Compare the altitudes of the following pressure levels on the two soundings. Circle the following pressures which were at **higher** altitudes over Miami (MFL) than over Caribou (CAR):

925 mb   850 mb   700 mb   500 mb   400 mb   300 mb   200 mb   100 mb

23. Constant-pressure surfaces are those that can be imagined as surfaces in the atmosphere on which the air pressure is the same, for example, the 500-mb surface. Comparing the pressure surfaces from 700 mb to 100 mb, the top of the plotted soundings, indicates that those constant-pressure surfaces slope [(***downward***) (***upward***)] from the warm air over Miami to the colder air over Caribou.

24. In general, as one moves poleward, one would expect that the altitudes of a constant-pressure surface would become [(***higher***) (***lower***)].

25. This poleward altitude change is in response to [(***higher***) (***lower***)] average air column temperatures.

26. Assume that you were to fly from Miami to Caribou maintaining a 30,000-foot altitude as indicated by your pressure altimeter. Using a pressure altimeter, you are actually flying along a constant-pressure surface. (To visualize this flight, you can compare the altitudes of the 300-mb levels of the two stations, a pressure that is found near 30,000 feet.) As you approached Caribou, your aircraft would actually be at a [(***higher***) (***lower***)] altitude than that indicated by your altimeter.

27. If you were to fly from Miami to Caribou while maintaining an <u>actual</u> altitude of 30,000 feet (~9640 m), the air pressure outside your plane would [(***gradually increase***) (***remain the same***) (***gradually decrease***)].

<u>Suggestions for further activities:</u> The course website shows upper air information for selected stations around the U.S. plotted on Stüve diagrams and in detailed text listings. Actual altitudes of different pressure levels are found on online upper air text data listings. You might print out the text data for a reporting station near you and plot these data on a blank Stüve diagram, which you can print from the website **Extras** section. You can compare your plots to the website version. See if you can find differences for fair versus stormy weather situations.

Recall that you can also obtain Stüve diagrams and text data for locations in the U.S. and around the world at a site provided by Plymouth State University (PSU). Below the table of cities on the "Stüves for Selected Cities in the U.S." page, click on the link ("click here" near bottom of page) for additional Stüve diagrams and text data. Once at the PSU site, click on "map" and select a region to find a station identifier. Proceed as directed to acquire the information you are seeking.

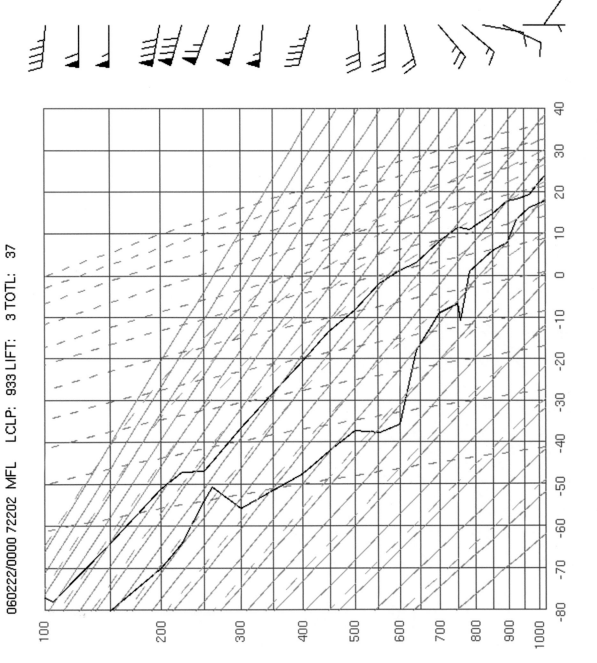

060222/0000 72202 MFL   LCLP: 933 LIFT: 3 TOTL: 37

Figure 7. Stüve diagram of Miami (MFL) sounding for 00Z 22 FEB 2006.

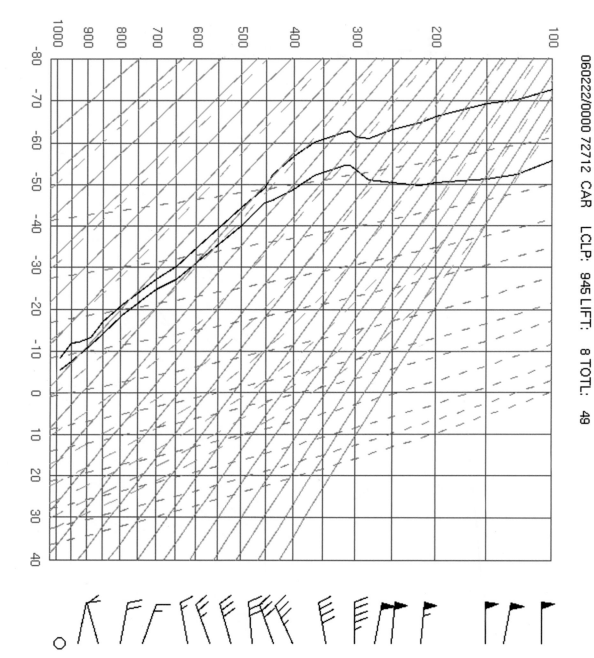

Figure 8. Stüve diagram of Caribou (CAR) sounding for 00Z 22 FEB 2006.

Investigation 6A: CLOUDS, TEMPERATURE, AND AIR PRESSURE

Objectives:

Clouds are an ever-present feature of Earth's atmosphere. A cloud is a visible suspension of tiny water droplets and/or ice crystals formed when water vapor condenses or deposits within the atmosphere. Clouds develop where air ascends and dissipate where air descends. Air temperature changes arising from air pressure changes play major roles in determining where clouds occur.

After completing this investigation, you should be able to:

- Describe how air temperature changes as air pressure changes.
- Make clouds appear and disappear in a hypothetical bottle.
- Describe the role condensation nuclei play in enhancing cloud formation.
- Explain how most clouds form in the atmosphere.

Introduction:

Cloud formation and dissipation are closely related to temperature and pressure changes in the atmosphere. Vertical motions play a primary role as air rising or sinking in the atmosphere experiences pressure changes. These pressure changes, in turn, bring about temperature changes that can result in condensation and cloud formation, or evaporation and cloud dissipation.

The relationship between air pressure and temperature can be explored in the following thought demonstration. Place a thin liquid crystal temperature strip in a clean plastic 2-liter or larger beverage bottle sealed with its cap. A liquid crystal temperature strip works well because it is very sensitive to the temperature changes of its immediate environment, in this case, the surrounding air in the bottle. [It is recommended that this experiment be done if possible. The temperature strips are available where aquarium supplies are sold, or at *www.ametsoc. org/amsedu/AERA/ed_mats.html*. Secure the temperature strip with a piece of tape to hang at the center of the bottle. Screw the cap on tightly.]

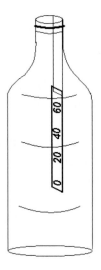

Exert pressure on the bottle so that its volume decreases. Reading the temperature strip after a few seconds have elapsed will show that the temperature of the air in the bottle rises. [Place the capped bottle so that about half of its length extends beyond the edge of a desk or table. Standing and with one hand on each end, push down on both ends of the sealed bottle so that it bends in the middle and partially collapses.]

Release the pressure so that the bottle expands again. It will be seen that as the bottle returns to its original shape the air temperature in the bottle falls. [After a half-minute or so, stop pushing down on the ends of the bottle. Try the bottle squeeze-and-release sequence several times while continuing to carefully observe temperature changes of the air in the bottle. Repeated trials confirm that a predictable relationship exists between air temperature and changes in air pressure.]

Air pressure and temperature relationships

1. Compressing the air by squeezing the bottle was accompanied by a(n) [(***decrease***) (***increase***)] in the temperature of air inside the bottle.

2. The expansion of air that occurred when the bottle was allowed to return to its original shape and volume was accompanied by a(n) [(***decrease***) (***increase***)] in the temperature of air inside the bottle.

3. These observations indicate that when air is compressed, its temperature increases, and when air expands, its temperature [(***decreases***) (***increases***)].

4. Air pressure in the open atmosphere always decreases with an increase in altitude. This happens because air pressure is determined by the weight of the overlying air. Air rising through the atmosphere expands as the pressure acting on it lowers and, in turn, its temperature [(***decreases***) (***increases***)].

5. Air sinking in the atmosphere is compressed as the air pressure acting on it increases, and its temperature [(***increases***) (***decreases***)].

Making clouds appear and disappear

Now imagine unsealing the bottle and adding some water; then reseal. After a few minutes the water will evaporate to saturate the bottle volume. [Pour a few milliliters of water in the bottle and then twist and turn the bottle to wet the inner surface. Pour out the excess water. Cap the bottle and let stand for a couple of minutes so enough water evaporates to achieve saturation within the bottle.]

Next reopen the bottle to introduce some smoke to the volume. The smoke is being added to the air because atmospheric water vapor requires particles (nuclei) on which to condense. In the atmosphere, particles acting in the same way are called *cloud condensation nuclei*. [Place the bottle on its side, open the bottle, and push down to flatten the bottle to about half its normal diameter. Have another person light a match, blow it out, and insert the smoking end into the open bottle. Quickly release your pressure on the bottle so it returns to its original shape and the smoke from the extinguished match flows inside. Quickly cap the bottle tightly.]

Now apply and release pressure on the bottle as before, noting the temperature changes. When the bottle is allowed to spring back to its original shape, the temperature lowers—and a cloud appears in the bottle! The cloud is evidenced by a change in air visibility. Repeating the process of applying and releasing pressure will cause the cloud to appear and disappear.

6.   The cloud forms when the pressure acting on the saturated air lowered and the temperature [(*__increased__*) (*__decreased__*)].

7.   Most clouds in the atmosphere form in a similar way as the cloud in the bottle. With the temperature change due to expansion, some of the water vapor in the saturated air must _____ , thereby forming cloud droplets.

8.   Once you have a cloud in the bottle, make the cloud disappear. The cloud disappears when the air temperature is raised by [(*__compression__*) (*__expansion__*)]. The change in temperature results in evaporation of the cloud droplets.

9.   It can be inferred from this investigation that in the open atmosphere where it is cloudy, air is generally [(*__rising__*) (*__sinking__*)]. Where it is clear, the air is generally moving in the opposite direction.

10. Generally, high pressure areas in the atmosphere tend to be clear because air in them experiences [(*__upward__*) (*__downward__*)] motion. Low pressure areas tend to have clouds because air in them experiences motion in the reverse direction.

Vertical motion, pressure change and temperature change are of major importance in the formation and dissipation of most clouds. However, another major factor is at work. At any given temperature, there is a maximum concentration of water vapor that can ordinarily occur in a volume of air. This condition called *saturation*, occurs when the temperature and dewpoint are equal. (The dewpoint is the temperature to which the air must be cooled at constant pressure to reach a relative humidity of 100%) Air always contains some water vapor, but usually less than the maximum possible for its temperature. Cloud formation requires saturation so that, with further cooling, excess water vapor can change to the liquid (or solid) state. Thus, the atmosphere must undergo some process whereby saturation is achieved and further cooling takes place if clouds are to form.

The cloud-in-a-bottle investigation shows how atmospheric processes can produce saturation by changing air pressure. Lowering air pressure leads to lower air temperatures and, if enough water vapor is available, saturation is achieved.

As directed by your course instructor, complete this investigation by either:

1.   *Going to the Current Weather Studies link on the course website, or*
2.   *Continuing to the Applications section for this investigation that immediately follows in this Investigations Manual.*

Investigation 6A: CLOUDS, TEMPERATURE, AND AIR PRESSURE

Applications

Water vapor and clouds in the open atmosphere

The accompanying map shows a major weather system that produced precipitation across the southern U.S., with up to 3.5 inches of rain reported in parts of Texas. Figure 1 is the surface map for 00Z 26 FEB 2006 (7 PM EST Saturday evening). The low-pressure center of the system was shown along the Florida panhandle associated with a stationary front to the east and a cold front to the west. Humid air from the Gulf of Mexico pushed generally northward and upward over the frontal systems and brought saturation, cloud development and precipitation. A second Low to the north over New York City was bringing snow to New England.

11. This Figure 1 map shows a broad precipitation shield marked by the radar shadings from eastern Texas to North Carolina associated with the Florida Low. The sky conditions at Charleston, South Carolina were [(*clear*) (*partly cloudy*) (*overcast*)].

12. Shaded radar echoes indicated that there [(*was*) (*was not*)] precipitation falling in the Charleston area. The three dots symbol of the present weather condition confirms the radar report.

13. The Charleston temperature was 53 °F and the dewpoint was 52 °F.

14. This difference between temperature and dewpoint of only one degree indicated the near-surface air [(*was very near*) (*was far from*)] saturation.

15. The sky coverage and precipitation reported on the station model and detected by radar indicated that there [(*must*) (*must not*)] have been saturated air above ground level at map time.

Figure 2 is the Stüve diagram from the Charleston (CHS) rawinsonde observation at the same time as the Figure 1 surface map, 0000Z 26 FEB 2006 *(060226/0000)*. The plotted curve to the right (higher values) on a Stüve diagram is the vertical temperature profile; the curve to the left (generally lower values) is the vertical dewpoint profile. (Temperatures and dewpoints are read by using the same scale in degrees Celsius appearing along the base of the diagram.) The plotted dewpoint is the temperature to which the air would have to be cooled at its current pressure level to become saturated with water vapor. (While saturation is assured if the temperature and dewpoint were equal, in examining radiosonde data, when the air temperature and dewpoint of rising air above the surface are within 5 Celsius degrees, meteorologists assume that clouds are possible in the area.)

16. Compare the Charleston temperature and dewpoint profiles displayed on the Stüve diagram (Figure 2). The profiles [(***are***) (***are not***)] consistent with the reports on the Figure 1 surface map concerning sky cover and precipitation.

The following selected Upper Air text data for Charleston are among the values which are plotted on the Stüve diagram. Surface station data are presented in the top line of the table, followed by successively lower pressure and higher altitude readings.

Sounding Data for CHS (72208)
00Z 26 FEB 2006

PRES	HGHT	TMPC	DWPC	RELH
1017	15	12.6	12.1	97
1000	158	10.8	10.5	98
983	305	10.3	10.0	98
947	610	9.2	8.8	98
925	807	8.4	8.0	97
913	914	8.0	7.6	97
880	1219	6.8	6.2	96
850	1504	5.6	4.9	95
848	1524	5.6	4.9	95
817	1829	4.2	3.5	95
808	1918	3.8	3.0	95
787	2134	3.8	2.9	94
762	2395	3.6	2.7	94
758	2438	3.3	2.4	94
730	2743	1.1	0.3	94
722	2831	0.4	-0.4	94
700	3080	0.2	-0.6	94
651	3658	-2.7	-4.2	89
603	4267	-5.7	-8.0	84
586	4487	-6.9	-9.4	82
557	4877	-9.1	-11.9	80
500	5710	-13.9	-17.5	74

Key:

PRES - Air pressure in millibars
HGHT - Elevation above sea level in meters
TMPC - Temperature in Celsius degrees
DWPC - Dewpoint in Celsius degrees
RELH - Relative humidity in %

17. The reported surface temperature in the table (also plotted on the Stüve) was 12.6 °C and the dewpoint was 12.1 °C. Based on such a small difference between air temperature and dewpoint, the air just above the surface at Charleston was likely [(***saturated***) (***unsaturated***)].

18. The radiosonde upper-air text data from the Charleston sounding shows that, as the instrument package ascended, the pressure (PRES) consistently [(***increased***) (***decreased***)].

19. During this ascent, the temperature (TMPC) generally [(***increased***) (***decreased***)]. (The layers from 850 to 848 mb and from 808 to 787 mb were *isothermal*.)

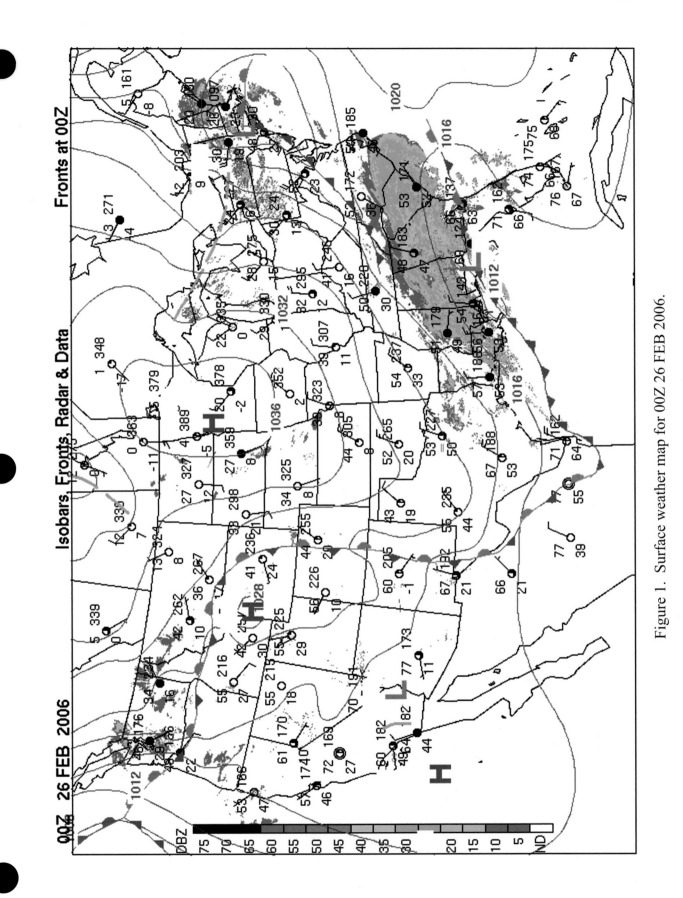

Figure 1. Surface weather map for 00Z 26 FEB 2006.

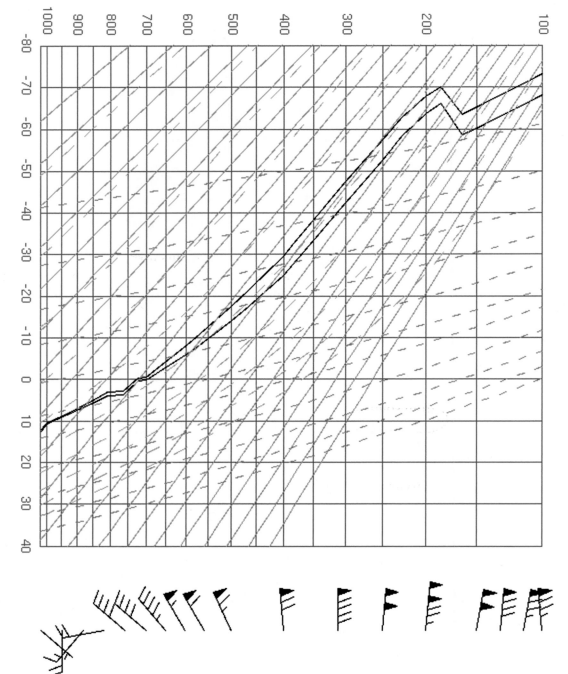

Figure 2. Stüve diagram for Charleston (CHS), SC sounding at 0000Z 26 FEB 2006.

20. **With the above text data as a guide, on the Stüve diagram, highlight the portions of the profile above the surface where the temperature and dewpoint (DWPC) curves are within one degree of each other.** The text data show that at these levels the relative humidities (RELH) were greater than 90%. [(***True***) (***False***)]

21. This small temperature and dewpoint difference, or alternatively, the high relative humidity condition, and the moderate rain reported at Charleston, indicated that the rising air during the ascent quickly became and remained [(***saturated***) (***unsaturated***)].

22. Therefore from near the surface to the 700-mb level, clouds probably [(***did***) (***did not***)] exist through that section of the troposphere over Charleston at the time of the sounding.

23. The separation of temperature and dewpoint values from about the 700-mb level upward indicated slightly drier air. If we arbitrarily assume the air was saturated from about 1000 mb to 700 mb, we can take these levels to be the approximate base and top, respectively, of the cloud layer over Charleston at that time. According to the pressure-level heights (HGHT in m) listed above, the thickness of the atmosphere with this layer of clouds extended through a depth of about [(***300***) (***3000***) (***30,000***)] meters.

24. We can assume from our experience in the first portion of this investigation that the vertical motion in the atmosphere over Charleston was [(***upward***) (***downward***)], which led to cloud formation. This vertical motion direction is consistent with the movement of the palm of your hand in the *hand-twist model* of the Low. These clouds produced the precipitation that was reported around the area.

The lowest level winds at Charleston, shown at the base of the wind profile to the right of the sounding, were from the northeast at about 5 knots. Wind directions from about 880 mb to 700 mb were generally from southerly directions at 20 to 45 knots, off the Gulf and Atlantic and overrunning the frontal surfaces. This airflow would force the air aloft leading to the widespread precipitation along the Gulf Coast.

Suggestions for further activities: You might compare Stüve diagrams for the station nearest you with surface cloud reports or with satellite observations to see ways whereby the existence of clouds can be determined. If you have periods of fog or predictions for it, you might check meteograms to follow the temperature and dewpoint values over time. (Fog is a cloud in contact with Earth's surface.)

Another process achieving saturation is the mixing of hot, humid air with cold, dry air in the formation of contrails (condensation trails - cloud-like streamers frequently observed to form behind aircraft flying in clear, cold air). This process is described at: *http://cimss.ssec.wisc. edu/wxwise/class/contrail.html*.

Investigation 6B: RISING AND SINKING AIR

Objectives:

As air moves vertically in the atmosphere, it experiences changes in the surrounding atmospheric pressure. These changes in pressure allow a rising parcel (a term used in meteorology to imply a small volume or body of air) to expand as surrounding pressures decrease, and cause a sinking parcel to be compressed as surrounding pressures increase. Rising, unsaturated air expands and cools at a rate of 9.8 C° per 1000 m (5.5 F° per 1000 ft). This is called the *dry adiabatic lapse rate*. Sinking unsaturated air warms at the same rate.

An unsaturated (relative humidity less than 100%) air parcel, when rising and cooling, may reach saturation. Upon saturation, further ascent will continue the expansional cooling. But, some heating will take place within the parcel because of condensation (or deposition at low temperatures). This warming occurs as latent heat is released to the environment when water vapor condenses into droplets or deposits as ice crystals. The simultaneous cooling by expansion and warming by condensation or deposition results in a **net** (observable) cooling rate, called the *saturated (or moist) adiabatic lapse rate*, that is lower than the cooling rate for unsaturated air. Although variable, the saturated adiabatic lapse rate averages about 6 C° per 1000 meters (3.3 F° per 1000 ft).

After completing this investigation, you should be able to:

- Describe how to use a Stüve diagram to follow atmospheric temperatures and pressures.
- Determine the temperature of air that rises or sinks in the atmosphere.
- Describe how the water vapor saturation of air can affect atmospheric temperatures.

Introduction:

The Figure 1 Stüve diagram for this investigation includes lines representing the adiabatic processes of dry (unsaturated) and saturated air. The solid, straight lines sloping from lower right to upper left in the body of the chart graphically represent the dry adiabatic lapse rate, showing visually the temperature change of an unsaturated air parcel that is undergoing vertical motion in the atmosphere. The dashed, curved lines sloping from lower right to upper left represent the temperature change of saturated air undergoing vertical motion, the saturated adiabatic lapse rate. **Locate an air parcel with temperature 17 °C and pressure 1000 mb by placing a dot on the chart on the 1000 mb horizontal line where 17 °C would occur.**

1. If this air rises as unsaturated (dry) air from 1000 mb, determine its temperature at 500 mb by following the *dry adiabatic lapse rate* line passing through the starting point, up to 500 mb. At 500 mb, the temperature of the unsaturated air parcel is about **[(-5) (-35) (-45)]** °C.

2. If this air rises as <u>saturated</u> air from 1000 mb, determine its temperature at 500 mb by following the *saturated adiabatic lapse rate* line passing through the starting point, up to 500 mb. At 500 mb, the saturated air parcel's temperature is approximately [(***-15***) (***-25***) (***-35***)] °C.

3. At 500 mb, the temperature of the unsaturated air parcel is [(***lower than***) (***the same as***) (***higher than***)] the temperature of the saturated air parcel.

4. This comparison demonstrates that rising unsaturated, clear air cools [(***more***) (***less***)] than rising saturated, cloudy air over the same interval.

5. Begin once again with unsaturated air at 17 °C and 1000 mb. Because it is unsaturated, its relative humidity initially is [(***greater than***) (***equal to***) (***less than***)] 100%.

6. As this air rises, assume it becomes saturated at 800 mb. From 1000 mb to 800 mb, it will follow a [(***dry***) (***saturated***)] adiabatic lapse rate line.

7. Being saturated at 800 mb, its relative humidity is now [(***greater than***) (***equal to***) (***less than***)] 100%.

8. As the air continues to rise, it will follow a [(***dry***) (***saturated***)] adiabatic lapse rate line.

9. Continue the ascent to 500 mb. The air parcel temperature is now approximately [(***-18***) (***-27***) (***-34***)] °C.

10. This temperature is [(***higher than***) (***equal to***) (***lower than***)] the temperature achieved by the unsaturated parcel that ascended dry adiabatically the entire way to 500 mb in item 1.

11. If condensation was occurring during the ascent from 800 mb to 500 mb, the air parcel would have [(***gained***) (***lost***) (***had no change in***)] water vapor during the ascent.

12. Throughout this saturated portion of the ascent, the relative humidity of the air parcel is [(***greater than 100%***) (***100%***) (***less than 100%***)].

13. Assume that all the water that condensed (or deposited) during the ascent was immediately lost as precipitation from the parcel. Therefore, if the air parcel at 500 mb begins to descend, it will warm slightly by compression and immediately become an unsaturated parcel. As the parcel sinks back to the 1000-mb level, it will warm at the dry adiabatic lapse rate, as shown by following the dry adiabatic lapse rate line down from the point at 500 mb. When it arrives back at 1000 mb, its temperature is [(***17***) (***27***) (***37***)] °C.

14. This parcel's final temperature is [(***higher than***) (***the same as***) (***lower than***)] its beginning temperature when it was initially at 1000 mb.

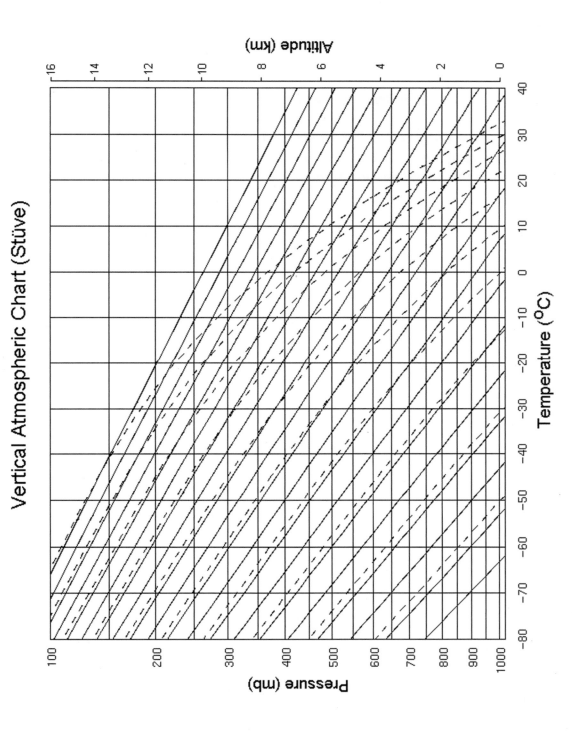

Figure 1. Vertical Atmospheric (Stüve) Chart with adiabats.

15. The relative humidity of this air parcel is now [(**_greater than_**) (**_equal to_**) (**_less than_**)] what it was when it began its journey at 1000 mb.

16. The change from the initial parcel temperature to the final parcel temperature at the 1000-mb level was caused by condensation (or deposition) which [(**_releases_**) (**_absorbs_**)] latent heat.

As directed by your course instructor, complete this investigation by either:

    1. Going to the Current Weather Studies link on the course website, or
    2. Continuing to the Applications section for this investigation that immediately follows in this Investigations Manual.

Investigation 6B: RISING AND SINKING AIR
Applications

Rising and sinking air motions occurring in the atmosphere may be produced by several situations. Rising motion can be caused by approaching fronts, convergence of winds blowing into a surface low pressure center which forces air aloft, localized daytime solar heating, or orographic flow over rising terrain. Conversely, sinking motion can occur with near-surface divergence of air in Highs or by air flow over descending terrain.

Occurrences similar to this Stüve example of rising and sinking air are common in mountainous areas, resulting in higher temperatures on the mountains' leeward slope (the side facing away from the prevailing wind). *Chinook winds* occurring east of the Rocky Mountains are examples of compressional warming of sinking air. Rapid City, South Dakota is frequently subject to Chinook winds.

17. At 00Z 10 OCT 2005, Rapid City, South Dakota reported a temperature of 45 °F and dewpoint of 39 °F. This difference of several degrees indicate that the near-surface air at Rapid City [(***was***) (***was not***)] saturated at that time.

18. Figure 2 is Stüve diagram for Rapid City (RAP), SD for 00Z 10 OCT 2005. The Stüve diagram for Rapid City indicated that the surface air [(***was***) (***was not***)] saturated as evidenced by the separation of the temperature and dewpoint values at the surface.

19. Therefore, air rising from the surface at Rapid City would initially be [(***unsaturated or "dry"***) (***saturated***)].

20. This rising air would therefore cool at the [(***dry***) (***saturated***)] adiabatic rate.

21. In the layer from the surface (897 mb) up to 850 mb, the temperature profile "parallels" the [(***straight, solid dry***) (***dashed, curved saturated***)] adiabatic lapse rate lines on the Stüve diagram.

22. Assuming rising air, this path indicates that the ascending air was cooling at the [(***dry***) (***saturated***)] adiabatic lapse rate.

23. From text data for the Stüve diagram Rapid City sounding (not provided here), the surface temperature was reported to be 7.0 °C at an altitude of 1029 m while the 850 mb temperature was 2.6 °C at an altitude of 1469 m. The temperature difference was _____ C° and the altitude difference was _____ m.

24. Therefore, the lapse rate was _____ C°/m or 10 C°/1000 m.

25. This lapse rate in the rising air at Rapid City was [(***very close to***) (***very different from***)] the dry adiabatic rate of 9.8 C°/1000 m.

26. From 850 mb to about 775 mb the air over Rapid City continued cooling but at a rate less than dry adiabatic. At 850 mb, the temperature and the dewpoint were [(***equal***) (***far apart***)].

27. The temperature and dewpoint profiles on the Stüve diagram are superimposed from 850 mb upward through a considerable vertical distance. Therefore, the air [(***was***) (***was not***)] saturated and clouds probably did exist over Rapid City. The conditions in this layer were consistent with the sky conditions over Rapid City and the indicated precipitation in the area as shown on the surface map for the same time.

28. From 850 mb up to 775 mb the temperature profile shows [(***cooling***) (***isothermal***) (***inversion***)] conditions.

29. This 850 mb to 775 mb portion of the profile approximately follows the nearby dashed line on the diagram representing the [(***dry***) (***saturated***)] adiabatic lapse rate. (This suggests that the radiosonde was sensing cloudy conditions.)

30. From 775 mb up to about 670 mb humidity conditions suggest clouds also existed but there was a temperature inversion from 775 mb to 740 mb. Atmospheric processes in addition to forcing air aloft must have been occurring. This was inferred from the change in wind direction reported to the right of the Stüve diagram from northerly below about 700 mb to southerly above that pressure level.

    Above about 520 mb the separations of the temperature and dewpoint profiles by more than 5 degrees suggested that clouds [(***did***) (***did not***)] continuously exist at all levels above Rapid City.

Investigation 6A (Clouds, Temperature, and Air Pressure) involved the relationship between air temperature and air pressure changes. The Stüve diagrams employed in this investigation graphically display this relationship with sets of lines drawn to represent temperature changes which occur when saturated or unsaturated air undergoes vertical motion. Observed temperature and dewpoint profiles, demonstrated by the Rapid City soundings, frequently provide convincing evidence that ascending air actually behaves according to this relationship!

Suggestions for further activities: You might print out the text data of rawinsonde observations and plot them on a blank Stüve diagram (available on the website) when Highs, Lows, and fronts pass nearby. Then compare local cloud and sky conditions with the temperature and dewpoint profiles you have plotted.

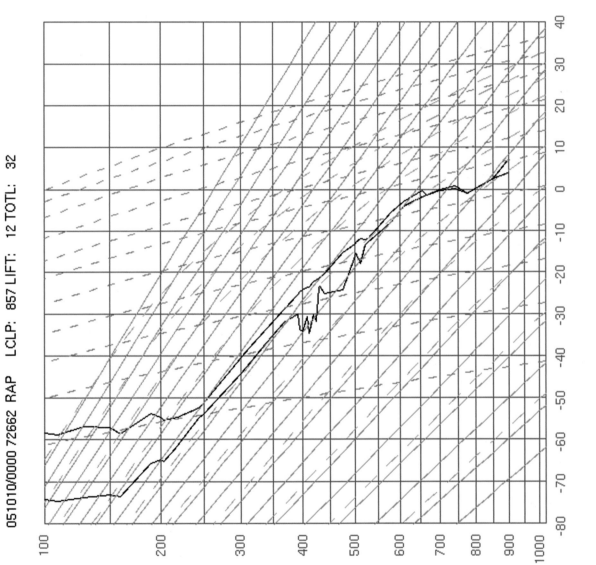

051010/0000 72662 RAP   LCLP: 857 LIFT: 12 TOTL: 32

Figure 2. Stüve diagram for Rapid City (RAP) for 0000Z 10 OCT 2005.

Investigation 7A: PRECIPITATION PATTERNS

Objectives:

Rain and snow are not random and capricious acts of nature. This is especially evident when weather-radar echo patterns signifying precipitation are viewed along with weather maps and satellite images for the same times.

The basic mechanism for the formation of clouds and precipitation is the uplift and consequent cooling of air by expansion. In fact, uplift of air along the sloping surface of a front is the principal mechanism whereby the circulation in Lows produces clouds and precipitation. Clouds and precipitation also may be associated with the upward branch of a convection current, uplift of air along the windward slopes of a mountain range, or convergence of surface winds. One of the most useful tools in following the development and movement of areas of precipitation is weather radar.

After completing this investigation, you should be able to:

- Describe different mechanisms leading to the formation of clouds and precipitation in low pressure systems.
- Locate areas of precipitation based on weather radar depictions.
- Indicate the general relationship between the uplift of air and the formation of clouds and precipitation.

Introduction:

1. Recall that a *front* is a line drawn on a surface weather map that marks a narrow transition zone between air masses differing in density (due to contrasts in temperature and/or humidity). An *air mass*, in turn, is a huge volume of air covering perhaps tens of thousands of square kilometers having generally uniform temperature and humidity characteristics.

    A mass of cold, dry air is [(***denser than***) (***not as dense as***)] a mass of warm, humid air. Warmer (lighter) air is forced to rise above the sloping frontal surface overlying colder (denser) air.

2. Ascending unsaturated (clear) air [(***expands***) (***is compressed***)], cooling at about 10 Celsius degrees per 1000 meters of ascent (5.5 Fahrenheit degrees per 1000 feet).

3. The warmer air rising above the frontal surface expands and cools as it ascends, and its relative humidity [(***increases***) (***decreases***)]. If saturation is achieved, clouds develop and from those clouds, rain or snow may fall.

4.   The relative humidity of saturated (cloudy) air is ___100___ %.

5.   Clouds (and perhaps precipitation) can develop in the ascending branch of a convection current, along a front, and up the windward slopes of a mountain range. The ascending branch of a convective current may produce an upwardly billowing cloud known as a [(*cumulus*) (*stratus*) (*cirrus*)] cloud.

6.   Prevailing winds blow from west to east across North America. Winds that blow onshore from the Pacific Ocean are forced up the windward slopes of the Cascade Mountain Range in the Pacific Northwest. Hence, the heaviest precipitation falls on the [(*western*) (*eastern*)] slopes of the Cascades.

Hc air rising on the slope & condenses & falls as water

As directed by your course instructor, complete this investigation by either:

1.   *Going to the Current Weather Studies link on the course website, or*
2.   *Continuing to the Applications section for this investigation that immediately follows in this Investigations Manual.*

Investigation 7A: PRECIPITATION PATTERNS
Applications

Weather radar consists of a pulsed beam of microwave energy that is reflected by raindrops and snowflakes that are in the beam's path. Some of that returned microwave energy reaches a receiver that displays these so-called *echoes* as colored images on a computer screen. NOAA's National Weather Service and other agencies operate more than 110 weather radars at various sites nationwide. The composite of all echoes received by these radars is routinely plotted on a surface weather map. In addition, echo intensity is rated by category ranging from weak to strong. Heavy rain (or hail) reflects more microwave energy than light rain and thus produces more intense echoes.

7. Figure 1 shows two radar images from the Fort Campbell, Kentucky (HPX) site. The shaded irregular shapes appearing in the top Figure 1a *reflectivity* image represent areas where rain was falling at 1852Z on 7 April 2006. The shadings provide information on the echo intensity, from which the rates of precipitation can be correlated. The intensity scale is depicted to the right of the image. The innermost red shades surrounded by yellow and then green shades indicate the most intense rainfall rates. The radar site is located in the center of the image area just north of Clarksville, TN across the KY-TN border. Shown in the bottom Figure 1b is the storm total precipitation amount during the hour following the 1852Z reflectivity image. The greatest accumulation is shown with the red shadings using the scale to the right in that image.

    Look at the Figure 1a reflectivity view. The greatest reflectivity values as shown by the shading tend to be found in [(***separate round or oval blobs***) (***long lines of uniform color***) (***a single large circle over the entire area***)]. This pattern gives rise to the terminology of storm "cells".

8. Cellular reflectivity patterns, including the strong gradients, as seen most notably in going from no echo to intense echo on the southwest sides of the cells like the two in west central Tennessee, suggest this precipitation event is primarily produced by [(***thunderstorms***) (***hurricanes***) (***a general rain area***)].

9. Look at the Figure 1b *one-hour precipitation total* image. The reflectivity intensities can be related to a precipitation rate by the computer and the accumulated total precipitation amount over the time interval can be displayed. Routinely delivered NWS radar products usually provide 1-hour and storm total precipitation amounts. The shadings shown depict the total amount of precipitation in inches across the area as given in the scale to the right of this portion of the image. The greatest one-hour precipitation totals are associated with streaks that trend from lower left to upper right. This movement to the northeast is the typical direction of movement of storm cells with the mid-tropospheric winds. The western ends of the precipitation total tracks are generally [(***not related***) (***closely related***)] to the location of the most intense cells at the beginning of the one-hour period.

10. Over this one-hour period the thunderstorm cells, particularly the cell located just to the north of Nashville, TN, dropped prodigious amounts of rainfall. The Figure 1b scale indicates the greatest total rainfall amounts estimated by the radar north of Nashville were approximately [(**_0.5_**) (**_1.0_**) (**_2.0_**)] inch(es). Meteorologists use these rainfall estimates along with local ground conditions (e.g., dry or saturated soils) and terrain (including stream locations and capacities) to warn of the potential for flash flooding.

As noted, clouds and precipitation commonly occur along fronts, in the upward branch of convection currents, along the windward slopes of mountain ranges (due to orographic lifting), and where surface winds converge. Often the most expansive area of precipitation forms in association with fronts. Figure 2 shows a frontal system passing across the central U.S. that spawned deadly severe weather including thunderstorms with many tornadoes.

Figure 2 is the surface weather map for 02Z 13 MAR 2006. A complex wavy frontal system stretched from eastern Canada across Maine to a Low centered over eastern Kansas and western Missouri. From the Low center one cold front arched southward across Oklahoma and Texas while another short segment of cold front continued westward into Colorado. Also shown as a curve with open, half circles is a dry line extending from the Low center, ahead of the cold front, southward into Texas and northern Mexico. A *dry line* is a boundary separating warm and humid air from warm, but drier air. The humidity difference leads to a density difference and the dry line behaves like a cold front as a lifting mechanism. (Note: the frontal positions on the 02Z map are from 00Z, and therefore should be taken as approximate.) A thin rectangle across eastern Iowa, southern Wisconsin and northern Illinois covers the approximate area shown by Figure 3.

Compare the temperatures and dewpoints at Little Rock, AR, with Oklahoma City, OK, and Amarillo, TX. Little Rock's temperature and dewpoint are 78 °F and 59 °F, respectively. Oklahoma City's are 74 °F and 25 °F, while Amarillo's are 46 °F and 3 °F. Little Rock's conditions were indicative of the warm, humid air of the warm sector of the storm system, between the warm front and the cold front/dry line to the west. Conditions at Oklahoma City represented the warm, dry air, while Amarillo was clearly in the cold, dry air following the passage of the cold front. With these conditions, the air at those cities was progressively denser from east to west.

11. At map time, radar echoes likely were produced by thunderstorm precipitation, indicated by red dots and blobs within yellow-shaded areas. (Intensities are shown by the scale to the left of the Figure 2 map.) Blue and green shades signified generally light precipitation. The thunderstorms were located generally [(**_across Colorado and Nebraska_**) (**_from eastern Oklahoma to southeastern Iowa_**)].

12. The southern portion of the area of thunderstorm activity likely had [(**_the cold front and dry line_**) (**_the warm front_**)] as the main lifting mechanism to initiate convection.

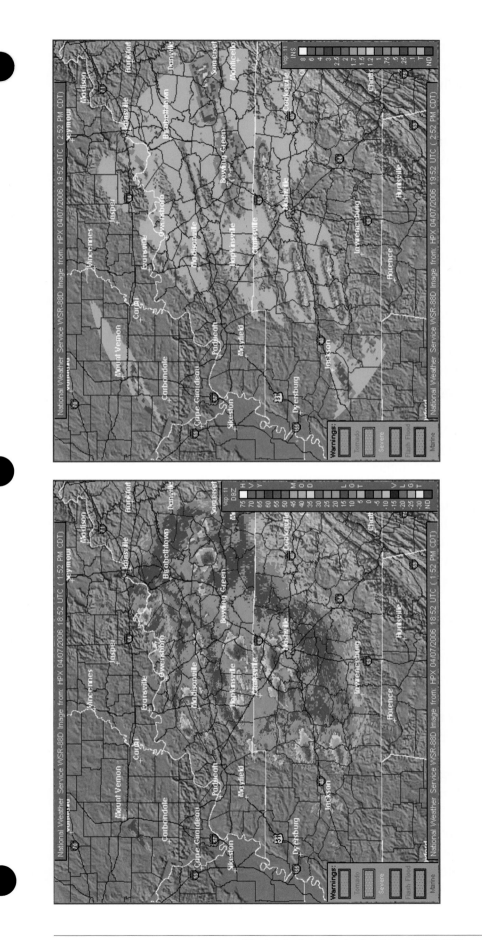

Figure 1. (a) Reflectivity display from Fort Campbell, KY radar at 1852Z 07 APR 2006 and (b) the one-hour total precipitation at 1952Z.

13. The northern portion of the area of thunderstorm activity was likely the result of lifting by [(***the cold front and dry line***) (***the warm front***)]. Also, a broad arc of snow was falling from Wisconsin westward to South Dakota and western Kansas north of the Low center.

Figure 3 is a composite view of (a) the reflectivity (precipitation intensity) display from the NWS Quad Cities (four-city metropolitan area on the Iowa-Illinois border) radar at 0254Z 13 MAR 2006 on the left and (b) the one-hour total precipitation detected at 0245Z on the right. These display times are about three-quarters of an hour following the map conditions of Figure 2. The most intense echoes are shown in the left reflectivity image in red as they were on the surface map. The arching band of precipitation across the middle of the view is the intense thunderstorm band just north of the warm front. The largest red blob to the lower right in the Springfield, IL area is a "supercell" thunderstorm producing heavy rains and severe weather.

14. Compare the positions of the thunderstorm cells in the (a) reflectivity view on the left to the (b) one-hour precipitation totals view on the right. Generally each elongated swath of relatively large total precipitation has a relatively intense reflectivity cell located at its northeast end. This implies that the individual intense cells were generally tracking towards the [(***south-southeast***) (***east-northeast***)].

15. The color coding indicates that the total precipitation estimated by the radar over the preceding hour from the southeastern supercell thunderstorm near Springfield was about [(***0.5 to 1.0***) (***1.0 to 1.5***) (***2 to 3***)] inches.

16. Figure 4 is the total precipitation measured by rain gauges at selected stations across the contiguous U.S. for the 24-hour period ending at 12Z 13 MAR 2006. This map is linked from the course website under **Surface** products, "24 Hour Precipitation", and includes the period of the surface map and radar images. The greatest precipitation total shown is [(***0.61***) (***1.00***) (***1.37***)] inches, located along the Indiana-Kentucky border.

Rain gauges are not available at every location where rain falls and radars only provide estimates of precipitation, so the value noted in Figure 3(b) does not appear on Figure 4. Local precipitation values at locations between gauges can be substantially greater than reported values.

17. Precipitation reports across the central U.S. region shown in the Figure 4 map [(***are***) (***are not***)] generally located where the radar echoes existed on the Figure 2 map.

Suggestions for further activities: When precipitation is expected or occurring in your area, you can consult local weathercasts for observations of the location and total amounts over a particular time period. You may wish to explore the current radar information provided by NOAA's NWS Radar page, linked from the **Radar** section of the website. Most browsers will allow you to run animations of the images (loop) or you can select a regional scale image below the large view. Precipitation reflectivity, radial velocity and storm total view and animations are available from individual stations by clicking on the map.

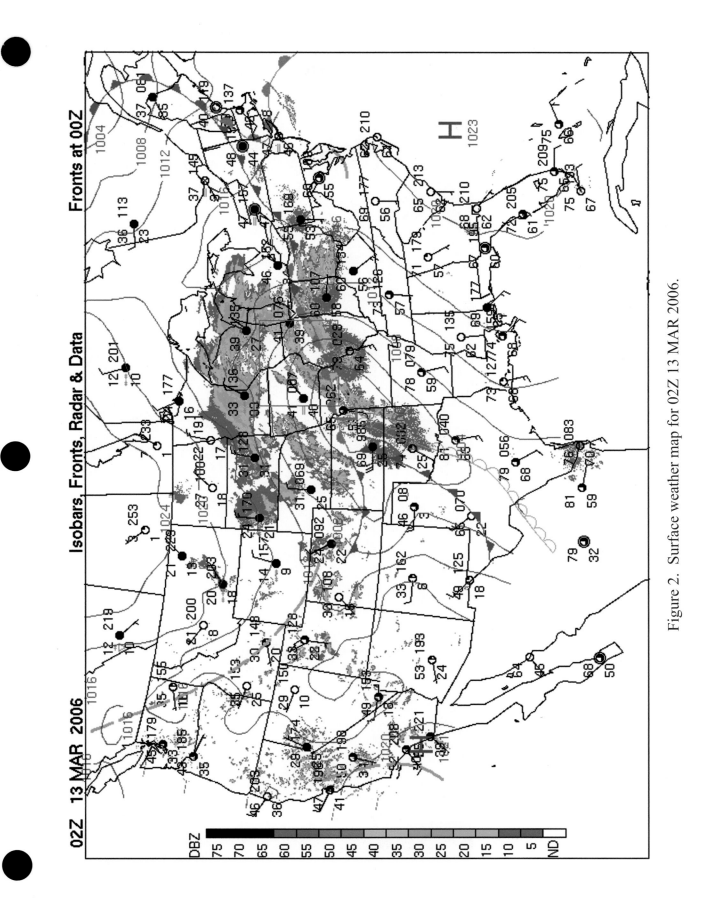

Figure 2. Surface weather map for 02Z 13 MAR 2006.

Figure 3. (a) Reflectivity display from NWS Quad Cities radar at 0254Z 13 MAR 2006 and (b) the one-hour total precipitation at

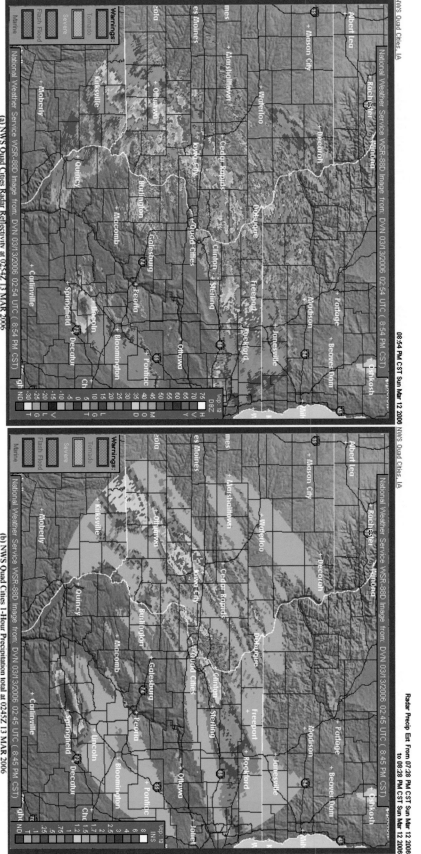

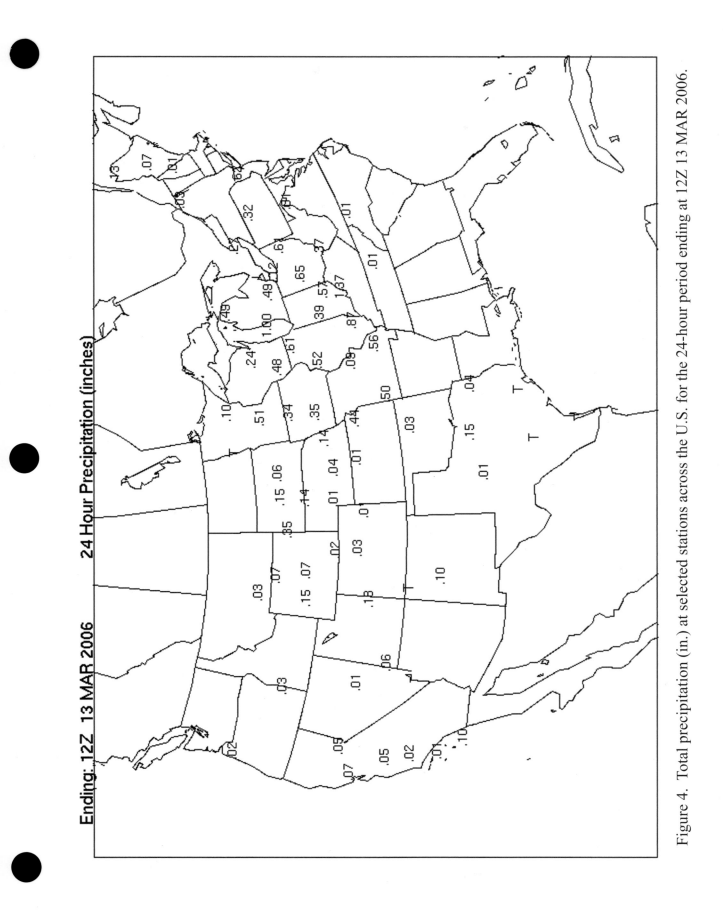

Figure 4. Total precipitation (in.) at selected stations across the U.S. for the 24-hour period ending at 12Z 13 MAR 2006.

Investigation 7B: DOPPLER RADAR

Objectives:

Weather radar provides information on storm size, shape, intensity, and direction of movement. With the advent of Doppler radar, the circulation within a storm can also be determined. For instance, air motions that indicate possible tornado development can be detected. This information can provide the public with advance warning of severe weather and save lives.

After completing this investigation, you should be able to:

- Describe aspects of the actual wind that are detected by Doppler radar.
- Determine the speed of the wind towards or away from the radar site.
- Construct the wind pattern as detected by Doppler radar.

Materials: Red and green pens or pencils.

Introduction:

Radar detection of motion is based on the *Doppler effect*, the change in frequency (or phase) of a sound or electromagnetic wave reaching a receiver when the receiver and source are moving relative to one another. A frequency shift occurs when a radar signal is reflected from a moving target such as a cluster of raindrops. If the raindrops are moving toward the radar, the reflected signals returned to the radar have a higher frequency than if the target were stationary. On the other hand, if the raindrops are moving away from the radar, the returned signal's frequency is lowered. The magnitude of the frequency shift is a measure of how fast the raindrops are moving directly toward or away from the radar.

Doppler weather radar is especially useful for detection of severe weather conditions. One of the most devastating and potentially deadly of severe weather phenomena is the tornado. A tornado is a rapidly rotating column of air in contact with the ground. Tornadoes are almost always associated with thunderstorms.

Before tornadoes develop their intense, ground-level circulation, a broader-scale horizontal rotation is often evident within the parent thunderstorm. This internal thunderstorm rotation is called a *mesocyclone*. As the air entering the thunderstorm begins to swirl in the mesocyclone, raindrops are carried along and reflect radar energy back toward the radar antenna.

1. Figure 1a is a schematic view of a radar beam detecting a mesocyclone, depicted as a rotating cylinder embedded within a severe thunderstorm. As viewed from above, the mesocyclone's rotation is typically counterclockwise. Figure 1b is a view from above

with the size of the mesocyclone exaggerated (not to scale). The dashed lines represent the radar beam in positions 1 through 5 as it rotates through the mesocyclone. The arrows drawn around the mesocyclone column in Figure 1b represent the actual wind at dots located at the tails of the arrows. Each arrow shows the instantaneous direction of air movement at that point, and the length of the arrow represents the speed of that wind. In this example, the actual winds circulating around the mesocyclone all have the same speed, as shown by arrows whose lengths are [(***the same***) (***different***)].

2. From one location to another around the mesocyclone, the wind directions are [(***the same***) (***different***)].

3. Doppler radar detects only motions that are directly toward or away from the radar. At two locations within the rotating wind pattern no air motion is detected by the Doppler radar beam. At those points, the actual wind blows along paths perpendicular to the radar beam (dashed line). Hence, the Doppler radar senses no Doppler wind speed at these locations. These two locations are sensed by the radar when its beam is in the [(***1***) (***2***) (***3***) (***4***) (***5***)] position(s). **Draw a small circle around each of the dots associated with those two arrows to denote this zero Doppler wind speed.**

4. Two arrows on the column circle are along the direction of the radar beam, one directly towards the radar and one directly away. These two locations are sensed when the radar beam is at the [(***1***) (***2***) (***3***) (***4***) (***5***)] position(s). Because these arrows are oriented directly toward or directly away from the radar site along the beam direction, the radar will sense the full wind speed, toward and away, respectively.

    Where the wind arrow is oriented directly toward the radar, use a green pencil to trace a bold, green arrow of the same length and direction atop the wind arrow. Where the wind arrow is oriented directly away from the radar, use a red pencil to trace a bold, red arrow of the same length and direction atop the wind arrow. [The NWS color convention uses "cool" colors such as green and blue for motions toward the radar and "warm" colors such as red and orange for those away from the radar.]

5. At the other four arrow locations shown around the mesocyclone, wind arrows are neither directly toward or away, nor perpendicular to the radar beam direction. Where the radar beam direction and the actual wind arrow make an angle other than 0 or 90 degrees, Doppler radar senses only the component of the total motion that is directly toward or away from the radar. **For the two arrows that are directed partly toward the radar, use the green pencil to draw approximately half-length green arrows, from the location dots, that are aimed directly toward the radar along the dashed beam direction.** These two locations are at the [(***1***) (***2***) (***3***) (***4***) (***5***)] position(s).

6. **For the two arrows that are directed partly away from the radar, use the red pencil to make similar half-length red arrows, drawn from the location dots, that are aimed directly away from the radar.** These two locations are at the [(***1***) (***2***) (***3***) (***4***) (***5***)] position(s).

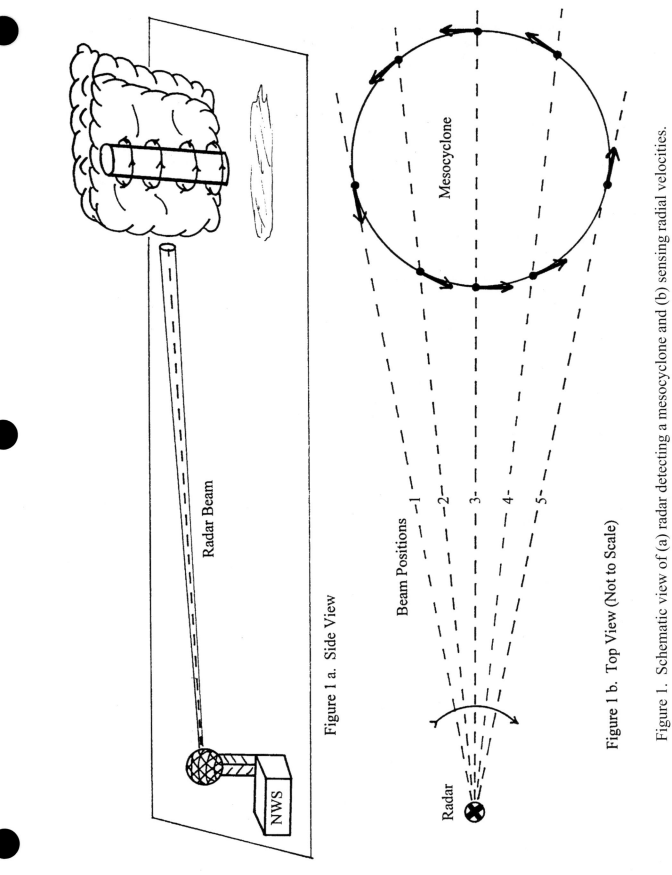

Figure 1 a. Side View

Figure 1 b. Top View (Not to Scale)

Figure 1. Schematic view of (a) radar detecting a mesocyclone and (b) sensing radial velocities.

Finally, with the green pencil, shade across the semi-circular area of the mesocyclone where the arrows are green. Shade the lightest from near the zero position, becoming darker where the green arrow is longest. With the red pencil, shade across the portion of the mesocyclone where the arrows are red. Graduate the shading from lightest near the zero position, becoming darker where the red arrow is longest.

7. Observe the colored arrows of your mesocyclone depiction. These are the Doppler winds as detected by the radar utilizing the Doppler effect. Circle either T for true, or F for false, for each of the following statements based on the colored arrow pattern of the radar display associated with the mesocyclone.

    a. T   F   The green arrows are directed toward the radar.
    b. T   F   The red arrows are directed away from the radar.
    c. T   F   Along the radar beam, when in position 3, the Doppler wind speed is zero.
    d. T   F   The green shaded area depicts air motion towards the radar.
    e. T   F   The red shaded area depicts air motion away from the radar.

The color scheme you have drawn on Figure 1b represents the severe weather "signature" of a mesocyclone on a Doppler weather radar display. The signature has regions of green and red appearing on opposite sides of a radial line from the radar's location. Meteorologists have identified other Doppler radar patterns associated with fronts, gust fronts and outflow boundaries from thunderstorms, wind shear, and other forms of severe weather.

As directed by your course instructor, complete this investigation by either:

  1. Going to the Current Weather Studies link on the course website, or
  2. Continuing to the Applications section for this investigation that immediately follows in this Investigations Manual.

Investigation 7B: DOPPLER RADAR
Applications

As noted in the first part of this investigation, Doppler radar detects the motions of particles directly toward or away from the radar site. While the targets producing this echo of energy are usually raindrops, ice crystals or hailstones, other particles in the atmosphere can scatter radar energy as well. Small aerosols (haze droplets, dust particles) and even insects can scatter the beam. In this way, NOAA's NWS Doppler radar can "see" air motions utilizing these particles even in "clear air", or non-precipitation cases. Figure 2 consists of side-by-side views of (a) the reflectivity (echo intensity) from precipitation and (b) the radial velocity of those targets relative to the radar site. The radar views were from essentially the same time on 14 MAR 2006 from the NWS Doppler radar which is located just northwest of State College (CCX), PA. A yellow dot in the right (b) velocity view marks the radar site.

8. The blue and green shadings in the (a) reflectivity view on the left denote light precipitation—in this case snow. The snow indicated that there [(___were___) (___were not___)] scattering targets spread across the radar's area of view. This distribution of snowfall provided the reflected radar energy that allowed the precipitation to be displayed.

9. In the (b) radial velocity view on the right, green areas indicate winds with a radial component *towards* the radar and red denotes a radial component of the wind *away* from the radar. The narrow band of light pinkish-gray shading oriented generally south–north through the radar site indicates 0 "Doppler wind speed". This "zero-speed" situation occurs when the radar beam direction is [(___perpendicular___) (___parallel___)] to the actual wind direction and no wind motion component is oriented directly towards or away from the radar.

10. **At the center of (b) radial velocity image through the yellow dot where the radar is located, draw a short arrow (a cm or two in length) perpendicular to the lightly shaded "0-Doppler" line. Place an arrow head on the eastern ("red") end to show the actual wind direction.** This air motion, as shown by your arrow, is from the [(___south___) (___west___) (___east___) (___north___)].

11. The transmitted radar beam is not as curved as the Earth's surface over which it travels so at increasing distances from the radar site in the center, the beam is detecting air motions at progressively higher altitudes. If wind speed and direction were constant at all altitudes, the "0-Doppler" line in the image would be straight and perpendicular to the wind direction. The light shaded, "0-Doppler" line [(___was___) (___was not___)] oriented approximately in a straight line across the displayed echo area.

12. Figure 3 is a regional display of surface weather conditions across the Northeast U.S. at 19Z. The station representing State College is shown in central Pennsylvania reporting a temperature of 37 °F. The surface wind at State College at 19Z was from the [(___south___) (___west___) (___east___) (___north___)] at about 20 knots.

13. So at the time of the radar image (about 1920Z), not long after the plotted observations, the wind direction [(***was***) (***was not***)] consistent with the arrow you drew on the image.

14. The "0-Doppler" line orientation suggests that the wind directions at higher elevations were approximately the same as those at the surface. A computer model analysis of wind direction at 18Z at 850 mb (approximately 5000 feet above sea level or about 3800 feet above the ground) over State College showed winds of about 40 knots from the west. This higher level wind direction was [(***consistent with***) (***contrary to***)] the radar velocity display.

When wind direction changes with altitude, the "0-Doppler" line in the velocity display becomes "S" shaped or exhibits other more complex curvature.

Storm systems are continually moving across Earth's surface. NWS radar views display the "base" radial velocity as was used in this investigation as well as the "storm relative" radial velocity. The storm relative view shows air motions within an apparently stationary storm cell. This is especially important in determining air motions for severe weather situations. Another example of this use will be considered in a later investigation dealing with tornadoes.

Suggestions for further activities: The radar images in this investigation were from sites located via "NWS Radar Page" link from the course website. Another source of radar imagery is *http://www.intellicast.com/*. More information about the WSR 88-D radar system can be found at: *http://www.crh.noaa.gov/radar/radinfo/radinfo.html*. Also, a discussion of Doppler technology, including storm relative velocities, can be found at: *http://www.crh .noaa.gov/lmk/soo/88d/index.php* with additional images at: *http://www.crh.noaa.gov/lmk/ soo/88dimg/index.php*.

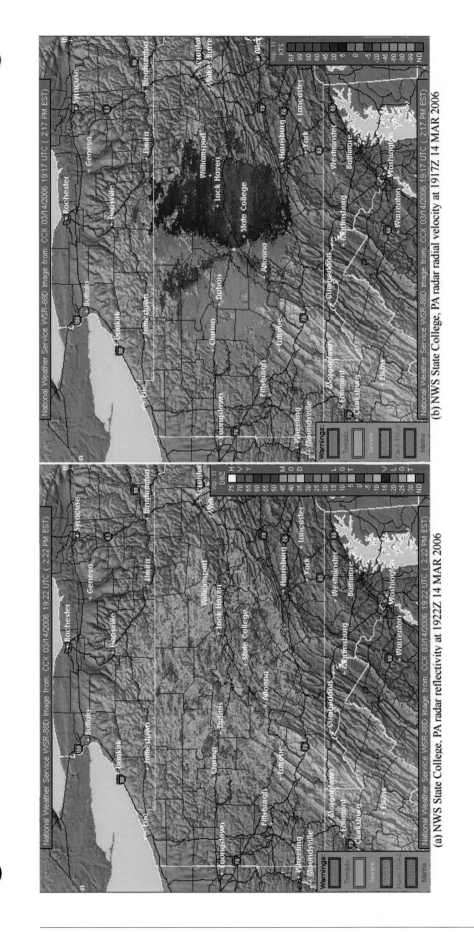

(b) NWS State College, PA radar radial velocity at 1917Z 14 MAR 2006

(a) NWS State College, PA radar reflectivity at 1922Z 14 MAR 2006

Figure 2. Reflectivity (a) and radial velocity (b) on 14 MAR 2006 from the NWS Doppler radar near State College (CCX), PA.

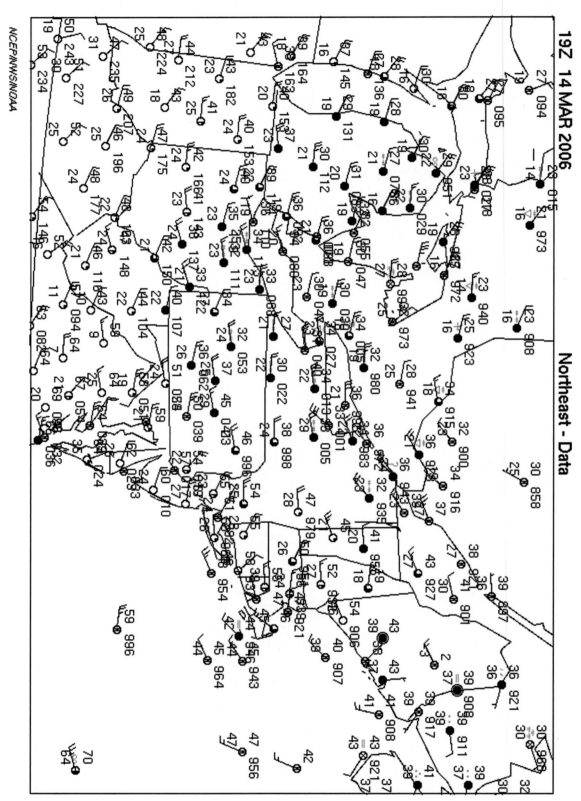

Figure 3. Regional surface weather map of the Northeast U.S. at 19Z 14 MAR 2006.

Investigation 8A: SURFACE WEATHER MAPS AND FORCES

Objectives:

Although the atmosphere is a gaseous fluid, it is a system with physical mass that responds to gravity and other forces such as that arising from pressure differences (gradients). Gravity constrains the atmospheric shell to a thin layer over the solid and liquid surface of the planet. Frictional coupling with the planetary surface causes the atmosphere to rotate with the planet. By isolating the forces that act on a parcel of air, we can explain observed air motions and the various scales of atmospheric circulation.

After completing this investigation, you should be able to:

- Describe the horizontal forces that act on air parcels.
- Show the directions toward which these atmospheric forces act.
- Relate these horizontal forces to the winds reported on weather maps.

Materials: Two "3x5" cards (or two cards 3 inches by 5 inches cut from stiff paper), scissors, tape, and pen or pencil.

Introduction:

Pressure Gradient Force

An air pressure gradient exists wherever air pressure varies from one place to another. This change in pressure over distance results in a force that puts air into motion.

1. The diagram to the right represents a portion of a surface weather map on which are plotted three straight, parallel isobars. Note that the isobars are uniformly spaced and drawn with a 4-mb interval. [(**_High_**) (**_Low_**)] pressure is located across the top of the diagram.

    1008 ——————————

    1004 ———————•——
                      A

    1000 ——————————

2. The diagram shows a pattern of air pressure changing over distance. Assuming that the atmosphere is initially calm, the only force acting horizontally on a parcel of air represented on the diagram at Point A is a pressure gradient force. **Draw an arrow starting at Point A that depicts the direction the pressure gradient force would act.** Your arrow shows the pressure gradient force acting directly towards [(**_highest_**) (**_lowest_**)] pressure. This force is directed perpendicular to the isobar lines. The horizontal pressure gradient gives rise to a force that causes the air parcel at A to begin moving in the direction towards which the force is acting.

Coriolis Effect

Everywhere on Earth, except at the equator, objects moving freely across Earth's surface travel along curved paths. This turning is produced by Earth's rotation and is called the **Coriolis Effect**. The following demonstrates the impact of Earth's rotation on horizontally-moving objects.

Directions: First construct a rotating card device with two 3x5 file cards (or two cards 3 inches by 5 inches made from stiff paper). Following the diagram below, (i) cut an approximately two and one-half inch straight slit down the middle of one card (A), and (ii) cut a slit about one and one-half inch long in the other card (B). Fit the cards together as shown (iii), and lay them flat on the desk or table in front of you. Tape card (A) to the table with the long slit as shown (dotted rectangles). Bend up the lower left and right corners of the loose card (B) to use as tabs. Pull the loose card horizontally towards you until the ends of the cuts meet to form a point of rotation. Be sure the moving card (B) can turn clockwise and counterclockwise around the point of contact. Make an **X** to mark the spot around which the card rotates.

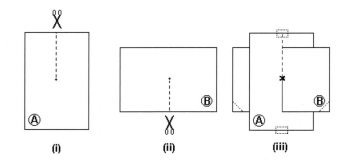

(i)   (ii)   (iii)

3. Orient the cards in the "cross" position as shown in the drawing. Place your pencil point at **X**. With the cards motionless, carefully draw a line <u>on the loose card</u> (B) along the cut-edge and directly away from you. The line you drew represents a path that is **[(_straight_) (_curved_)]**.

4. Now investigate how rotation affects the path of your pencil line. Again, begin with the cards in the "cross" position and your pencil point at **X**. As you slowly pull the lower left tab of the loose card towards you, slowly move your pencil point away from you along the cut-edge while drawing its path <u>on (B)</u>. The loose card is rotating counterclockwise as you do this. The line you drew is **[(_straight_) (_curved_)]**.

5. You actually moved the pencil point along a path that was both straight **and** curved at the same time! This is possible because motion is measured relative to a frame of reference. In this investigation, there are two different frames of reference; one fixed and the other rotating. When the pencil-point motion was observed relative to the fixed card and its cut-edge, its path was **[(_straight_) (_curved_)]**.

6. When the pencil motion was measured relative to the rotating card, its path was

[(***straight***) (***curved***)]. This apparent deflection of motion from a straight line in a rotating system is called the **Coriolis Effect** for Gaspard Gustave de Coriolis (1792-1843), who first explained it mathematically. Because Earth is a rotating system, objects moving freely across its surface, except at the equator, exhibit curved paths. This includes air parcels moving horizontally.

7. Now imagine yourself <u>far above the North Pole</u> and looking down on the Earth below. Think of the loose card (B) as being part of the Earth's surface and that X represents the North Pole. From this perspective, Earth appears to rotate counterclockwise. You can observe the pencil point's motion relative to the Earth's surface (B). You see that as the pencil point moves along the cut-edge and away from the **X**, it draws a path on the rotating surface that [(***is straight***) (***curves to the right***) (***curves to the left***)].

8. Now imagine yourself <u>far above the South Pole</u> and looking down on the Earth below. Again, think of the loose card (B) as being part of the Earth's surface and that X represents the South Pole. From this perspective, Earth appears to rotate clockwise. Rotating the loose card clockwise by pulling on the lower-right tab, you can observe that as the pencil point moves along the cut-edge and away from the **X**, it draws a path on the rotating card that [(***is straight***) (***curves to the right***) (***curves to the left***)].

9. The effect of Earth's rotation on the path of objects moving across its surface is greatest at the poles, and diminishes to zero at the Equator. In summary, the Coriolis Effect causes objects freely moving horizontally over the Earth's surface in the Northern Hemisphere to appear to curve to the [(***right***) (***left***)]

10. The Coriolis Effect causes objects in the Southern Hemisphere to curve to the [(***right***) (***left***)].

When investigating atmospheric motions, it is informative to analyze the forces acting on the air. However, the rotating-card activity you just completed shows that the observed curved motions are due to a rotating frame of reference and not due to a force. Consequently, an imaginary ***Coriolis "force"*** is invented to be applied along with real forces to describe motions of objects. The Coriolis force producing such curved motion is defined as always acting perpendicular to the direction of motion, to the right in the Northern Hemisphere to explain rightward turning, and to the left in the Southern Hemisphere to describe leftward turning.

<u>Pressure Gradient Force, Coriolis Effect, Friction, and Weather Maps</u>

11. On the following weather map segment, consider an air parcel at rest at Point A. An initial horizontal pressure gradient force [(***is***) (***is not***)] acting on the parcel.

12. Once horizontal motion has begun at this Northern Hemisphere location, the air parcel's path will be deflected to the [(***right***) (***left***)].

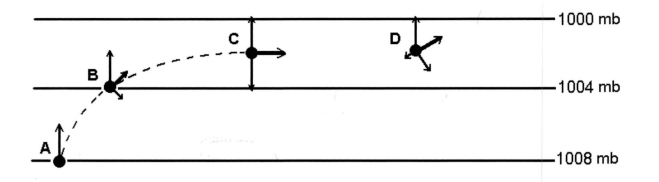

13. The moving air parcel follows the dashed curved path shown on the map. The thick arrow at Point B shows the parcel's direction of motion at that location. At that instant, the longer thin arrow represents the _____ force.

14. The shorter thin arrow represents the _____ force, which is acting at a right angle and to the right of the direction of motion.

15. As the air parcel speeds up, the Coriolis Effect increases and the parcel's motion continues to be deflected to its right. This continues until the parcel reaches Point C where the magnitude of the Coriolis Effect finally equals that of the pressure gradient force (which continues to act toward lowest pressure). At Point C the Coriolis Effect will be acting directly opposite to the pressure gradient force. The two forces are in balance. From Point C and onward, the air parcel will flow [(*perpendicular*) (*parallel*)] to the isobars. This flow is known as the **geostrophic** wind.

16. Point D shows the effect of friction on moving air. The **force of friction**, represented by the smallest arrow drawn from Point D, always acts opposite to the direction of motion and slows the moving object. The slowing causes the Coriolis Effect to decrease. As shown by the thick arrow at Point D, the direction of airflow changes and air flows obliquely across isobars towards [(*lower*) (*higher*)] pressure.

17. It is the presence of the frictional force added to the pressure gradient force and the Coriolis Effect that causes air to spiral [(*inward*) (*outward*)] in surface-map Lows and outward in Highs.

   An additional force acts on horizontally moving air if the isobars are curved. That force, called the *centripetal force*, is not treated in this investigation.

As directed by your course instructor, complete this investigation by either:

   1. *Going to the Current Weather Studies link on the course website, or*
   2. *Continuing to the Applications section for this investigation that immediately follows in this Investigations Manual.*

Investigation 8A: SURFACE WEATHER MAPS AND FORCES
Applications

Figure 1 is the surface weather map (Isobars, Fronts, Radar & Data) for 12Z, Monday morning, 20 March 2006. At map time the central U.S. was experiencing a range of precipitation types from snow in the northern plains to severe thunderstorms and heavy rains across the southern plains. These weather conditions were related to two main pressure centers, a broad High in central Canada and a Low in northeastern New Mexico. Another weaker Low was developing along the front in eastern Texas.

18. The general circulation pattern about the New Mexico Low as inferred from winds reported from Colorado to west Texas was generally [(***clockwise and outward***) (***counterclockwise and inward***)].

This pattern is consistent with the depiction of surface winds in the *hand-twist model* of a Low used earlier in Investigation 1A. The eastern Texas Low was developing a similar circulation pattern.

19. The circulation pattern about the southern side of the Canadian High, centered beyond the map edge to the north, was generally [(***clockwise and outward***) (***counterclockwise and inward***)].

This pattern is consistent with the depiction of surface winds in the *hand-twist model* of a High in Investigation 1A.

20. Wichita, Kansas, reported coded pressure digits of "**067**". This is decoded to a sea-level pressure of __1008__ mb for Wichita.

21. Minneapolis, MN reported coded pressure digits of "**289**". This is decoded to a sea-level pressure of __1028.9__ mb for Minneapolis. (A portion of the Minneapolis station circle is cut by the 1028-mb isobar label.)

22. The pressure difference over the distance from Wichita to Minneapolis is then __20__ mb. (Several isobar lines are interrupted by labels. Where cut, complete the isobar line through the label space to better see the pattern.)

23. The horizontal pressure gradient force is the dominant force in bringing about large-scale horizontal air motions. The strength of the pressure gradient force depends on the pressure difference over distance and is inferred from the spacing of isobars. With a straight-edge, draw a line connecting Wichita and Minneapolis. Between the stations of Wichita and Minneapolis, the number of isobars (in the standard sequence of Investigation 1B) is __6__ .

24. The orientation of the line you drew is approximately [(***parallel***) (***perpendicular***)] to the isobars. Place a bold arrowhead on your line at the Wichita end.

25. The resulting arrow generally represents the orientation of the pressure gradient force which is directed from [(***lower to higher***) (***higher to lower***)] pressures.

26. Your arrow (and the horizontal pressure gradient force in this region) is directed generally toward the [(***southwest***) (***southeast***) (***northwest***) (***northeast***)].

27. By comparison, a line from Tampa, FL, to Greensboro, in western NC, a comparable distance to that from Wichita to Minneapolis, crosses ___ isobar line(s) and spans a pressure difference of 5.7 mb.

28. The horizontal air pressure gradient was stronger across the [(***Florida-North Carolina***) (***Kansas-Minnesota***)] area.

These pressure gradient magnitudes are reflective of the wind speeds reported for those areas: 15 kts at Kansas City and Wichita and 5 kts at Tampa and Greensboro. The pressure gradient force is the primary determiner of wind speed. Strong pressure gradients (closely spaced isobars) are usually associated with higher wind speeds. Examples in northeast Montana and Saskatchewan, Canada, show 20-knot winds associated with another area of relatively strong pressure gradient.

29. Consider the station report at Kansas City, MO (a portion of the data is cut by the 1016-mb isobar label). The wind reported at Kansas City was 15 knots directed generally toward the [(***east***) (***north***) (***west***) (***south***)].

30. The reported wind showing the air motion at Kansas City [(***was***) (***was not***)] in the same direction as the horizontal pressure gradient that you drew near that location.

31. Moving air does not flow directly from higher toward lower pressure because it also experiences the **Coriolis Effect**. In the Northern Hemisphere, the Coriolis Effect is directed to the [(***right***) (***left***)] of the direction of motion.

32. Consequently, the Coriolis Effect acting on the wind at Kansas City would be directed generally toward the [(***east***) (***north***) (***west***) (***south***)].

33. A third force acting on air moving near the Earth's surface is **friction**. Friction, which always acts in the direction opposite to motion, retards the movement of the air. The direction of the frictional force on the air at Kansas City was generally towards the [(***east***) (***north***) (***west***) (***south***)].

The frictional force, having slowed the air and reduced the Coriolis Effect, brings about the flow of air along a path cutting across the isobars towards lower pressure. In this way, air spirals into Lows and out of Highs as shown with the *hand-twist model*.

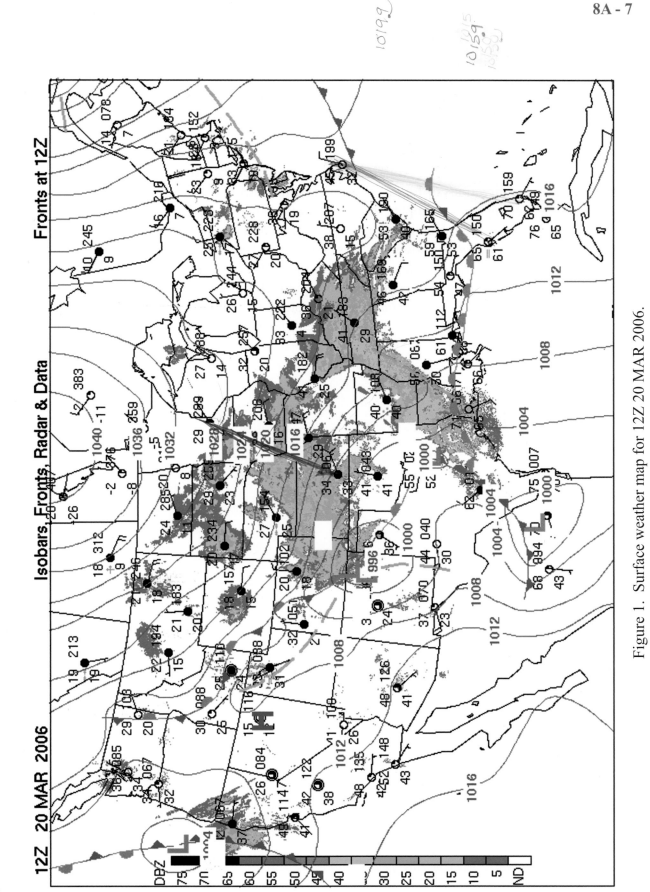

Figure 1. Surface weather map for 12Z 20 MAR 2006.

Also, the circulation patterns are determiners of weather conditions. The flow about the eastern Texas Low was bringing warm, humid Gulf air northward over the front to fuel thunderstorms. To the north, in the cold air, the wind directions about the New Mexico Low and Canadian High were toward progressively rising terrain producing orographic lifting and upslope snows over the northern plains.

Suggestions for further activities: You might call up the "Isobars, Fronts, Radar, & Data" map to identify the directions of forces associated with winds in passing weather systems. An interesting challenge is to compare the weather maps such as we have used with those for locations in the Southern Hemisphere. For example, *http://www.bom.gov.au/weather/ national/charts/synoptic.shtml* shows the latest surface analysis for Australia. Observations can be found at: *http://weather.noaa.gov/weather/ccworld.html*, which may be plotted on the Australian map. A map of current conditions for South Africa can be found at: *http://www .weathersa.co.za/Imagery/SeaLevelMap.jsp*. One note, Southern Hemisphere wind arrows are drawn by convention with the "feathers" on the *opposite side*, pointing toward lower pressure. Why might that be?

Investigation 8B: UPPER-AIR WEATHER MAPS

Objectives:

Weather as reported on surface weather maps provides us primarily with a two-dimensional view of the state of the atmosphere, that is, weather conditions observed at the Earth's surface. Atmospheric conditions reported on upper-air weather maps provide the third dimension, that is, conditions at various altitudes above the Earth's surface. Hence, for a more complete understanding of the weather, we need to consult both surface and upper-air weather maps.

After completing this investigation, you should be able to:

- Describe the topography of upper-air constant-pressure surfaces based on height contours, including the identification of Highs, Lows, ridges, and troughs.
- Identify the general relationship between height contours and the temperature of the underlying atmosphere.
- Describe the relationship between the height contours and wind direction on upper-air weather maps.

Introduction:

Upper-air weather maps differ from surface weather maps. Whereas surface weather conditions are plotted on a map of constant altitude (normally sea level) from observations that are collected at least hourly, upper-air weather conditions are plotted on maps of constant air pressure from radiosonde observations at 12-hour intervals. The altitude at which the particular pressure is located is reported on these maps. For example, an upper air observation is made by releasing a balloon-borne instrument package to the atmosphere. As the balloon rises, the air pressure decreases. The altitude at which the pressure of 850 mb occurs is referred to as the 850-mb height. Every 12 hours, upper-air maps are drawn for various pressure levels including 850 mb, 700 mb, 500 mb, and 300 mb.

Plotted on upper-air maps are temperature (in °C), dewpoint (in °C), wind speed (in knots), wind direction, and height of the pressure surface above sea-level (coded in tens of meters). Become familiar with the upper-air station model depicted on the following page. The upper air station is located at the end of the wind shaft opposite the speed "feathers" surrounded by the plotted data.

UPPER AIR STATION MODEL LEGEND
(500 mb)

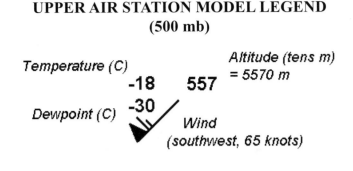

While the course website provides upper air maps utilizing the station model above with the dewpoint shown directly, several NOAA and other web maps display the dewpoint depression. The *dewpoint depression* is the number of Celsius degrees that the dewpoint is <u>below</u> the plotted temperature. This should cause no confusion when seen on a map because the dewpoint can never be greater than the air temperature so that the dewpoint depression will always be some positive number. On the other hand, upper air temperatures and dewpoints for most levels are negative Celsius values. Hence, on upper-air maps a positive value is generally the dewpoint depression and a negative value is the dewpoint.

Also, the dewpoint depression is more useful than the dewpoint because it indicates how close the air is to saturation and hence, cloud formation. That is, the plotted dewpoint depression shows the likely presence of clouds. Meteorologists generally assume that clouds are present (at the station or within the region) when the dewpoint is within 5 Celsius degrees of the air temperature, *i.e.* the dewpoint depression is 5 or less.

The plotted altitude of the pressure level of the map is a coded value. That is, only the three most significant digits of the value are plotted. To decode the plotted value the following table shows the Standard Atmosphere altitude of the pressure surface, and the missing digits needed to decode the three plotted numbers (xxx).

Upper Air Map (mb)	Standard Altitude (m)	Coded Digits
850	1457	1xxx
700	3012	(2/3)xxx
500	5579	xxx0
300	9164	xxx0

The 700-mb level may lie below 3000 m necessitating placing a 2 in front of the plotted values to make the meaningful choice in the decode.

1. Figure 1 is the 500-mb map for 12Z 28 DEC 2005. Meteorologists use 500-mb maps because horizontal winds at that level steer weather systems across the Earth's surface. Hence, the so-called *steering winds* at 500 mb can be used to predict the track of a Low-pressure system.

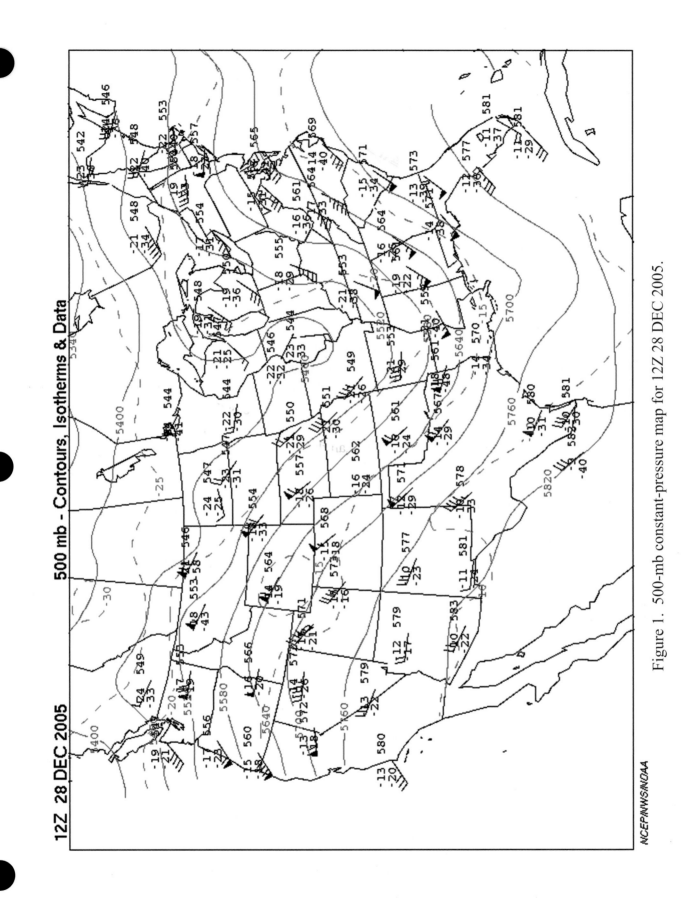

Figure 1. 500-mb constant-pressure map for 12Z 28 DEC 2005.

Solid lines on the 500-mb map join locations where the 500-mb pressure level is at the same altitude. These lines, called *contours of height*, are drawn at intervals of 60 m. The coded height values on the map are in **tens** of meters. Contour values are in **whole** meters. At 12Z 28 DEC 2005, the lowest reported height for a pressure reading of 500-mb was _____ m. For your answer, rely on individual coded station reports.

2. The highest reported 500-mb height on the map was _____ m.

3. The 500-mb map and other constant-pressure upper-air maps are actually topographic maps. That is, the contour pattern reveals the "hills" and "valleys" of the constant-pressure surface. The contour pattern indicates that, in general, the 500-mb surface (the surface where the air pressure is everywhere 500 mb) is at a [(***higher***) (***lower***)] altitude in southern Canada than in the southern United States.

4. Contour lines on constant-pressure upper-air maps separate regions that have higher altitudes from those areas that have lower altitudes than the value of that contour line. The area north of the 5460-m contour line generally near the U.S.-Canadian border is a region where 500-mb altitudes are the [(***lowest***) (***highest***)] on the map. Conversely, the area to the south of the 5820-m contour along the Mexican-U.S. border are the highest.

5. The wave pattern of most contour lines consists of topographic ridges and troughs, that is, elongated crests and depressions, respectively. A broad [(***trough***) (***ridge***)] appears on the Figure 1 map in the central U.S.

6. On the same map, a [(***trough***) (***ridge***)] appears in the Southwestern U.S.

As demonstrated in Investigation 5B, air pressure drops more rapidly with altitude in a column of cold air than in a column of warm air. Hence, the height of the 500-mb surface is lower where the underlying air is relatively cold. Conversely the 500-mb surface is higher where the underlying air is relatively warm.

7. Therefore, the air below the 500-mb region of lowest heights in Figure 1 must be [(***colder***) (***warmer***)] than the air below the surrounding higher 500-mb surfaces.

8. The upper air station model also gives the air temperature at 500 mb. The plotted station data show that the general decline in temperature at 500 mb as latitude increases is accompanied by a(n) [(***increase***) (***decrease***)] in the altitude of the 500-mb surface.

9. Suppose that at 12Z on 28 DEC 2005 you board an airplane and fly non-stop directly from Minneapolis, MN to Miami, FL. En route, the plane cruises along the 500-mb surface. Flying from Minneapolis to Miami, the aircraft's cruising altitude [(***increases***) (***decreases***) (***does not change***)].

10. At the same time, the air temperature outside the aircraft [(***rises***) (***falls***)].

11. A relationship exists between the orientation of height contours and wind direction on 500-mb maps, especially at higher wind speeds. As seen in Figure 1, wind direction is generally [(*__perpendicular__*) (*__parallel__*)] to nearby height contour lines.

As directed by your course instructor, complete this investigation by either:

1. *Going to the Current Weather Studies link on the course website, or*
2. *Continuing to the Applications section for this investigation that immediately follows in this Investigations Manual.*

Investigation 8B: UPPER-AIR WEATHER MAPS
Applications

Figure 2 is the surface map for 00Z 22 MAR 2006. These surface conditions occurred 36 hours after those that were shown on the Figure 1 surface map in Investigation 8A. On the Figure 2 map the storm system from the southern plains had tracked eastward becoming one Low centered off the North Carolina coast and another spread over Georgia with an extension northward into the Virginias. Cold air associated with a high-pressure system was influencing the center of the nation while another weak storm system was found in Arizona. The fronts associated with yet another system can be seen off the Washington and Oregon coasts poised to invade the Northwest. Circulation of the High centered in central Canada off the map area is generally clockwise and outward which is consistent with the surface winds in the *hand-twist model* of a High.

The isobars associated with the High are elongated southward along a line almost directly down the center of the country. This extension is called a "ridge". The large-scale flow to the east side of the ridge line is bringing cold air southward over the eastern half of the country. The circulation around the eastern Lows brought humid Atlantic air over the colder air at the surface to produce widespread cloudiness and snow (shown by radar in the Mid-Atlantic region). Some lake effect snow can also be seen to the lee (downwind) of Lakes Superior and Michigan/Huron, caused by the flow of cold air over the relatively warmer lake waters.

12. Flow in the cold air to the west of the ridge line is bounded by the [(***cold***) (***warm***) (***stationary***)] front stretching from eastern Mexico to western Canada where the dense cold air cannot get over the mountains. Generally, air temperatures at stations to the west of the front are higher than those to the east.

13. At Nashville, Tennessee, where the temperature was 38 °F, the wind was blowing from the [(***south-southeast***) (***north-northwest***)] at about 10 knots.

14. The pressure gradient force everywhere on the map is directed from [(***lower to higher***) (***higher to lower***)] pressures and perpendicular to the isobars.

15. Therefore, at Nashville, the pressure gradient force was generally directed toward the [(***northwest***) (***southeast***)].

16. The Coriolis Effect at Nashville was directed toward the [(***north-northeast***) (***west-southwest***)].

17. And the frictional force acting on the wind at Nashville was directed toward the [(***south-southeast***) (***north-northwest***)].

Figure 3 is the 500-mb constant-pressure map for 00Z 22 MAR 2006. This upper-air map depicts the atmospheric conditions found at the 500-mb pressure level over the coterminous U.S. and adjacent areas of Canada and Mexico at the same time as the conditions shown on the Figure 2 surface map. These mid-tropospheric conditions were associated with the air masses, storm systems, fronts, and weather plotted on the surface map at that time. Weather systems often extend from the surface well into the troposphere, hence the need to examine upper-air maps to describe them three-dimensionally.

On the Figure 3, 500-mb map, the plotted report for Oakland, the northern station in California, shows that at 500 mb over the station, the conditions were:

18. temperature: [(*-16*) (*-21*)] (°C)
19. dewpoint: [(*-28*) (*-35*)] (°C)
20. wind direction: [(***northwest***) (***southeast***)]
21. wind speed: about [(*35*) (*65*)] (kt)*
22. height: [(*5570*) (*5470*)] (m) *

*[Note: When winds of 50 knots or higher are reported, a pennant is used on the station's wind shaft to signify a 50-knot increment in speed. Also, the altitudes of the constant-pressure surfaces on upper air charts are given in coded values (as is the case with the air pressures on surface maps). On 500-mb maps, the height is plotted in tens of meters. Decoding requires adding a **0** to the plotted number. That is, a plotted 500-mb height value of 556 is actually 5560 m. Contour lines are labeled on the map with the actual height value.]

23. The following is an excerpt from a rawinsonde text report for the same time as the Figure 3, 500-mb map. (Current rawinsonde text reports can be found from the website: "Upper Air Data - Text".) **Using the values reported at the 500-mb level, plot an upper air station model for 500 mb using the station circle to the right of the data table.** Round temperature (in degrees Celsius, *TMPC*) and dewpoint (in degrees Celsius, *DWPC*) to the nearest whole degree. (Mid-way values are rounded up if positive and down if negative.) Wind speed (in knots, *SKNT*) is rounded to the nearest 5 knots. (Wind direction is given in degrees clockwise from north, *DRCT*.) Be sure to plot the reported height (in meters, *HGHT*), as the coded height in tens of meters.

Date:		00Z 22 MAR 2006					
PRES	HGHT	TMPC	DWPC	RELH	DRCT	SKNT	Station
832	1620	12.8	-9.2	21	330	3	
753	2438	4.9	-11.9	28	160	13	
700	3026	-1.1	-12.1	43	170	19	O
500	5600	-21.7	-29.7	48	240	57	
400	7220	-30.1	-45.1	22	235	72	

Compare the station model plot you drew to the 500-mb map. The station you have plotted is [(***Wilmington, Ohio***) (***Albuquerque, New Mexico***)].

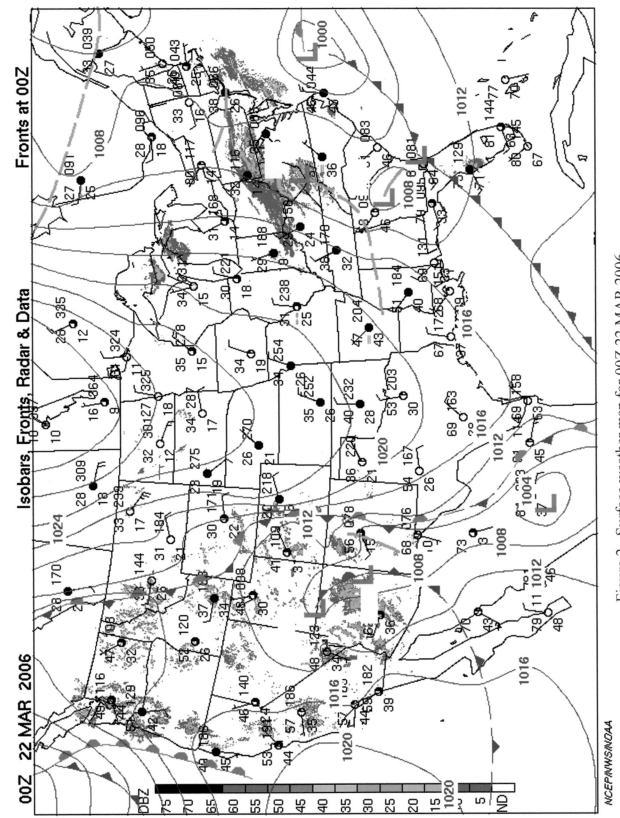

Figure 2. Surface weather map for 00Z 22 MAR 2006.

NCEP/NWS/NOAA

24. The 500-mb heights (heights above sea level where the air pressure is 500 mb) are analyzed by drawing contour lines through locations having the same altitude as the value of the contour line. To better visualize the contour pattern, highlight the 5580-m contour by tracing over it. [The 5580-m contour curves from the Arizona-Mexico border through northern Kansas and then across northern North Carolina into the Atlantic.] The overall contour pattern of the 500-mb map shows:

    a. (*a trough over the eastern U.S.*)
    b. (*a ridge over the south-central U.S.*)
    c. (*a trough over the western U.S.*)
    d. (*all a, b and c choices*)

25. Examine the winds and contours across the map area. Comparing the area over Mississippi to South Carolina with the area over California to Washington as an example, generally, wind speeds on the 500-mb map are faster where the height contour lines are [(*closer together*) (*farther apart*)]. This relationship between the spacing of contours and wind speeds at 500 mb is similar to the relationship between spacing of isobars and wind speeds on surface weather maps.

26. On Northern Hemisphere surface maps, the wind circulation about well-developed Lows is counterclockwise and inward while that about Highs is clockwise and outward. This across-isobar flow is due to the presence of friction near the Earth's surface. At 500 mb, far above the influence of surface friction and as evidenced by the Figure 1 and 3 maps, wind directions (especially at higher wind speeds) are generally [(*parallel to the contours*) (*across the contours toward lower heights*)].

27. Compare the temperatures at 500 mb for Dodge City, in western Kansas, and Las Vegas, in southern Nevada, as representative of those air columns. Between Earth's surface and 500 mb, the air column over Kansas is generally [(*warmer*) (*cooler*)] than the column over Nevada.

28. The height of the 500-mb pressure surface over Kansas is generally [(*higher*) (*lower*)] than the 500-mb height over Nevada. This relationship should be familiar from Investigation 5B and leads to the terminology of upper air troughs and ridges.

The flow at the 500-mb level is often termed the steering level for broad-scale weather systems, the Highs and Lows of surface weather maps. As a general forecasting guideline, a well-defined surface Low will move with the 500-mb wind direction at one-half the 500-mb wind speed. The flow over South Carolina on the Figure 3, 500-mb map is directed <u>toward</u> the east. The complex area of low-pressure shown on the Figure 2, 00Z surface map over the southeastern U.S. would therefore be expected to continue to move eastward at relatively high speeds.

<u>Suggestions for further activities:</u> You might try making a height-contour analysis by printing an unanalyzed 500-mb map ("500 mb - Data") from the website. You can then

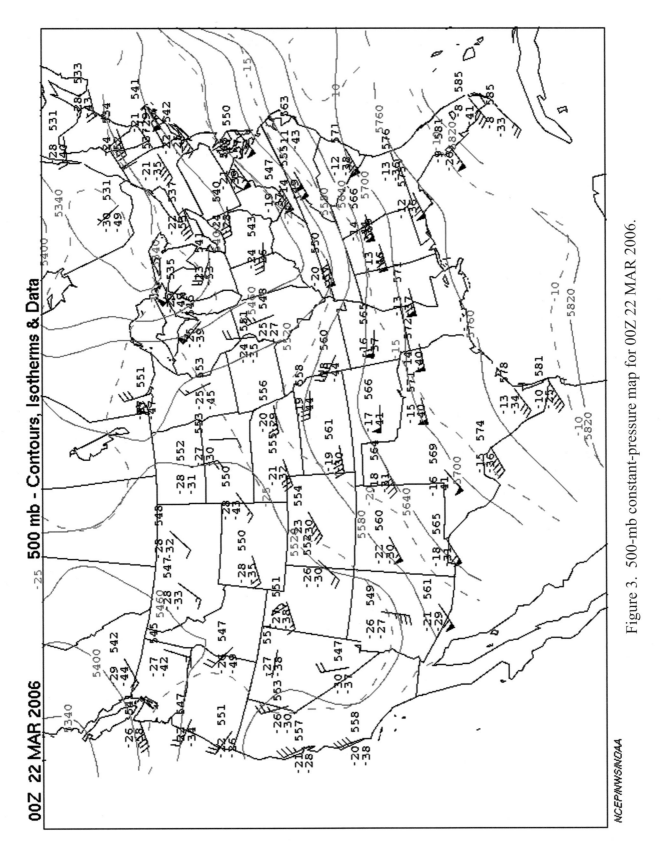

Figure 3. 500-mb constant-pressure map for 00Z 22 MAR 2006.

compare your hand-analyzed pattern to the computer-analyzed map with contours. Also, compare upper-air map patterns to surface weather maps and the weather conditions you experience locally. See if you can link upper-air troughs and ridges with surface Lows and Highs.

Investigation 9A: WESTERLIES AND THE JET STREAM

Objectives:

At the planetary (global) scale in the middle and upper troposphere, the prevailing upper-air westerlies encircle middle latitudes in a wave-like pattern. These winds are important components of day-to-day weather in that they steer storm systems from one place to another and are ultimately responsible for the movement of air masses. Surveying the basic characteristics of these upper-air tropospheric westerlies is key to understanding the variability of midlatitude weather.

A jet stream may exist as a relatively narrow river of strong winds within the westerlies. The jet stream that occurs over the polar front and near the tropopause has an important influence on the weather of middle latitudes. This so-called *polar front jet stream* exists where relatively cold air at higher latitudes comes in contact with warm air from lower latitudes. In addition, this jet stream provides upper-air support for the development of low pressure systems.

After completing this investigation, you should be able to:

- Describe the wave patterns exhibited by the meandering upper-air westerlies.
- Determine the location of the polar front jet stream on an upper-air weather map.
- Explain the general relationships between the jet stream in the upper-air westerlies and the paths air masses and storms take.
- Describe how atmospheric temperature patterns are associated with the upper-air circulation and the jet stream.

Introduction:

1.   The upper-air westerlies flow generally from west-to-east around the planet in a wave-like pattern of ridges and troughs as shown below. Ridges are topographic crests and troughs are elongated depressions on constant-pressure surfaces. (Refer to Investigation 8B to review features on upper-air maps, including ridges and troughs.) In the figure below, the "H" locates a ridge and "L" locates troughs.

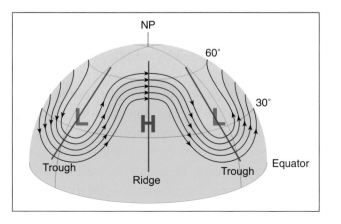

The upper-air westerlies exhibit clockwise (anticyclonic) curvature in ridges. As shown in the drawing above, a line can be drawn that divides a ridge into two roughly symmetrical sectors. The line is known as a *ridge line*. Note that west of the ridge line, winds are from the southwest (a warm weather direction) and east of the ridge line, winds are from the northwest (a cold weather direction). We conclude that winds to the west of a ridge line favor [(***cold***) (***warm***)] air advection while winds to the east of a ridge line favor cold air advection.

2. The upper-air westerlies curve counterclockwise (cyclonic) in troughs. As shown in the drawing above, a line can be drawn that divides a trough into two roughly symmetrical sectors. The line is known as a *trough line*. Note that west of the trough line, winds are from the northwest (a cold weather direction) and east of the trough line, winds are from the southwest (a warm weather direction). We conclude that winds to the west of a trough line favor [(***cold***) (***warm***)] air advection while winds to the east of a trough line favor warm air advection.

    Ridges and troughs usually progress from west to east so that as a ridge line shifts eastward, a location that had been experiencing cold air advection then experiences warm air advection, and a location that had been experiencing warm air advection then experiences cold air advection.

3. Upper-air winds steer low-pressure systems as well as air masses. A surface Low that is centered to the east of a trough line and west of a ridge line will be expected to move toward the [(***northeast***) (***southwest***)].

The wavy pattern of the upper-air westerlies consists of ridges alternating with troughs. The distance between successive ridge lines or, equivalently, between successive trough lines is the *wavelength*. At any one time, usually between 3 and 5 waves encircle the Earth in the middle latitudes.

With time the wave pattern of the upper-air westerlies changes. These changes may involve a change in the number of waves, the wavelength, or the amplitude of the wave. At one extreme, shown in the left drawing below, upper-air westerlies blow almost directly from west to east with little sign of ridges or troughs. This westerly flow pattern is described as *zonal*. At the other extreme, shown in the right drawing below, upper-air westerlies blow in huge north/south loops with high amplitude ridges and troughs. This westerly flow pattern is described as *meridional*. The circulation patterns displayed below are actually opposite extremes of many possible patterns exhibited by middle latitude upper-air westerly waves.

4. When the upper-air westerly flow pattern is zonal, the source region for much of the air over the lower 48 states is the Pacific Ocean. On the other hand, when the upper-air westerly flow pattern is meridional, the source regions for air masses over the lower 48 states are Canada (where winds are from the northwest) or Mexico or the Gulf of Mexico (where winds are from the southwest). Hence, from west to east across the lower 48 states, temperatures are likely to be more variable with a [(***zonal***) (***meridional***)] flow pattern.

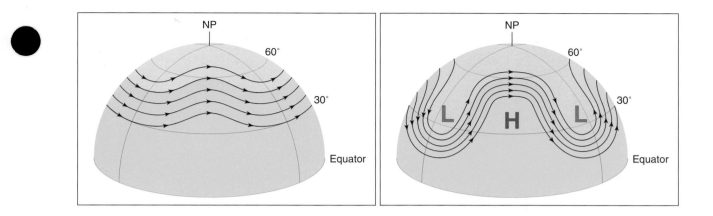

5. Fundamental to the formation of the polar-front jet stream within the westerlies is the physical property that warm air is less dense than cold air when both are at the same pressure. Air pressure drops [(***more***) (***less***)] rapidly with increasing altitude in cold air than in warm air.

The polar front represents the boundary between higher latitude cold air and lower latitude warm air. This temperature contrast extends from the Earth's surface up to the altitude of the polar front jet stream. As demonstrated in Investigation 5B, the effect of temperature on air density means that the air pressure at any given altitude above the surface is higher in the warm air column than in the cold air column. Hence, a horizontal pressure gradient is directed across the front from the warm side toward the cold side. In response, the horizontal wind initially blows from warm air toward cold air but is soon deflected by the Coriolis Effect. Consequently, the wind blows parallel to the polar front with the cold air to the left when facing in the direction towards which the air is flowing (in the Northern Hemisphere). Furthermore, where cold and warm air reside side by side, the magnitude of the horizontal pressure gradient increases with increasing altitude. This causes the horizontal wind to strengthen with altitude and reach its maximum speed in the polar front jet stream.

6. When the polar front jet stream is south of a Northern Hemisphere locality, the weather at that location is relatively [(***warm***) (***cold***)].

7. As a component of the planetary-scale upper-air westerlies and similar to the winds at 500 mb, the polar front jet stream steers low pressure systems. Hence, middle latitude storms generally move from [(***west to east***) (***east to west***)].

As directed by your course instructor, complete this investigation by either:

1. *Going to the Current Weather Studies link on the course website, or*
2. *Continuing to the Applications section for this investigation that immediately follows in this Investigations Manual.*

Investigation 9A: WESTERLIES AND THE JET STREAM
Applications

8. Examine Figure 1, the upper-air map of winds at the 300-mb level at 00Z 14 APR 2006 (average 300-mb height is about 9 km above sea-level). **Using a pencil, lightly shade stations that have wind speeds of 70 knots or higher (triangular pennant and two long barbs). Then lightly shade the area between such stations to form a broad band where wind speeds are 70 knots or higher. Draw a dark, heavy, smooth, curved arrow across the map through the core of highest wind speeds. Add an arrowhead to represent wind direction.** The large arrow you drew on your map approximates the location of the polar front jet stream across the lower 48 states.

    Examine Figure 2, the upper-air map of winds at the 300-mb level at 12Z on 13 JAN 2006, upper tropospheric conditions at a more energetic time. **Using a pencil, again lightly shade the region(s) where winds are at least 70 knots. Finally, draw a heavy dark arrow and arrowhead through the high-speed core of the jet stream winds.**

    The pattern of winds in Figure 2 indicates a [(*__ridge__*) (*__trough__*)] over the central states. The flow pattern in the same region is meridional.

9. On average, one would expect temperatures at similar latitudes to be similar. Zonal wind patterns, as in Figure 1, also tend to preserve this relationship. However, given the wind pattern of Figure 2, at 12Z on 13 JAN 2006, surface air temperatures over western Oregon are likely to be [(*__lower__*) (*__higher__*)] than surface temperatures over Wisconsin. This is reflected in the 300-mb temperatures plotted on the map.

10. Across the United States, Lows tend to follow the path of the polar front jet stream. At map time, a storm was centered in southern Illinois. From Figure 2, this storm was likely to move towards [(*__Virginia__*) (*__the Great Lakes__*) (*__Florida__*)].

11. Knowledge of the location of the jet stream and upper-air winds in general is very important for commercial aviation and can result in fuel savings and shorter flight times. At Figure 2 map time, an airline flight from New Orleans, Louisiana to Denver, Colorado would take [(*__less time__*) (*__more time__*)] than a flight along the same route from Denver to New Orleans.

Figure 3 is the surface map for 00Z 27 MAR 2006. At map time much of the eastern U.S. was under the influence of high pressure centered from the Great Lakes to the Ohio Valley. This High was associated with the relatively cool air that had influenced much of the country over the prior several days. It was slowly moving eastward to be replaced by a storm system located in the western plains, marked by *L*s in South Dakota, Nebraska and Oklahoma. Another high-pressure area is coming ashore in the Pacific Northwest. The expansive eastern High displays the usual clockwise and outward wind circulation pattern.

12. This means, on the west side of the High, winds were generally from the [(***north***) (***south***)] bringing warmer, more humid air from the Gulf across the central U.S. ahead of the advancing storm system and cold front. The winds on the east side of the High and those between the Dakotas' Low and Idaho High to the west were generally from the north bringing colder air from Canada into those areas of the U.S.

13. Figure 4 is the 500-mb constant-pressure map for 00Z 27 MAR 2006, the same time as the surface map. Recall that the 500-mb level shows conditions in the <u>middle</u> troposphere. At the 500-mb level, the highest wind speeds plotted on the map are [(***less than***) (***the same as***) (***greater than***)] the highest wind speeds observed at the surface.

14. Figure 5 is the 300-mb constant-pressure map for 00Z 27 MAR 2006, the same time as the surface and 500-mb maps. The conditions shown at 300 mb were representative of those in the <u>upper</u> troposphere. The 300-mb heights reported at individual stations are in 10s of meters. The heights of the 300-mb pressure level were within several hundred meters of [(***5500***) (***9200***) (***12,500***)] meters.

15. These 500-mb and 300-mb maps had contour patterns that showed:
    a. (***an East coast trough, a central U.S. ridge, and a trough over the Rocky Mountain States***)
    b. (***an East coast trough and a ridge over the Rocky Mountain States***)

16. Using the conventional wind speed threshold of 70 knots for defining a jet stream, there [(***was***) (***was not***)] evidence for a jet stream on the 00Z 27 MAR 2006 300-mb constant-pressure map.

17. The highest wind speed plotted on the 300-mb map was about _____ knots (two pennants) at Grand Junction, Colorado. **Lightly shade the area across the western U.S. from Washington State to western Kansas including Grand Junction and between neighboring stations where wind speeds are 70 knots or greater. Also similarly shade the Southeastern U.S. area where wind speeds were greater than 70 knots.** The jet stream location as indicated by the 300-mb wind speeds you shaded generally curved southward around the west sides of the troughs in the western U.S. and eastern U.S.

18. Comparing the highest wind speeds plotted at the surface, 500-mb and 300-mb levels, wind speeds typically [(***decrease***) (***remain the same***) (***increase***)] with increasing altitudes above Earth's surface.

19. Commercial jet aircraft routinely fly at altitudes near the 300-mb level. If an aircraft were flying from Seattle, Washington, to Denver, Colorado, at 00Z on 27 MAR 2006 at about the 300-mb level where wind speeds are highest, the aircraft's speed relative to the ground ("ground speed") would be about 75 or more knots [(***faster***) (***slower***)] than its speed relative to the air through which it is moving ("air speed").

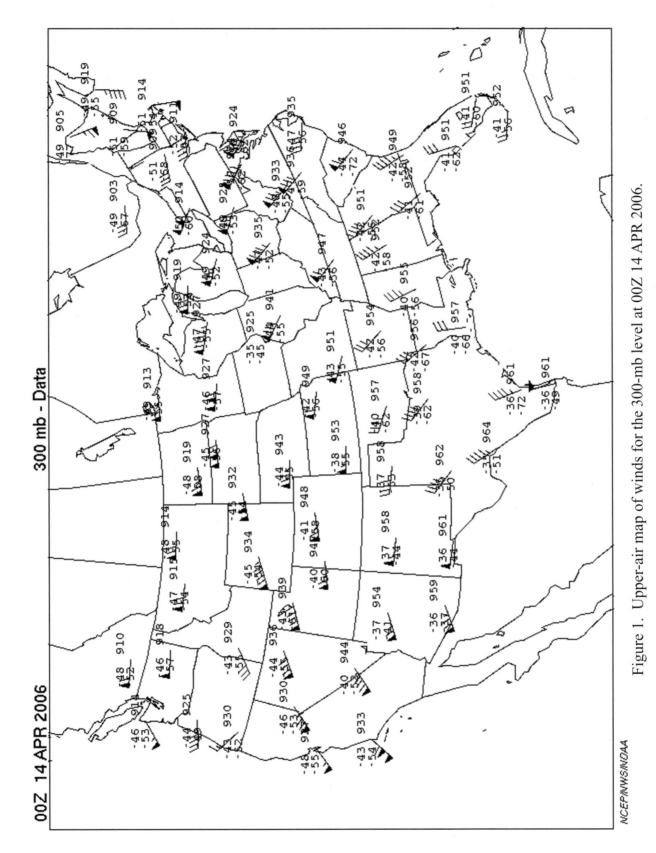

Figure 1. Upper-air map of winds for the 300-mb level at 00Z 14 APR 2006.

20. Compare temperatures in Pennsylvania and Iowa on both the surface and 500-mb maps at 00Z on 27 MAR 2006. Temperatures at both levels over Pennsylvania are [(***higher***) (***lower***)] than those over Iowa.

21. These temperature contrasts suggest a column of air over Pennsylvania that was [(***warmer***) (***colder***)] than the column over Iowa.

22. The heights of the 300-mb level over Pennsylvania are [(***higher***) (***lower***)] than the heights of the 300-mb level over Iowa. This relationship between air column temperatures and upper-level pressure heights is consistent with the pressure block discussion in Investigation 5B.

The surface and low-level warm and cold air advection patterns noted in item 12 brings cold air southward to lower the upper-level heights under troughs and warm air northward to raise the upper-level heights under ridges. Thus, the upper-level patterns of ridges and troughs are created, maintained and destroyed with passing lower-level weather systems. The atmosphere is truly three-dimensional!

Dashed lines on the 300-mb map are isotachs (lines of equal wind speed) that encircle regions of particular wind speeds. For example, in Figure 5 a 90-knot isotach was found across the Utah-Colorado border. Such regions of higher wind speeds within the jet stream are called *jet streaks*. Often jet streaks are associated with springtime severe weather outbreaks. The "spreading" of the 300-mb flow moving across eastern Nebraska and Kansas also provides the broad upper level divergence of air that causes the surface Low to deepen (develop).

Suggestions for further activities: You might try shading areas of highest wind speeds on the 300-mb chart to identify jet streaks. See if you can spot relationships between jet streaks and the location of associated surface low-pressure systems. Also, for developing storm systems in the central U.S., you might see if the positions of the low pressure/low height centers are successively more westerly with height (surface to 700 mb to 500 mb to 300 mb), as is expected with cold air being advected southward on the west side of storm centers. Does this fit with the discussion of warm and cold air columns and their relationship to heights of pressure levels?

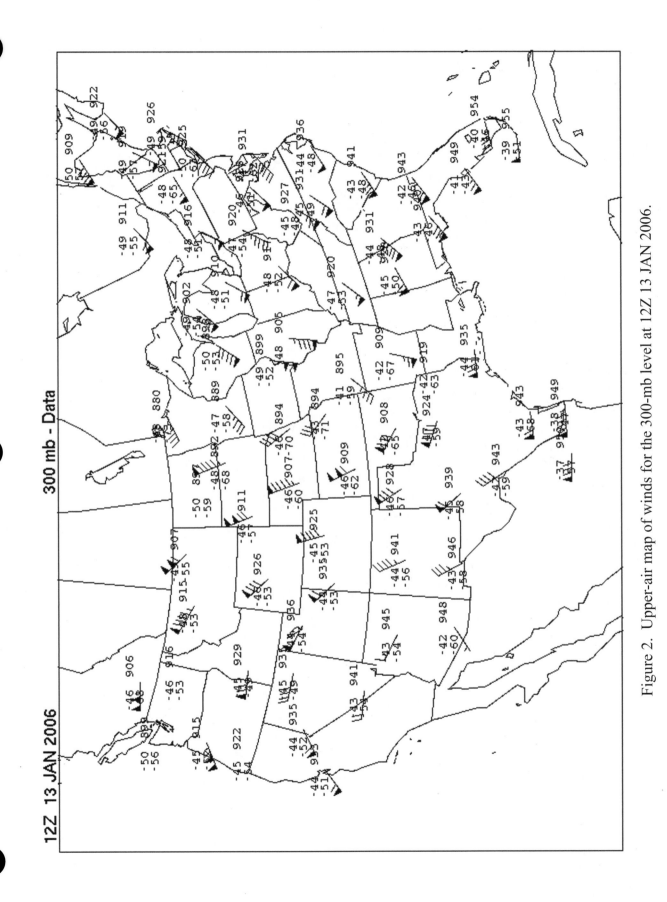

Figure 2. Upper-air map of winds for the 300-mb level at 12Z 13 JAN 2006.

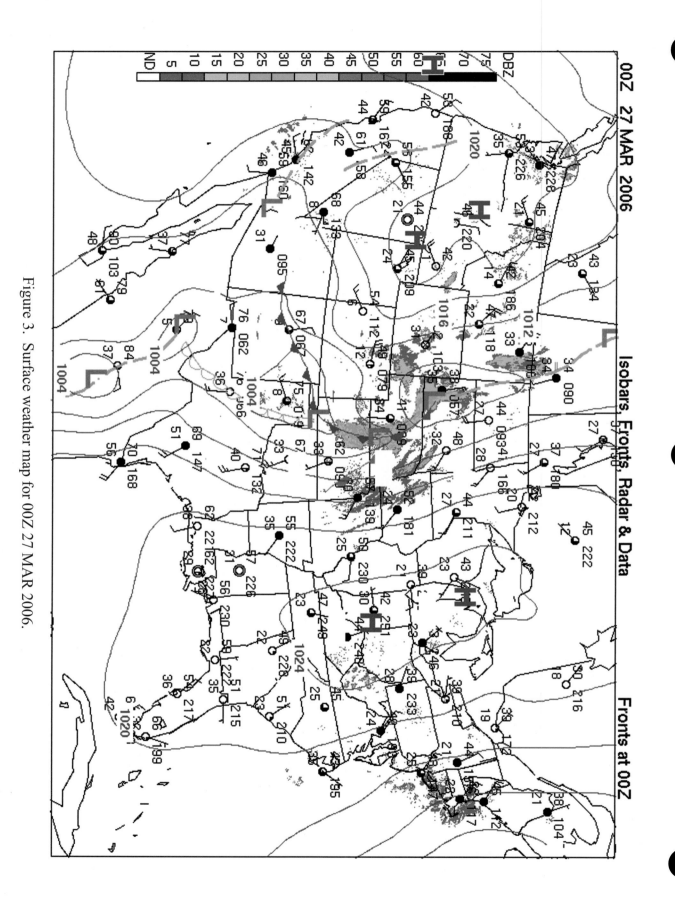

Figure 3. Surface weather map for 00Z 27 MAR 2006.

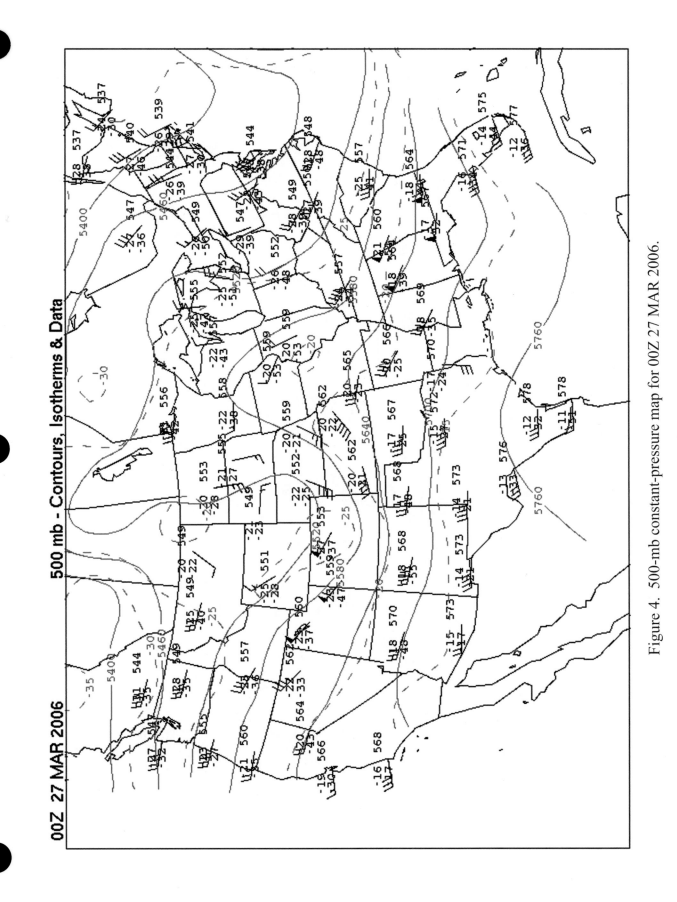

Figure 4. 500-mb constant-pressure map for 00Z 27 MAR 2006.

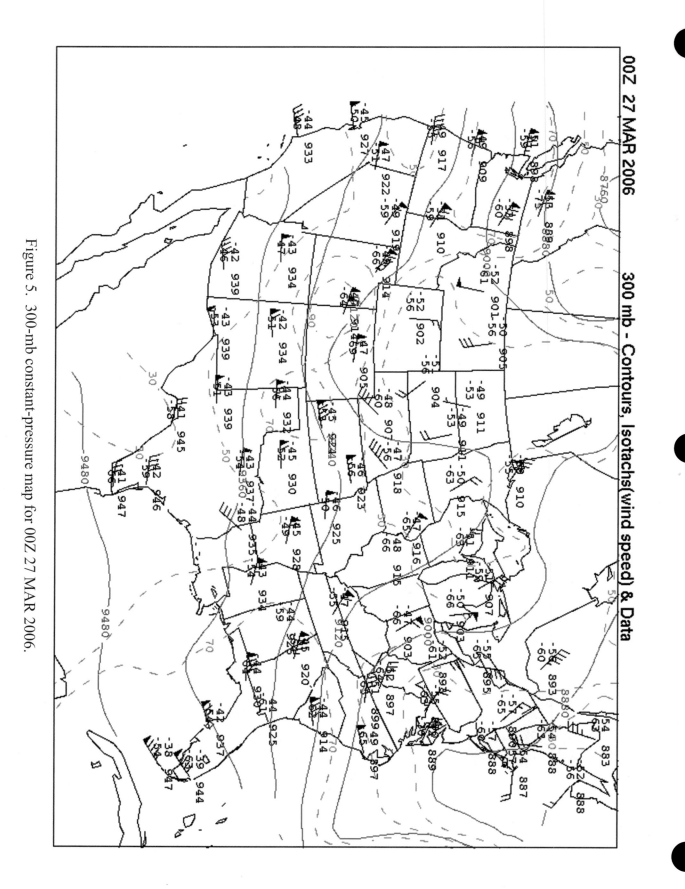

Figure 5. 300-mb constant-pressure map for 00Z 27 MAR 2006.

Investigation 9B: ¡EL NIÑO!

Objectives:

The tropical Pacific covers nearly one-fifth of Earth's surface area and stretches about one-third the way around the globe. The tropical Pacific Ocean and the overlying atmosphere are a coupled system that makes its presence felt far beyond its boundaries. Its influence on world-wide weather and climate can have major ecological, societal, and economic consequences. Every 3 to 7 years this coupled ocean/atmosphere system takes on conditions termed El Niño, which typically persists for 12 to 18 months and may alternate with the less frequent La Niña. El Niño is one example of the variability of weather and climate on time and spatial scales that go beyond the basic weather map.

After completing this investigation, you should be able to:

- Describe the neutral (long-term average) conditions of the tropical Pacific Ocean and atmosphere.
- Compare El Niño conditions to neutral conditions.
- Explain how atmospheric conditions during El Niño are transmitted beyond the tropical Pacific area.

Introduction:

Tropical Pacific during Neutral (Long-Term Average) Conditions

1. Examine Figure 1, the neutral (long-term average) conditions in the tropical Pacific Ocean from about Borneo in the western Pacific Ocean to the west coast of South America (greatly exaggerated in the vertical scale). The scene depicts the ocean surface with atmosphere above and a cross-section of the ocean below. Fair weather appears in the eastern tropical Pacific (near 80 degrees W) while the cloud diagram implies that [(*__fair__*) (*__stormy__*)] weather prevails in the western Pacific (near 120 degrees E).

2. The large-scale motions in the atmosphere show a convection cell (convective loop). The bold dark arrows show that air is rising in the stormy weather area of the western Pacific and [(*__rising__*) (*__sinking__*)] in the eastern tropical Pacific.

3. The bold black arrow along the ocean surface in the convective loop represents the *trade winds* and points in the direction toward which the prevailing winds are blowing in the equatorial region. As indicated by the arrows, winds during neutral (long-term average) conditions blow toward the [(*__east__*) (*__west__*)] along the equator.

4. The large white, open arrows provide surface ocean current information. The surface current arrows indicate that during neutral conditions, surface water flows towards the [(*__east__*) (*__west__*)] driven by the prevailing winds.

5. Colored areas on the top of the block diagram denote sea surface temperatures (SST) during neutral conditions. The red colored area in the western Pacific denotes the highest SST. These highest SST occur under [(***considerable cloudiness***) (***clear skies***)] in the tropical Pacific. This SST pattern is caused by relatively strong trade winds pushing sun- warmed surface water westward, as indicated by the direction of surface currents.

6. Strong trade winds also cause the warm surface waters to pile up in the western tropical Pacific so that the sea surface in the western Pacific is somewhat higher than in the eastern Pacific. Transport of surface waters to the west also causes the *thermocline* (the transition zone between warm surface water and cold deep water shown by the blue layer in the ocean side view) to be [(***deeper***) (***shallower***)] in the eastern tropical Pacific than in the western Pacific.

7. Warm surface water transported by the wind away from the South American coast is replaced by cold water rising from below in a process called *upwelling*. Upwelling of cold deep water results in relatively [(***high***) (***low***)] SST in the eastern Pacific compared to the western Pacific.

8. Cold surface water cools the air above it, which leads to increases in the surface air pressure. Warm surface water adds heat and water vapor to the atmosphere, lowering the surface air pressure. These air-sea interactions result in tropical surface air pressure being highest in the [(***eastern***) (***western***)] tropical Pacific.

9. Whenever air pressure changes over distance, a force will move air from where the pressure is relatively high to where pressure is relatively low. The trade winds blow from east to the west because from east to west the surface air pressure [(***increases***) (***decreases***)].

10. Rainfall in the tropical Pacific is also related to SST patterns. There are reasons for this relationship. The higher the SST, the greater the rate of evaporation of seawater and the more vigorous is atmospheric convection. Consequently, during neutral conditions, rainfall is greatest in the western tropical Pacific where SST are [(***highest***) (***lowest***)].

Tropical Pacific During *El Niño*

11. Figure 2 shows atmospheric and oceanic conditions during *El Niño*. Compared to Figure 1 (neutral or long-term average conditions), the area of stormy weather during El Niño has moved [(***eastward***) (***westward***)]. While no two El Niño episodes are exactly alike, all of them exhibit most of the characteristics shown in the El Niño schematic of Figure 2. With the onset of El Niño, tropical surface air pressure patterns change. Compare El Niño conditions in the western and central tropical Pacific with the neutral conditions of Figure 1. During neutral conditions, surface air pressure in the central Pacific is higher (accompanied by fair weather) than to the west. During El Niño, the surface air pressure to the west is higher than in the central Pacific. This reversal in the atmospheric pressure pattern, called the *Southern Oscillation*, was first studied in an attempt to explain monsoon failure and drought in India.

12. In response to changes in the air pressure pattern across the tropical Pacific, the trade winds weaken (and wind directions can reverse, especially in the western Pacific as

shown by the bold dark arrows). No longer being pushed toward and piled up in the western Pacific, the warm surface water reverses flow direction. As shown by the surface currents arrows, the surface water during *El Niño* flows toward the east. As evident in the appropriate sea surface temperature shading, this causes SST in the eastern tropical Pacific to be [(***higher***) (***lower***)] than during neutral conditions.

13. In response to changes in surface currents, sea surface heights in the eastern tropical Pacific are higher than during neutral conditions. At the same time, the arrival of the warmer water in the east causes the surface warm-water layer to thicken. Evidence of this is the [(***shallower***) (***deeper***)] depth of the thermocline compared to neutral conditions.

Tropical Pacific During *La Niña*

14. Figure 3 shows atmospheric and oceanic conditions during *La Niña*. The tropical Pacific at times experiences trade winds stronger than neutral conditions with SST lower than usual in the eastern tropical Pacific and higher than usual in the western tropical Pacific. Because stronger trade winds produce stronger surface currents during *La Niña*, the warm water is pushed westward and colder water wells up to cause below-average sea-surface temperatures in the eastern tropical Pacific. It also follows that sea surface temperature in the western tropical Pacific must be [(***above***) (***below***)] its neutral condition average.

15. Changes in surface air pressure, areas of large-scale convection, and upper air flow patterns as shown in Figures 2 and 3 alter the planetary wind circulation and affect the weather elsewhere in the world. Figure 4 shows some weather patterns that have been statistically associated with *El Niño* conditions. This figure shows that during our Northern Hemisphere winter when *El Niño* is taking place, the southeastern states are usually [(***drier and warmer***) (***wetter and cooler***)] than normal. Figure 5 shows some weather patterns linked to *La Niña* conditions.

The planetary-scale circulation of the atmosphere along the Intertropical Convergence Zone (ITCZ) includes the northeasterly trade winds of the Northern Hemisphere converging with the southeasterly trades of the Southern Hemisphere. But this generalized picture does not describe all the fluctuations of the dynamic Earth-atmosphere system. Changing temperatures in the upper layers of the Pacific Ocean and the overlying atmosphere along the equator lead to the Southern Oscillation and El Niño/La Niña episodes. In much of 1997 and early 1998, for example, the tropical Pacific Ocean was experiencing an unusually strong *El Niño*. The effects of these tropical ocean-atmosphere conditions extended well beyond the tropics and may well have set the stage for the extensive storminess along the West Coast, relatively warm and dry weather in the Southeast, the mild winter in the northern states, and weather extremes elsewhere.

As directed by your course instructor, complete this investigation by either:

   1. Going to the Current Weather Studies link on the course website, or
   2. Continuing to the Applications section for this investigation that immediately follows in this Investigations Manual.

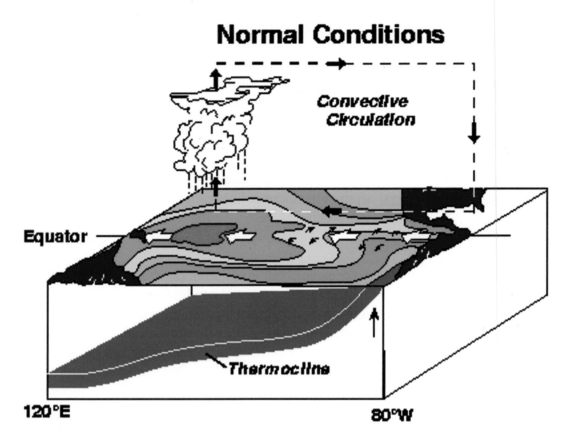

Figure 1. Atmospheric-oceanic block diagram of Neutral ("Normal") Conditions in the tropical Pacific Ocean.

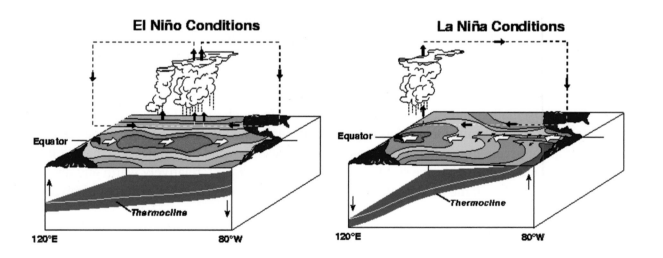

Figure 2. Diagram of El Niño Conditions in the tropical Pacific.

Figure 3. Diagram of La Niña Conditions in the tropical Pacific.

WARM EPISODE RELATIONSHIPS DECEMBER - FEBRUARY

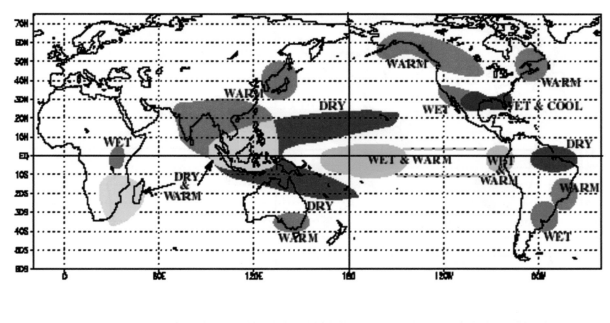

WARM EPISODE RELATIONSHIPS JUNE - AUGUST

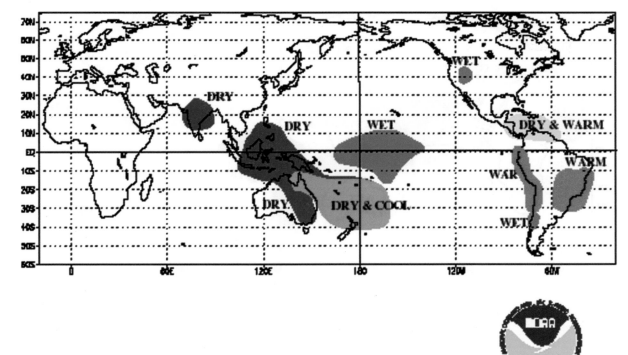

Climate Prediction Center
NCEP

Figure 4. Weather patterns statistically associated with El Niño conditions

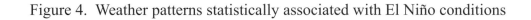

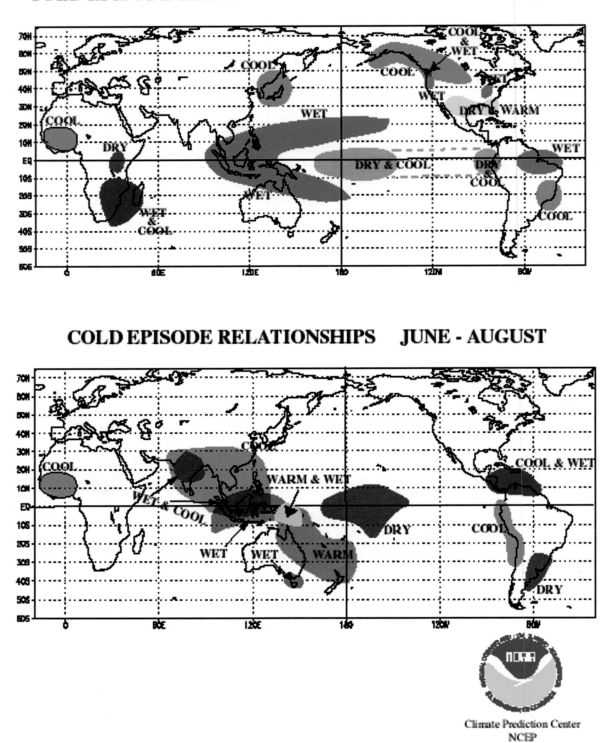

COLD EPISODE RELATIONSHIPS   DECEMBER - FEBRUARY

COLD EPISODE RELATIONSHIPS   JUNE - AUGUST

Climate Prediction Center
NCEP

Figure 5. Weather patterns statistically associated with La Niña conditions

Investigation 9B: ¡EL NIÑO!
Applications

16. Figure 6 is a depiction of the ocean surface temperatures and atmospheric surface winds in the tropics as measured primarily by an anchored-buoy array along the equator. The mapped area extends ten degrees of latitude north and south of the Equator and from near the South American coast on the east to near Indonesia on the west. The top view, labeled <u>November 1997 Means,</u> is the average sea surface temperatures (shaded with isotherms drawn at 0.5 Celsius degree intervals) and surface winds (as shown by arrows) for the month of November 1997, near the peak of the relatively strong 1997-98 El Niño episode.

    The sea surface temperatures across the region ranged from about 26 °C as the "coolest" in the southeast corner of the panel to about [(**_20_**) (**_25_**) (**_30_**)] °C as the "warmest" just south of the equator, west of center in the upper panel.

17. The highest SST were located in the neighborhood of about [(**_170 degrees W_**) (**_120 degrees W_**)] longitude in the Pacific.

18. The wind directions in the eastern Pacific were generally from the southeast. However, in the western Pacific, along the equator (from about 140 degrees E to 150 degrees W), winds were generally [(**_light_**) (**_strong_**)] and variable, blowing from the west in some locations and from the east in other locations.

19. These wind conditions generally [(**_were_**) (**_were not_**)] consistent with the depiction of the trade wind flow shown by the small dark arrows in the block diagram of "El Niño Conditions" of Figure 2.

20. The "El Niño Conditions" diagram shows that, due to the transport of warmer water eastward during the El Niño, SST in the eastern Pacific should be above the values of "Neutral Conditions". This condition of SST warmer than the long-term average is an example of a [(**_positive_**) (**_negative_**)] SST *anomaly*.

21. The bottom view of Figure 6 (<u>November 1997 Anomalies</u>) is a depiction of SST and wind *anomalies*, that is, departures of the observed values shown in the top view from the long-term average. (Note: Positive temperature anomalies are solid lines in intervals of 0.5 degree Celsius. Negative anomalies, though none appear in this graph, are displayed as dashed lines. A heavy line labeled **0** shows where no temperature anomaly exists, *i.e.* conditions are average.)

    The SST anomalies in the eastern Pacific were positive, with the greatest values being more than [(**_1.5_**) (**_4.5_**) (**_7.5_**)] Celsius degrees. SST anomalies across the tropical Pacific were all positive except for two small regions near the western corners of the image where temperatures were slightly below the long-term average (above and below the heavy "0" lines).

22. Figure 7 is a similar depiction of the tropical Pacific SST and wind conditions for November 1998, one year later than Figure 6, showing that *La Niña* conditions had replaced *El Niño*. In November 1998, sea-surface temperatures along the equator in the eastern Pacific were near 22 °C, several degrees [(***higher***) (***lower***)] than those in the same area in November 1997 during the *El Niño*.

23. Winds across the entire Pacific area of the depiction were now generally blowing from the [(***east***) (***west***)].

24. The lower panel of Figure 7, November 1998 *Anomalies,* shows that the Pacific SST anomalies denoted by the dashed lines along the equator were almost all [(***positive***) (***negative***)].

25. Anomaly values dropped below [(***-2***) (***-3***)] Celsius degrees. These relatively cool waters (compared to neutral conditions) are characteristic of *La Niña*.

For the latest five-day average conditions from the TAO buoy array, you can access *http://www.pmel.noaa.gov/tao/jsdisplay/*. The latest forecast for the tropical Pacific can be found at: *http://www.cpc.ncep.noaa.gov/products/analysis_monitoring/enso_advisory/index.shtml*. More information on El Niño can be found at: *http://www.elnino.noaa.gov/* and for La Niña at: *http://www.elnino.noaa.gov/lanina.html*. These pages also contain links to El Niño impacts on seasonal US weather patterns.

Typically the greatest extremes of SST occur prior to December as indicated by the November El Niño and La Niña images shown. For a comparison of the strong November 1997 El Niño conditions with those of other years, go to the TAO display page. From that page, click on the "Lat Lon plots" bar, then choose a Sea Surface Temperature plot, for a Monthly time range, include the year, month, and finally hit the **Make Plot!** bar. Tropical Pacific conditions for any month can also be found in this way.

Suggestions for further activities: You might investigate the El Niño/La Niña websites given above to determine the instrumentation used to obtain these *in situ* oceanic buoy measurements. Also, the sites display the Southern Oscillation Index (SOI). You can explore the discovery and meaning of this indicator of tropical Pacific conditions.

The El Niño theme page, *http://www.pmel.noaa.gov/tao/elnino/nino-home.html*, links to a three-dimensional animation of the tropical ocean conditions as El Niño evolves. Global impacts of El Niño are shown at: *http://www.cpc.noaa.gov/products/analysis_monitoring/ensocycle/elninosfc.shtml*, while global La Niña impacts are shown at: *http://www.cpc.noaa.gov/products/analysis_monitoring/ensocycle/laninasfc.shtml*.

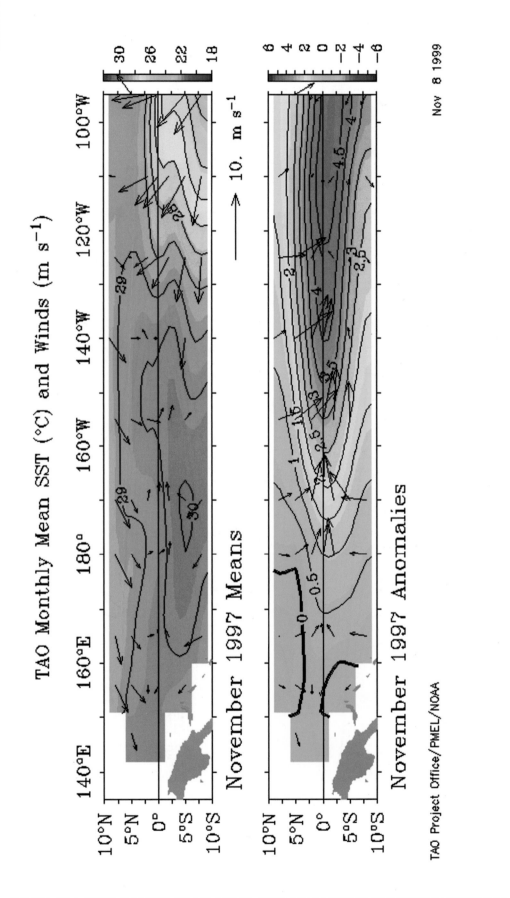

TAO Monthly Mean SST (°C) and Winds (m s⁻¹)

November 1997 Means

November 1997 Anomalies

TAO Project Office/PMEL/NOAA

Nov 8 1999

Figure 6. November 1997 oceanic means and anomaly conditions from TAO array.

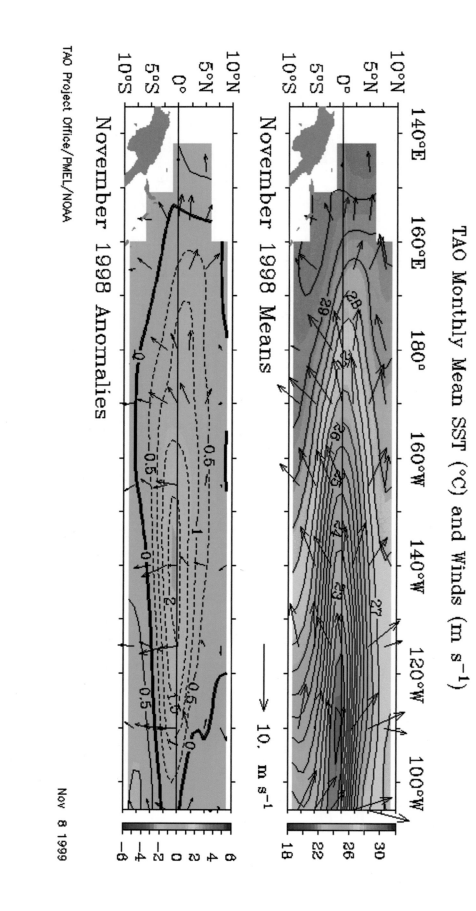

Figure 7. November 1998 oceanic means and anomaly conditions from TAO array.

Investigation 10A: THE EXTRA-TROPICAL CYCLONE

Objectives:

Extra-tropical cyclones (Lows or low pressure systems) are stormy weather makers, which spend much of their life cycles in the middle latitudes. The counterclockwise and inward circulation that characterizes surface winds in Northern Hemisphere cyclones brings contrasting air masses together to form fronts. And along those fronts clouds and precipitation may develop. As a cyclone travels along its track, the system progresses through its life cycle. Localities that come under the influence of a cyclone often experience sequential changes in weather. Understanding the types of weather associated with a typical extra-tropical cyclone aids in weather forecasting.

After completing this investigation, you should be able to:

- Describe the pattern of surface winds and weather about the center of an extra-tropical cyclone.
- Specify the type of weather associated with fronts that rotate about an extra-tropical cyclone's low-pressure center.
- Compare and contrast the weather associated with cold fronts and warm fronts.

Introduction:

1. Looking down on a Northern Hemisphere low-pressure system (cyclone), surface winds blow [(***clockwise and outward***) (***counterclockwise and inward***)] about the center.

2. The specific track across Earth's surface taken by a migrating extra-tropical cyclone is determined by large-scale horizontal winds blowing [(***near the Earth's surface***) (***in the middle and upper troposphere***)].

3. As a cyclone tracks across the continent, the system progresses through its life cycle. As a cyclone develops, the central pressure of the system [(***falls***) (***rises***)] and surface winds strengthen. At maturity, clouds cover a broad area about the low center and associated precipitation is widespread.

4. Figure 1 is a schematic of a typical extra-tropical cyclone at maturity. Shown are the positions of the cold and warm fronts along with isobars drawn at intervals of 4 mb. **Label the fronts with the appropriate symbols for a warm front and cold front.** Review the *hand-twist model* for low pressure systems (Investigation 1A). **Then, using the wind symbol on the station model as a guide, pencil in on the map the wind direction at points to the northeast, southeast, southwest, and northwest of the cyclone center.** To the south and east of the center of an extra-tropical cyclone, surface winds are likely to produce [(***warm***) (***cold***)] air advection.

5. To the north and west of the center of an extra-tropical cyclone, surface winds are likely to produce [(**_warm_**) (**_cold_**)] air advection.

6. Dewpoints are likely to be relatively high to the [(**_southeast_**) (**_northwest_**)] of the cyclone center.

7. As the cyclone tracks across the continent, the cold and warm fronts rotate about the center of low pressure. The motion of the storm system, then, is similar to that of a Frisbee®, that is, a Frisbee rotates as it sails through the air. Typically, the cold front rotates about the center of the low faster than the warm front. Hence, eventually the cold front catches up with and merges with the warm front forming an occluded front. At this stage in the life cycle of an extra-tropical cyclone (known as *occlusion*), the storm often begins to weaken as the central air pressure begins to [(**_rise_**) (**_fall_**)].

8. As a cyclone progresses through its life cycle and its cold front rotates toward its warm front, the area at the Earth's surface occupied by relatively warm and humid air [(**_shrinks_**) (**_increases_**)].

9. With the passage of a warm front, the air temperature usually rises and the dewpoint usually [(**_falls_**) (**_rises_**)].

10. With the passage of a cold front, the air temperature usually falls and the dewpoint usually [(**_falls_**) (**_rises_**)].

11. A shift in wind direction usually accompanies the passage of a front. With passage of the cold front, surface winds shift direction from the south to the [(**_southeast or east_**) (**_west or northwest_**)].

12. With passage of the warm front, surface winds shift direction from the east to the [(**_southeast or south_**) (**_west or northwest_**)].

13. Ahead of a surface warm front, warm and humid air rides up and over a wedge of cooler air (a process known as *overrunning*.) As the ascending warm air expands and cools, its relative humidity [(**_increases_**) (**_decreases_**)], and clouds may form.

14. Most cloudiness associated with a warm front develops over a broad area, often hundreds of kilometers wide, [(**_ahead of_**) (**_behind_**)] the front. From these clouds, light to moderate precipitation typically falls for 12 to 24 hours or longer.

15. As a cold air mass advances and a warm air mass retreats, the colder, denser air forces the warmer, lighter air to ascend either along or just ahead of the cold front. Uplift of warm air triggers cloud development and perhaps showery precipitation. In some instances, uplift is so vigorous that thunderstorms develop. Typically, the band of clouds and precipitation associated with a cold front is [(**_narrower_**) (**_wider_**)] than that associated with a warm front.

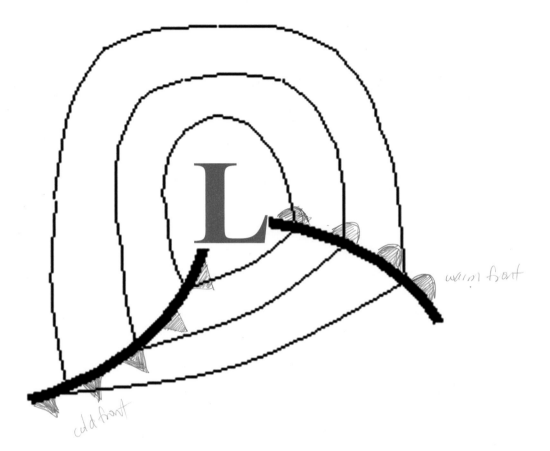

Figure 1. Schematic diagram of Northern Hemisphere extra-tropical (wave) cyclone.

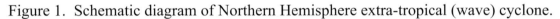

As directed by your course instructor, complete this investigation by either:

1. *Going to the Current Weather Studies link on the course website, or*
2. *Continuing to the Applications section for this investigation that immediately follows in this Investigations Manual.*

Investigation 10A: THE EXTRA-TROPICAL CYCLONE
Applications

16. The accompanying Figure 2 visible satellite image shows the broad, comma-shaped cloud pattern associated with a mature extra-tropical cyclone. The center of lowest air pressure at the Earth's surface at map time is designated by the "L" plotted over Iowa. Bold, heavy lines represent the location of an occluded front and a cold front associated with this low-pressure system. Clearing skies and generally fair weather follow the passage of the [(*occluded*) (*cold*)] front.

Let us now examine a weather pattern featuring a strong extra-tropical cyclone which was associated with deadly tornadoes in the Ohio River Valley region. The weather system developed as a low-pressure center in the Colorado area, a common location for *cyclogenesis* (storm formation), several days before and rapidly moved eastward across the Great Plains towards the Great Lakes area.

17. Figure 3 is the surface weather map for 00Z 03 APR 2006. At map time, the center of the system, shown by the lowest pressure, was in [(*southern Michigan*) (*western Tennessee*) (*southeastern Iowa*)].

18. From the Low center, a [(*cold*) (*warm*) (*stationary*)] front stretched southeastward to the North Carolina-Virginia border.

19. Also, from the Low a [(*cold*) (*warm*) (*stationary*)] front curved south and southwestward to the Texas-Oklahoma border.

20. The continuation of both fronts where little movement was occurring became [(*cold*) (*warm*) (*stationary*)] fronts extending eastward into the Atlantic and southwestward to Mexico, respectively.

21. Generally, surface air temperatures were warmest and dewpoints highest [(*north of the warm front*) (*southeast of the Low center between the warm and cold fronts*) (*behind (west of) the cold front*)].

22. Behind the cold front winds were generally from the northwest or west, while wind directions in the warm sector were generally from the [(*east or northeast*) (*southwest or south*)].

Radar echoes associated with the cyclonic system showed that precipitation was occurring mainly in a wide arc from the west to the northeast of the Low center, in a band along the warm front, and in a curve southward into the warm sector. In this particular system, the arc of thunderstorms is in the warm sector, ahead of the cold front rather than along it. This arc is called a *squall line*, shown by double dots and a dashed line. These thunderstorms, developing in the warm sector of the storm system between the cold and stationary fronts, became severe—producing hail, strong winds, and some tornadoes. One severe thunderstorm was responsible for 11 fatalities in western Tennessee in the hour following map time. (The tiny dot on the Arkansas-Tennessee border denotes this thunderstorm at map time.)

23. In addition to the lifting mechanisms of convergence with Lows and along fronts, precipitation formation requires humid air. Dewpoints in the warm sector, between the warm and cold fronts, were generally in the [(*30s and 40s*) (*50s and 60s*) (*70s and 80s*)] Fahrenheit. The humid air flow from the Gulf of Mexico provided the fuel for the thunderstorms associated with the extra-tropical cyclone.

24. Figure 4 is the infrared satellite view from 0015Z 03 APR 2006, essentially the same time as the surface weather conditions plotted on the Figure 3 map. **Sketch the locations of the cyclone's warm and cold fronts and squall line on the satellite image.** The white shading indicating the major areas of coldest cloud tops over the east-central U.S. at this time were located in [(*an arc where the squall line was located*) (*a broad patch along the warm front*) (*both locations*)].

25. These coldest cloud tops are also likely to be the [(*lowest*) (*highest*)] cloud tops.

26. This pattern of bright shading indicating highest cloud tops [(*was*) (*was not*)] generally coincident with areas of most intense precipitation and thunderstorm activity indicated by radar on the surface map. In all, the NOAA Storm Prediction Center received reports of 63 tornadoes, 326 hail and 324 wind damage cases in the 24-hour period from 6 AM CST on 2 April to 6 AM on 3 April.

The curvature of the clouds in the central U.S. suggests the "comma" cloud pattern usually associated with a mature extra-tropical cyclone. The comma has a broad head around the Low and a tail along the cold front (or squall line, in this case).

27. Figure 5 is the 300-mb constant pressure map for 00Z 03 APR 2006, the time of the surface map and satellite view. The upper level flow pattern associated with this cyclone is characterized by a [(*trough*) (*ridge*)] in the center of the country.

28. **Draw an arc through the southernmost parts of the curved contours from southeastern South Dakota to western Arkansas.** This axis of curvature of the storm at 300 mb is located somewhat to the [(*west*) (*east*)] of the storm's surface Low and cold front. This positioning is typical of a strong, developing extra-tropical cyclone and is related to the placement of the coldest air column below this 300-mb level (recall Investigation 5B).

29. The location of the 70-knot isotach enclosing an area from Wyoming to southern Missouri and northern Arkansas [(*is*) (*is not*)] evidence of a jet stream associated with this storm system. The 90-knot isotach in Colorado is a jet streak.

A broad area of horizontal divergence at the 300-mb level is located to the east of the trough

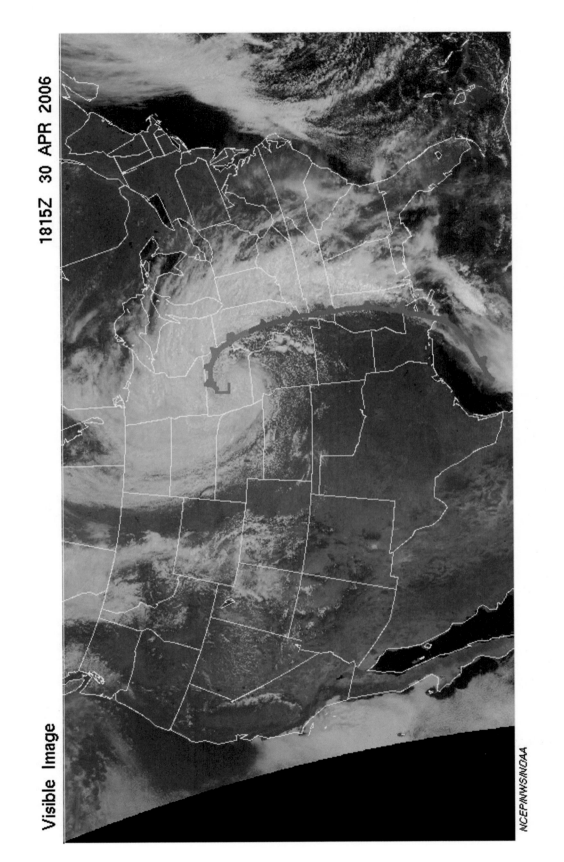

Figure 2. Visible satellite image of a mature extra-tropical cyclone and fronts on 30 APR 2006.

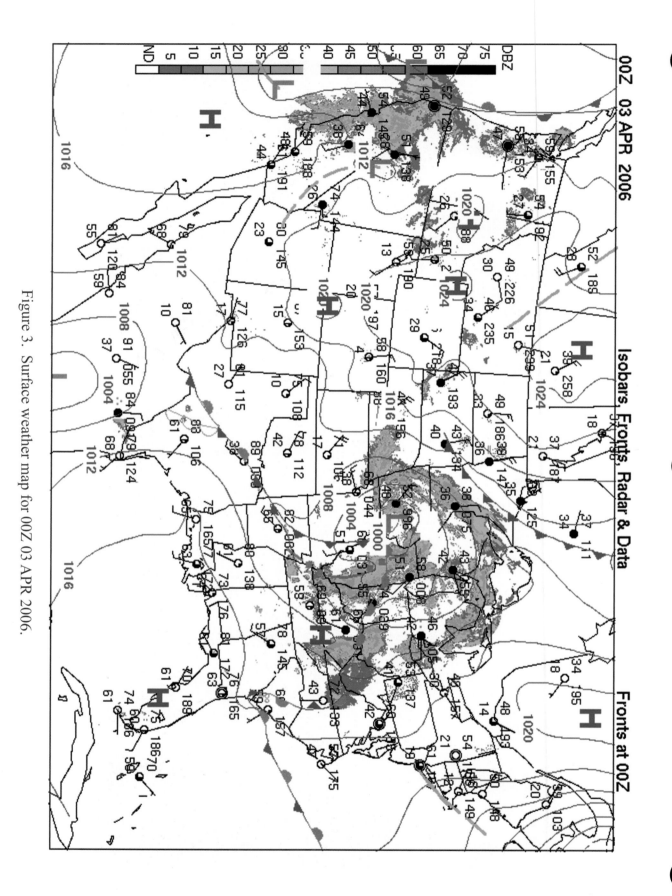

Figure 3. Surface weather map for 00Z 03 APR 2006.

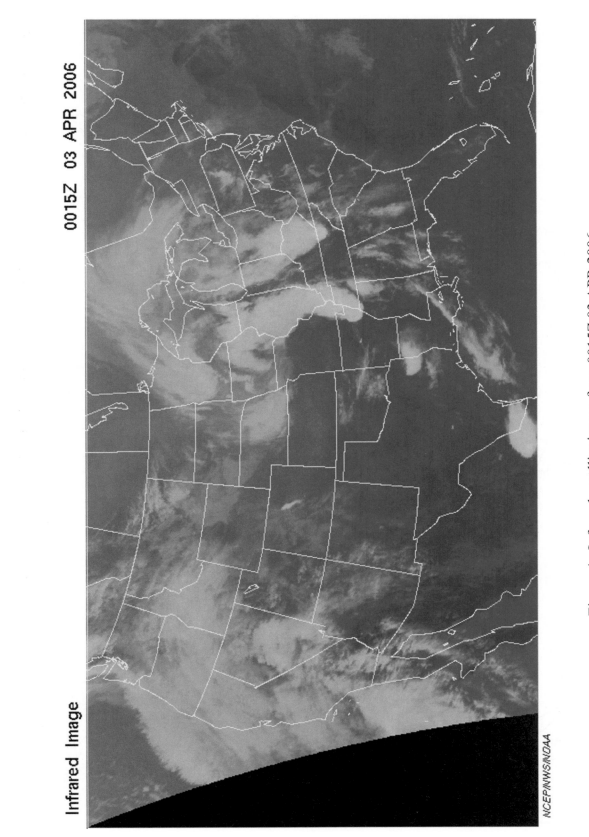

Infrared Image

0015Z 03 APR 2006

NCEP/NWS/NOAA

Figure 4. Infrared satellite image from 0015Z 03 APR 2006.

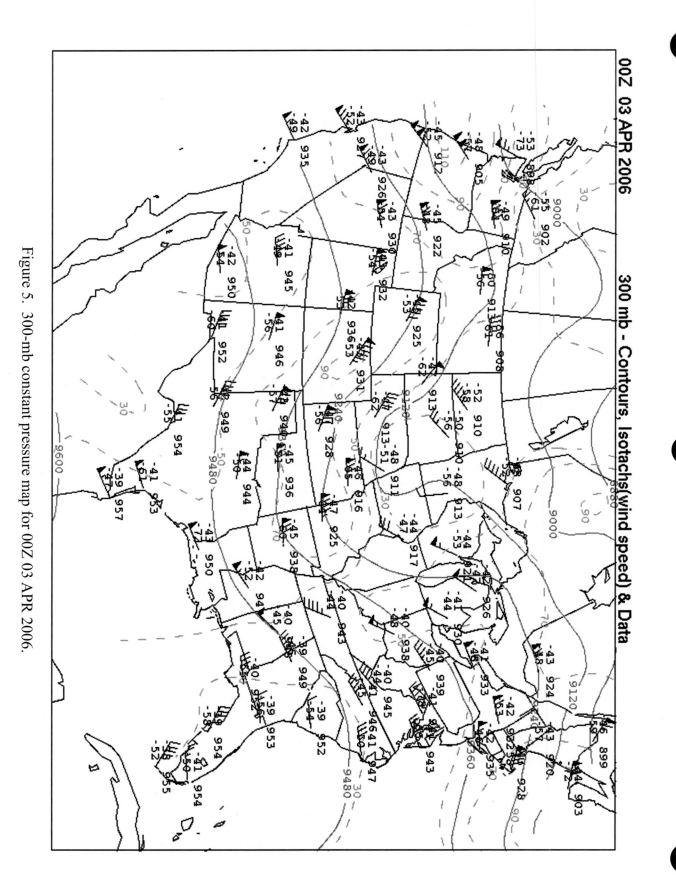

Figure 5. 300-mb constant pressure map for 00Z 03 APR 2006.

axis, shown by your line. Specifically, wind directions over northeastern Iowa to Wisconsin display the spreading flow pattern of divergence that supports the developing Low at the surface. In addition, horizontal divergence across Tennessee to northern Alabama contributed to the intensification of thunderstorms that brought deadly severe weather to that area.

Suggestions for further activities: NOAA weather radio, "State Surface Data - Text" on the course website, or local instrument readings and media reports are ways you can keep track of changes in hourly weather conditions that accompany cyclones as these systems and their fronts approach and cross your location, particularly when severe weather threatens. You can record these hourly weather conditions on a blank meteogram, available from the course website, under **Extras**, "Blank Metgram". Then you can compare these changing conditions with the general pattern expected from passing extra-tropical cyclones. (NOAA Weather Radio is particularly valuable when severe weather threatens your area as most weather radios are equipped with warning alarms that can be triggered by the National Weather Service when conditions warrant.)

Additional discussion of the extra-tropical cyclone with images can be found at: *http://ww2010.atmos.uiuc.edu/(Gh)/guides/mtr/cyc/home.rxml*. Also, from the *NWS Surface Analyses* link on the course website (**Surface** section), you can create a 24-hour surface analysis loop showing the movement of weather systems by selecting a region and clicking "Display Loop".

Investigation 10B: EXTRA-TROPICAL CYCLONE TRACK WEATHER

Objectives:

An understanding of the typical weather pattern associated with an extra-tropical cyclone in the middle latitudes enables us to forecast the sequence of changes in weather as the cyclone approaches and then moves away. As a general rule, the weather on one side of a storm track differs from the weather on the other side. The storm track is the path the low-pressure center takes as the system progresses through its life cycle. Facing in the direction towards which the cyclone is moving, the weather is usually colder on the left side of the storm track and warmer on the right side of the storm track. Typically, only localities on the right side of a storm track experience the passage of fronts. During the colder times of the year, the storm track can separate areas of snow from areas of rain.

After completing this investigation, you should be able to:

- Describe the sequence of changes in weather that typically takes place on the right (warm) side of a cyclone track.
- Describe the sequence of changes in weather that usually takes place on the left (cold) side of a cyclone track.

Introduction:

1. Figure 1 shows a winter low pressure system intensifying over eastern Colorado. Over the subsequent two days, the storm system tracks toward the Great Lakes region. Track A would take the cyclone center to the east of Detroit and Track B would take the cyclone center to the west of Detroit. In either case, the system would pass close enough to Detroit to have major consequences for the city's weather. The potential positions of the cyclone center along each of the two tracks (Track A and Track B) at 12-hour intervals are indicated by heavy dots. As the cyclone tracks toward the Great Lakes, the system progresses through its life cycle. The cold and warm fronts gradually rotate (counterclockwise as viewed from above) about the cyclone center with the faster cold front closing in on the slower warm front.

    Using the frontal positions shown in Texas as the starting point, pencil in the cyclone's estimated cold and warm frontal positions at 12-hour intervals along Track A. Draw the fronts from the low-pressure center at each location. With Track A, residents of Detroit [(***do***) (***do not***)] experience the passage of fronts.

2. Apply the *hand-twist model* of low pressure systems to the cyclone's position at 12-hour intervals along Track A. Assume that before the storm's arrival the wind at Detroit is blowing from the east. As the cyclone approaches the wind shifts from the east to the [(***southeast***) (***northeast***)].

3. Considering the wind shifts and frontal positions at Detroit as the cyclone passes through the region along Track A, the city is on the relatively [(***warm***) (***cold***)] side of the system.

4. **Using the cyclone's Track B frontal positions in Oklahoma as a guide, pencil in the associated cold front and warm front at 12-hour intervals.** With Track B, residents of Detroit [(***do***) (***do not***)] experience the passage of fronts.

5. **Apply the *hand-twist model* of low pressure systems to each of the storm's 12-hour positions along Track B.** Assume that initially the wind at Detroit is blowing from the east. As the storm approaches the wind shifts from the east to the [(***southeast***) (***northeast***)].

6. Considering the wind shifts at Detroit as the cyclone's center passes through Michigan along Track B, Detroit is on the relatively [(***warm***) (***cold***)] side of the system.

7. Substantial snowfall at Detroit is more likely if the cyclone takes Track [(***A***) (***B***)].

8. Showery precipitation is more likely at Detroit if the cyclone takes Track [(***A***) (***B***)].

9. As the cyclone approaches Detroit on either storm track, the air pressure at the city [(***falls***) (***rises***)].

10. As the cyclone moves away from Detroit, the air pressure at the city [(***falls***) (***rises***)].

11. The next weather system to affect Detroit is likely a cold [(***cyclone***) (***anticyclone***)] approaching from central Canada.

As directed by your course instructor, complete this investigation by either:

1. *Going to the Current Weather Studies link on the course website, or*
2. *Continuing to the Applications section for this investigation that immediately follows in this Investigations Manual.*

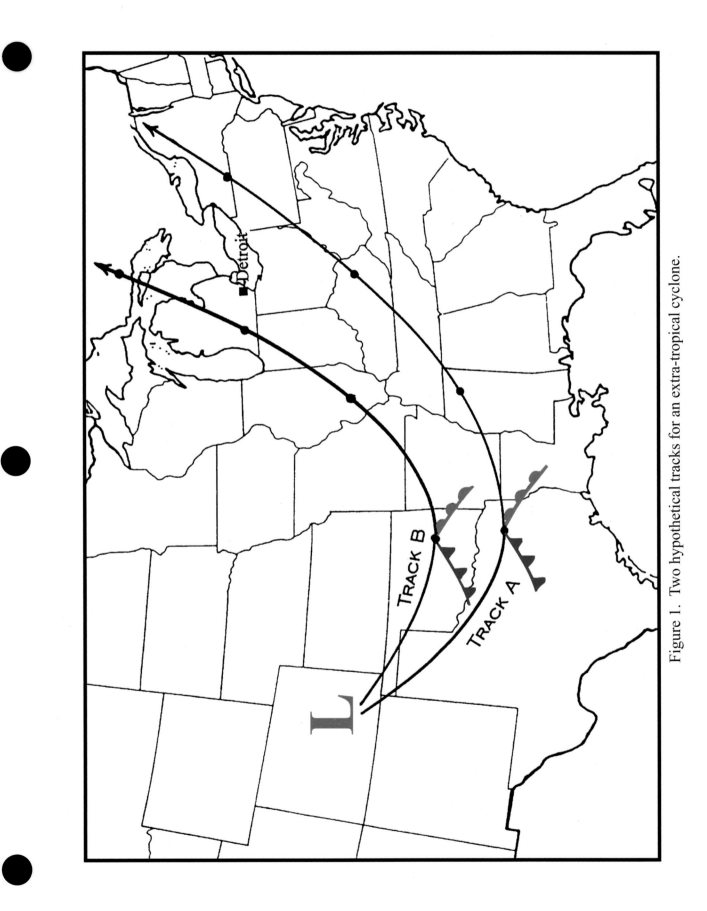

Figure 1. Two hypothetical tracks for an extra-tropical cyclone.

Investigation 10B: EXTRA-TROPICAL CYCLONE TRACK WEATHER

Applications

Extra-tropical cyclones continually form, migrate across the country and go through their life cycles to occlusion and dissipation. Successive cyclones are often separated by anticyclones (Highs). Investigation 10A examined one of these cyclonic systems in some detail (Investigation 10A, Figure 3). Also, an anticyclone could be seen along the west-central U.S.-Canadian border. And another in the series of extra-tropical cyclones that had been impacting the Northwest U.S. could be seen as its frontal system and accompanying precipitation moved ashore.

12. Review the Investigation 10A Figure 3 surface map (00Z 03 APR 2006). The pattern of wind directions about the Low centered in southeastern Iowa was generally [(***clockwise and outward***) (***counterclockwise and inward***)].

13. Meanwhile the circulation around the western Canadian High was generally [(***clockwise and outward***) (***counterclockwise and inward***)].

14. The majority of stations in the central U.S. about the Low and its fronts and squall line reported [(***fair weather***) (***overcast skies and precipitation***)].

15. Station models from west-central Canada across the northern Plains and Rocky Mountain states influenced by the High were generally consistent with [(***fair***) (***stormy***)] weather conditions.

16. Based on our previous investigations of the general direction of flow of mid- to upper-tropospheric winds in middle latitudes (specifically the Investigation 10A Figure 5 map of 300-mb winds), one would expect the systems depicted on the Figure 3 surface map to move generally toward the [(***west***) (***east***)].

The accompanying Figure 2 map of this Investigation is a forecast map. It is a sample of the kinds of maps available in the "Watches, Warnings, Advisories and Forecasts" section of the website under "Station model data-". These forecast conditions at stations across the country are produced by a computer model of the atmosphere using mathematical equations of the physical laws governing fluid motions, starting from the observed conditions at a given time. This particular numerical weather prediction model producing the forecast shown is the Nested Grid Model (NGM), so named for the mathematical scheme used in the calculations.

17. This forecast map was delivered on the website as a "Forecast - 36 Hour" map, meaning it is a projection of weather conditions 36 hours into the future. The "Valid" time, marked on the upper left corner of the printed map, is when these conditions are expected. The Valid time of the map is 12Z 04 APR 2006. Consequently, the forecast

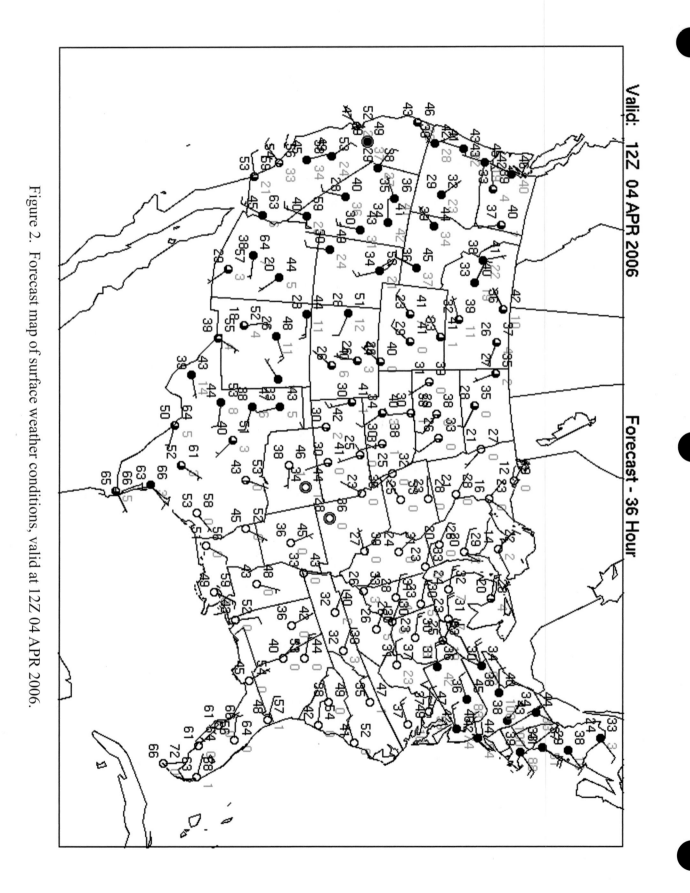

Figure 2. Forecast map of surface weather conditions, valid at 12Z 04 APR 2006.

would have been based on actual observations 36 hours earlier, that is, observations reported at [(__00__) (__12__)] Z on 03 APR 2006.

18. This original observation time [(__was__) (__was not__)] the same time as the surface observations appearing on the Investigation 10A Figure 3 surface map.

The forecast data for each station are presented in a "forecast station model" that is explained in the User's Guide, found under the *Extras* section on the website. The forecast conditions for the valid time of 12Z 04 APR 2006 at Minneapolis, Minnesota (in southeastern MN) were:

19. Temperature: _____ °F with dewpoint: **21** °F.
20. Wind: generally from the [(__southwest__) (__northwest__)] at about 1 - 2 knots.
21. Cloud cover: [(__clear__) (__one-half__) (__overcast__)].
22. Probability of Precipitation (provided in the "1 o'clock" position): [(__0__) (__15__) (__36__)] %.

23. Although symbols for weather systems (**H**s, **L**s, and fronts) are not shown on forecast maps, by analyzing wind directions, the sky conditions, and precipitation probabilities, weather systems may be located approximately. Overcast conditions were predicted over the Northeastern States for 12Z 04 APR. Another broad band of cloudy skies was located across the western quarter of the U.S. These stations generally [(__do__) (__do not__)] have higher probabilities of precipitation compared to other stations where less cloud cover is expected.

24. The portion of a circulation pattern of wind directions in the Northeastern States, which can be inferred about a spot over Connecticut, is [(__clockwise__) (__counterclockwise__)].

25. Based on this wind pattern, that location is likely to be the center of a [(__High__) (__Low__)]. **Lightly place an "H" or "L" on the map to mark this location.**

26. Most stations located east of a line from about central Minnesota to Arkansas have generally westerly or northwesterly winds except for New England. Furthermore, the wind directions west of the MN-AR line are generally from the southeast or south. **Lightly sketch a line along this position**. That pattern of wind directions suggests that an elongated [(__High__) (__Low__)] may be centered along the line you just drew. **Lightly place an "H" or "L" along the center of the line on the map to mark this location.**

27. Sky conditions at stations on both sides of the MN-AR line are generally [(__clear__) (__cloudy__)] and consistent with that pressure system.

28. The cloudy conditions and relatively higher precipitation probabilities across the mountainous West suggest that a [(__High__) (__Low__)] was probably located somewhere in the region. (Wind circulations often do not develop the classical *hand-twist* pattern in mountainous terrain.)

29. Figure 3 is the actual surface map of 12Z 04 APR 2006. This [(_**is**_) (_**is not**_)] the same time as the "Valid" time for the forecast weather conditions of the Figure 2 map.

30. The center of lowest pressure within the 1000-mb isobar along the East Coast is located in [(_**Pennsylvania**_) (_**Connecticut**_) (_**Maine**_)]. The position of the "**L**" printed on the map coincides with the "**L**" you placed in Item 22 above on the forecast map.

31. The center of highest pressure within the 1024-mb isobar is marked with an "**H**" located in [(_**South Dakota**_) (_**Missouri**_) (_**Illinois**_)]. The position of the "**H**" printed on the map is generally near the "**H**" you placed on the forecast map. **Finally shade the areas of precipitation as shown by radar echoes**. (To aid this process, you may wish to overlay the forecast map on the actual map.)

32. The areas of scattered precipitation shown by radar across the U.S. on the Figure 3 surface map generally [(_**did**_) (_**did not**_)] exist where overcast skies were expected on the Figure 2 forecast map.

33. Compare the weather conditions forecast on Figure 2 with those actually reported at 12Z 04 APR on Figure 3 for the several of the following stations: (a) San Diego, California, (b) Casper, Wyoming, (c) Minneapolis, Minnesota, (d) Nashville, Tennessee, (e) Tallahassee, Florida, and (f) Buffalo, New York. In terms of the values of temperature, winds, and cloud cover, the forecast conditions would generally have been [(_**a useful guide**_) (_**very misleading**_)] to residents of those cities.

Suggestions for further activities: Actual weather forecasts issued to the public by NOAA's National Weather Service are produced by meteorologists beginning with computer guidance information. You might use the website forecast maps to compare the NWS forecast weather conditions for your location with the conditions that actually occur at the forecast "Valid time". Forecasts issued by local radio and television stations or newspapers are usually based on NWS forecasts. (Generally, weather forecasts appearing in newspapers are the least accurate due to the long lead time needed to meet publication deadlines.)

For smaller scale wind systems such as the sea/lake breezes, a description is given of their formation and evolution at: _http://cimss.ssec.wisc.edu/wxwise/seabrz.html_.

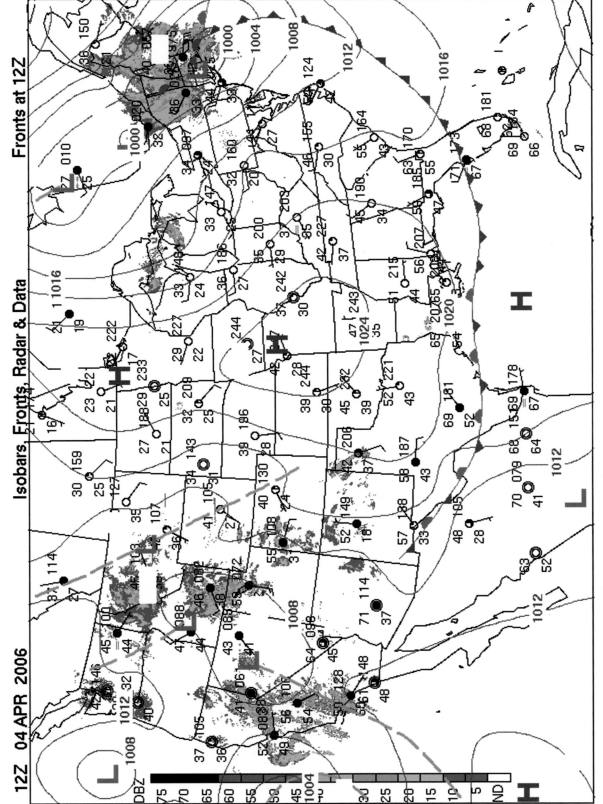

Figure 3. Actual surface weather map showing conditions at 12Z 04 APR 2006.

Investigation 11A: THUNDERSTORMS

Objectives:

A thunderstorm is one of nature's most awesome spectacles; and it is a major mechanism whereby heat energy is transported from Earth's surface into the atmosphere. Thunderstorms are also responsible for dangerous lightning, excessive rainfall that can lead to flash flooding, damaging surface winds, and tornadoes. Thunderstorms are the consequence of convection currents that surge to great altitudes within the troposphere (and sometimes into the lower stratosphere). At middle latitudes, surface heating by the sun can set the stage for thunderstorm development. However, convection forced by converging surface winds or uplift along a frontal surface or a mountain slope produces most midlatitude thunderstorms.

After completing this investigation, you should be able to:

- Describe the appearance of thunderstorms on visible satellite imagery.
- Identify probable locations of thunderstorms on infrared satellite imagery.
- List some of the modes of occurrence of thunderstorms.

Introduction:

1. As a general rule of thumb, the greater the altitude of the top of a thunderstorm cloud (cumulonimbus), the more intense is the thunderstorm cell. A relatively high thunderstorm top implies vigorous convection and a relatively [(***weak***) (***strong***)] updraft.

2. Within a thunderstorm cell, the temperature [(***falls***) (***rises***)] with increasing altitude primarily because of the expansion of rising air within the cloud.

3. An intense thunderstorm thus has a relatively [(***cold***) (***warm***)] cloud top.

4. On a visible satellite image, a large thunderstorm can appear as a bright white blotch, or cluster. The brightness of the blotch indicates that the cloud top has a relatively [(***high***) (***low***)] albedo for visible solar radiation.

As directed by your course instructor, complete this investigation by either:

1. *Going to the Current Weather Studies link on the course website, or*
2. *Continuing to the Applications section for this investigation that immediately follows in this Investigations Manual.*

Investigation 11A: THUNDERSTORMS
Applications

On Friday, 7 April 2006, an occluding low-pressure system with its accompanying warm and cold fronts swept across the central U.S. triggering an outbreak of severe thunderstorms. The Low and accompanying fronts progressed eastward during the early part of the weekend, bringing rain and severe weather to areas of the Eastern U.S. The accompanying circulation about the Low brought warm and humid air northward into the *warm sector*, the region between the warm and cold fronts. In addition to the low-level humid air and approaching cold front as a lifting mechanism, strong horizontal divergence at upper levels created the instability needed for explosive growth of cumulonimbus clouds. Twelve fatalities and considerable property damage occurred across Tennessee from tornadoes spawned by the thunderstorms that we investigate here. Ironically, the same area saw 24 fatalities just one week earlier from another severe thunderstorm outbreak noted in Investigation 10A.

Figure 1 is the surface weather map for 18Z 07 APR 2006. At map time the low-pressure system's central pressure was 996 mb, surrounded by a 1000-mb isobar encircling eastern Kansas and southern Missouri. Frontal positions from 15Z show a short occluded front extending westward along the northern edge of the lowest pressure with a warm front stretched eastward (with a loop) toward the Atlantic. A cold front is shown curved southward into eastern Texas. A second cold front was shown to the west as the leading edge of much colder air.

5.   Shaded areas across the U.S. denote radar echoes where precipitation was likely falling at map time. The shading scale to the left of the map indicates intensity of precipitation. The most intense echoes (red spots) were produced by a patch of precipitation over western Kentucky and Tennessee located [(***behind the cold front***) (***in the warm sector***) (***ahead of the warm front***)].

6.   The temperature and dewpoint at Nashville, TN, were 74 °F and 60 °F, respectively, indicating relatively [(***warm and humid***) (***cool and dry***)] air near the surface across that area.

7.   Meanwhile, the temperature and dewpoint at Oklahoma City, OK, behind the cold front were 73 °F and 32 °F, respectively, indicating relatively [(***warm and humid***) (***warm but dry***)] air in that region to the west of the initial cold front (essentially acting more as a dryline).

8.   Finally, the air at Chicago, IL, north of the surface warm front, had temperature and dewpoint values of 43 °F and 36 °F, respectively, which were [(***higher***) (***lower***)] than temperatures and dewpoints in the warm sector south of the warm front.

9.   Wind directions from the Gulf Coast northward to Nashville are from the [(***northwest***) (***south***)].

10. This representative wind direction at Nashville would likely be associated with the northward advection of [(***warm and humid***) (***cool and dry***)] air.

To develop, thunderstorm cells require (a) abundant moisture, (b) a lifting mechanism, and (c) supportive atmospheric conditions. Severe thunderstorms can occur where these conditions are very well organized. These conditions were fully met across western Kentucky and Tennessee on 7 April 2006.

Figure 2 is the satellite Visible Image for 1815Z 07 APR 2006, about the same time as the surface map. The oval of bright white clouds over Kansas was associated with the Low while the band eastward from Iowa across to New York and New England was located ahead of the warm front. No extensive cloudiness had formed along the initial cold front.

11. Across western Kentucky and Tennessee, the bright white blotches of cloudiness [(***do***) (***do not***)] generally align with the area where the radar reported the most intense precipitation echoes on the surface map (Figure 1).

    The blotches feature a sharp western edge of towering cumulonimbus clouds. Spreading eastward are feathery upper-level cirrus clouds as the thunderstorm tops are blown downwind by middle- to upper-tropospheric winds. Additional cumulus patches in southeastern Missouri and central Indiana are destined to build into thunderstorms as well.

12. Figure 3 is the satellite Infrared Image for 1715Z 07 APR 2006, the hour prior to the surface map and visible satellite image. At this time the thunderstorms were rapidly growing cumulus towers. **Compare the shading of the cloud towers in western Tennessee and Kentucky with the area from the Texas Gulf Coast northeastward to eastern Tennessee.** The western TN/KY cloud towers were [(***brighter***) (***darker***)] than the clouds scattered from TX to eastern TN.

13. This shading contrast implies that the cloud towers were [(***warmer***) (***colder***)] than the broad field of clouds to the south.

14. This temperature contrast also means that the cloud tower tops were [(***lower***) (***higher***)] than tops of clouds in the broad southern cloud field. The change in shading in the infrared satellite views can be used to gauge the vertical growth rate of thunderstorm tops. This may be seen in animations of the infrared images from hour to hour, such as is available from the course website, under **Satellite** section as "Latest IR Animation".

Figure 4 is the satellite Water Vapor Image for 1815Z 07 APR 2006, the same time as the visible image. Current water vapor images along with a six-image animation loop are also available from the course website. Satellite water vapor sensors are tuned to the infrared radiation that is absorbed and emitted by water vapor in the atmosphere, particularly between the 700- and 400-mb levels, roughly from 3 km to 7 km altitude in the middle troposphere. Thick clouds appear bright white in water vapor imagery. In cloudless regions, humid

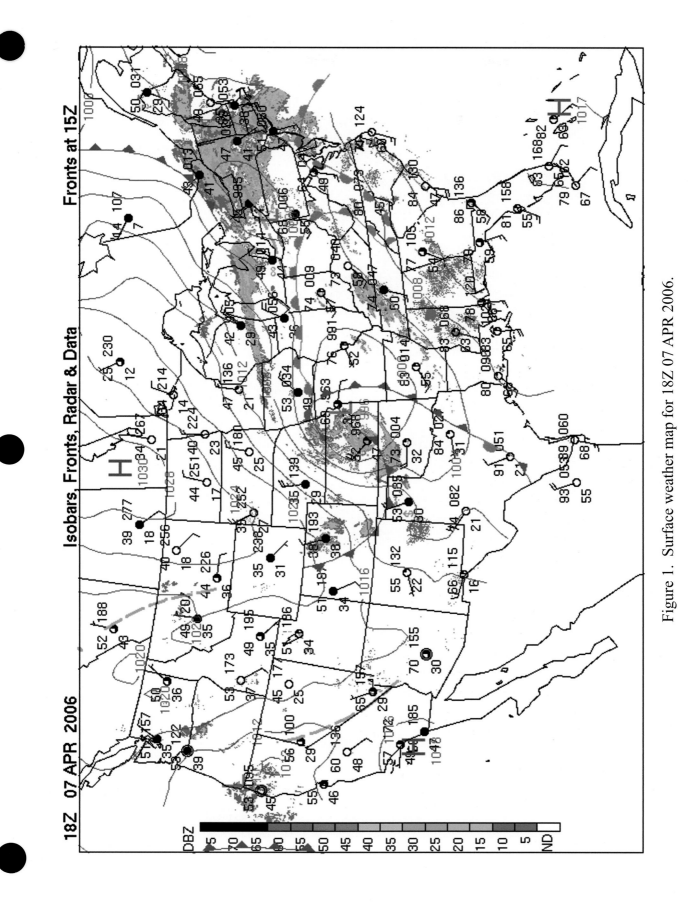

Figure 1. Surface weather map for 18Z 07 APR 2006.

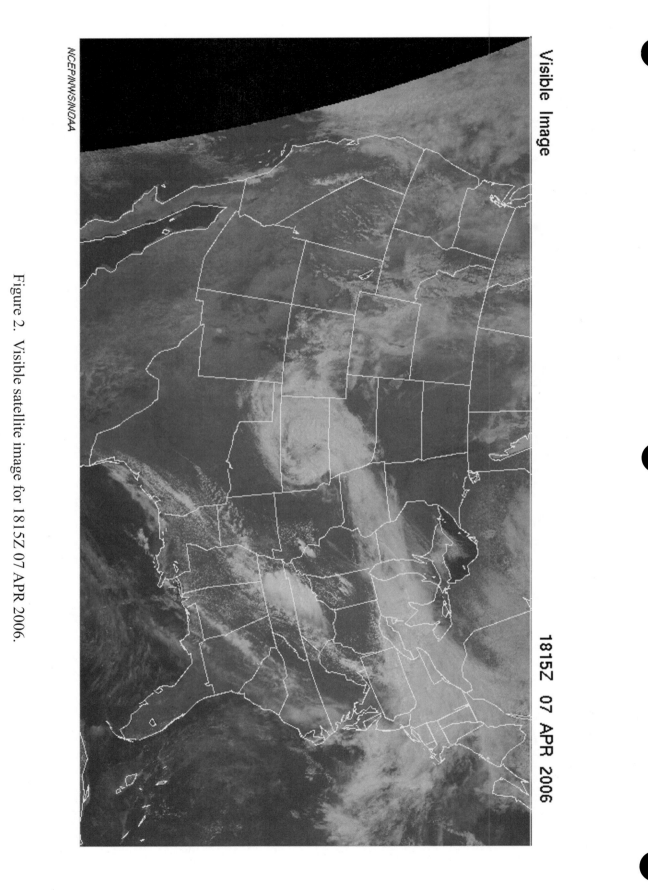

Figure 2. Visible satellite image for 1815Z 07 APR 2006.

Infrared Image

1715Z 07 APR 2006

NCEP/NWS/NOAA

Figure 3. Infrared satellite image for 1715Z 07 APR 2006.

mid-tropospheric areas (relatively high dewpoints) appear generally medium gray while relatively dry mid-levels (low dewpoints) appear dark. Although areas can be clear in visible and infrared imagery, extensive water vapor in the mid-troposphere can make the same areas appear medium gray in water vapor imagery.

15. A bright white blotch [(**_was_**) (**_was not_**)] located where the thunderstorms were shown on the radar (Figure 1) and visible satellite (Figure 2) views.

16. A broad swath of lighter gray shading from Texas northeastward to Ohio containing the KY-TN bright white blotch indicates air that is [(**_more_**) (**_less_**)] humid at mid-tropospheric levels than that shown around the Low center to the northwest or from the Gulf of Mexico to the Carolinas. One characteristic of severe thunderstorms is often drier air at mid levels. But in cases where water vapor concentrations are relatively high at mid levels, heavy rainfall and flash flooding are more likely.

17. The Figure 4 water vapor view also shows darker streaks bounding the medium gray area including the thunderstorm blob to the northwest and to the southeast. These darker streaks showed a relatively [(**_drier_**) (**_more humid_**)] flow of air at mid-tropospheric levels to either side of the thunderstorm area. This mid-tropospheric moisture gradient across the moisture flow (from 300-mb map, not shown) was associated with two regions of faster jet stream winds located to either side of the developing thunderstorms. The streaks indicated boundaries to the region of thunderstorm development at map time and were associated with the upper-level divergence.

On 7 April 2006, mainly during the late afternoon hours, NOAA/NCEP's Storm Prediction Center reported 64 tornadoes and 531 instances of hail from thunderstorm activity along with 173 reports of wind damage, from northern Louisiana spreading across the northern Gulf Coast states and into Virginia and the Ohio River Valley.

A thunderstorm cell typically progresses through its life cycle (towering cumulus, mature, and dissipating stages) in less than an hour. More prolonged periods of thunderstorm weather are associated with a multicellular thunderstorm, that is, a thunderstorm that is made up of many cells. Each of those cells may be at a different stage of its life cycle with new cells continually forming and old cells dissipating.

A multicellular thunderstorm may form a large nearly circular cluster known as a *mesoscale convective complex (MCC)*. An MCC is typically large enough to cover an area the size of the entire state of Iowa. Figure 5 is a NOAA enhanced infrared satellite image showing a MCC over the corner of Oklahoma, Kansas, Arkansas and Missouri on 24 April 2006. The brown shades are the highest (coldest) cloud tops. MCCs are most frequent in the summer in the central U.S. plains states.

Surface weather reports as shown on weather maps and meteograms, upper air data on constant-pressure maps and on Stüve diagrams, and radar summaries and satellite imagery (visible, infrared, and water vapor) complement each other to produce a three-dimensional

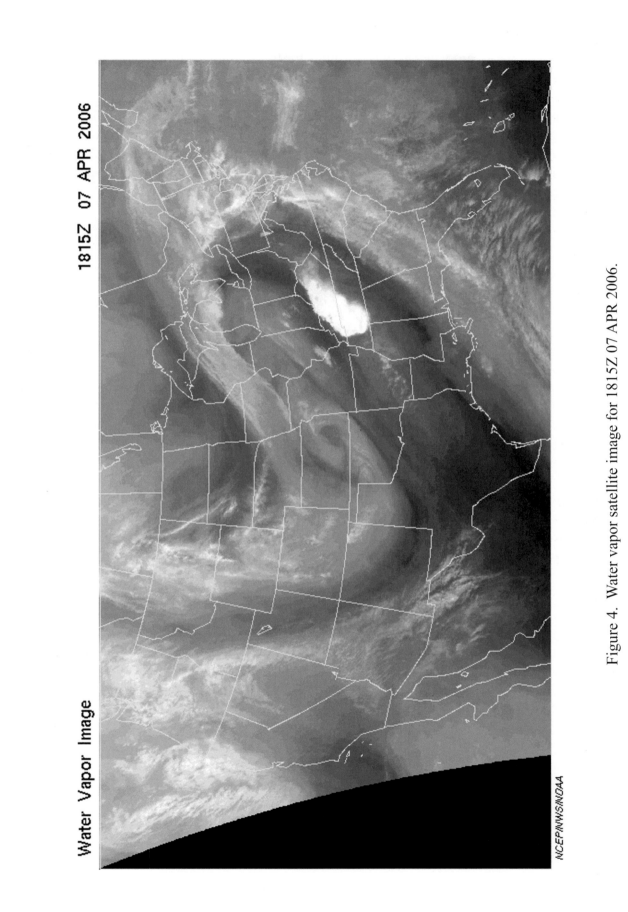

Figure 4. Water vapor satellite image for 1815Z 07 APR 2006.

picture of the atmosphere that evolves over time. From this present understanding, forecasts can be made and necessary watches and warnings for threatening weather issued to the public.

<u>Suggestions for further activities:</u> Compare visible, infrared, and water vapor satellite images for your region with radar views as various weather systems influence your local conditions. Other Internet sources for satellite views are the GOES website (*http://www.goes.noaa.gov/*) and the University of Wisconsin, Space Science and Engineering Center (*http://www.ssec. wisc.edu/data/*).

Figure 5. Mesoscale Convective Complex (MCC) in south-central U.S. on 24 APR 2006.

Investigation 11B: TORNADOES

Objectives:

A tornado can be the most violent weather system on Earth. Its strong winds can take lives and cause considerable property damage. Wind speed in a tornado, estimated from the extent of property damage, is the basis for rating these systems from 0 (weakest) to 5 (strongest) on the Fujita scale (F-scale). Most tornadoes are spawned by and travel with severe thunderstorms and generally exhibit a counterclockwise rotation as seen from above. The special weather pattern required for tornadic thunderstorms to develop is most common in spring and summer in the central United States.

After completing this investigation, you should be able to:

- List some of the characteristics of the path of an intense tornado.
- Describe the general weather conditions favorable for formation of tornadic thunderstorms.
- Explain why winds on one side of a tornado may be stronger than winds on the other side.

Introduction:

In the early evening of 3 May 1999, an outbreak of severe weather struck the southern Great Plains. Many tornadoes touched down in central Oklahoma, but the most devastating twister tracked through the suburbs and portions of downtown Oklahoma City.

A portion of the National Weather Service Public Information statement on this tornado read as follows: "JUST SOUTH AND EAST OF AMBER... THE TORNADO QUICKLY GREW TO CLOSE TO THREE-QUARTERS OF A MILE WIDE. ASPHALT PAVEMENT... ABOUT ONE INCH THICK... WAS PEELED FROM A SECTION OF RURAL ROAD /EW125 RD/ ABOUT FIVE MILES EAST OF STATE ROAD 92. THE FIRST DAMAGE RATED AT F4 WAS DISCOVERED ABOUT FOUR MILES EAST-NORTHEAST OF AMBER. F4 DAMAGE WAS OBSERVED CONTINUOUSLY FOR SIX AND ONE-HALF MILES... WITH ANOTHER AREA OF F4 DAMAGE ABOUT 2 MILES NORTHWEST OF NEWCASTLE. TWO AREAS OF F5 DAMAGE WERE OBSERVED. THE FIRST WAS IN THE WILLOW CREEK ESTATES... A RURAL SUBDIVISION OF MOBILE HOMES AND SOME CONCRETE SLAB HOMES IN BRIDGE CREEK. TWO HOMES WERE FOUND COMPLETELY SWEPT FROM THEIR SLABS... AND ABOUT ONE DOZEN AUTOMOBILES WERE CARRIED ABOUT ONE-QUARTER MILE. GRASS VEGETATION IN THIS AREA WAS COMPLETELY SCOURED TO MUD... AND SMALL CEDAR TREES WERE LEFT DE-BARKED AND DEVOID OF GREENERY. THE RIDGECREST BAPTIST CHURCH WAS DESTROYED NORTHEAST OF THE FIRST F5 DAMAGE AREA.

THE SECOND F5 DAMAGE WAS ONE MILE WEST OF THE COUNTY LINE IN BRIDGE CREEK... AND CONSISTED OF A CLEANLY SWEPT SLAB HOME WITH FOUNDATION ANCHOR BOLTS AND ANOTHER VEHICLE LOFTED ONE-QUARTER MILE. THE MAXIMUM WIDTH OF THE TORNADO IN BRIDGE CREEK WAS ABOUT ONE-MILE WIDE. THE TORNADO MAINTAINED A NEARLY STRAIGHT PATH TO THE NORTHWEST OF THE TURNPIKE EXCEPT WHEN IT MADE A SLIGHT JOG TO THE RIGHT AND MOVED DIRECTLY OVER THE 16TH STREET TURNPIKE OVERPASS

BEFORE RESUMING ITS ORIGINAL COURSE. THE TORNADO CONTINUED INTO THE NORTHERN SECTIONS OF RURAL NEWCASTLE... AND CROSSED THE TURNPIKE AGAIN JUST NORTH OF THE U.S. 62 NEWCASTLE INTERCHANGE. AT THIS LOCATION THE TORNADO NARROWED TO ABOUT ONE-QUARTER MILE WIDE AND THE DAMAGE INTENSITY DROPPED TO F2 BEFORE IT CROSSED THE SOUTH CANADIAN RIVER INTO NORTHERN CLEVELAND COUNTY."

Preliminary reports indicated 44 fatalities and over 700 injuries with this tornado. Approximately 11,000 homes were destroyed and total insured damage was about $750 million. The destruction throughout central Oklahoma from this outbreak was estimated to total about $1.2 billion.

1. As shown on the damage paths map in Figure 1 (north is at the top of the map), the tornadoes in this outbreak generally traveled [(***towards the northeast***) (***towards the southeast***)]. This is the general direction of movement of the majority of tornadoes that occur in the United States. [Map courtesy of NOAA's NWS, Norman, OK.]

2. The most devastating tornado in this outbreak was the one that tracked through Oklahoma City (center of map, continuous path beginning south of Amber, designated F5). The first reports of tornado damage along the track that led into Oklahoma City were at 7:17 PM CDT when multiple injuries occurred. Damage near the end of the path was reported at 8:10 PM CDT. Hence, this tornado was on the ground for at least _____ minutes.

3. The length of the tornado path on the ground was about [(***20***) (***40***) (***80***)] miles.

4. Therefore the tornado's forward speed averaged about [(***25***) (***45***) (***85***)] miles per hour.

5. Numbers associated with the tornado paths on the map are F-scale values. The "**F**" designations for tornadoes refer to levels of destruction based on the Fujita Tornado Intensity Scale. The Fujita scale and associated wind speeds are shown in the upper left corner of the map. The highest F-scale shown on the map with the Oklahoma City tornado was F-____. (For information on the new enhanced Fujita Tornado Intensity Scale implemented 1 February 2007, see *http://www.spc.noaa.gov/efscale*.)

6. Tornadoes are classified by the highest reported F-scale rating as assessed by related structural damage. The "5" value was shown in purple numbers at [(***1***) (***3***) (***8***)] point(s) along the damage path.

7. According to the Fujita scale, a tornado with this maximum rating is accompanied by winds estimated at _____ to _____ mi. per hour.

8. Often the strongest winds in a tornado occur on the side of the system where the internal tornadic winds are blowing in the same direction as the storm is moving. This is because tornadoes have both rotational motion around their low-pressure centers (usually counterclockwise when viewed from above) and translational motion across the Earth's surface. Where the tornado's movement across the Earth's surface adds to

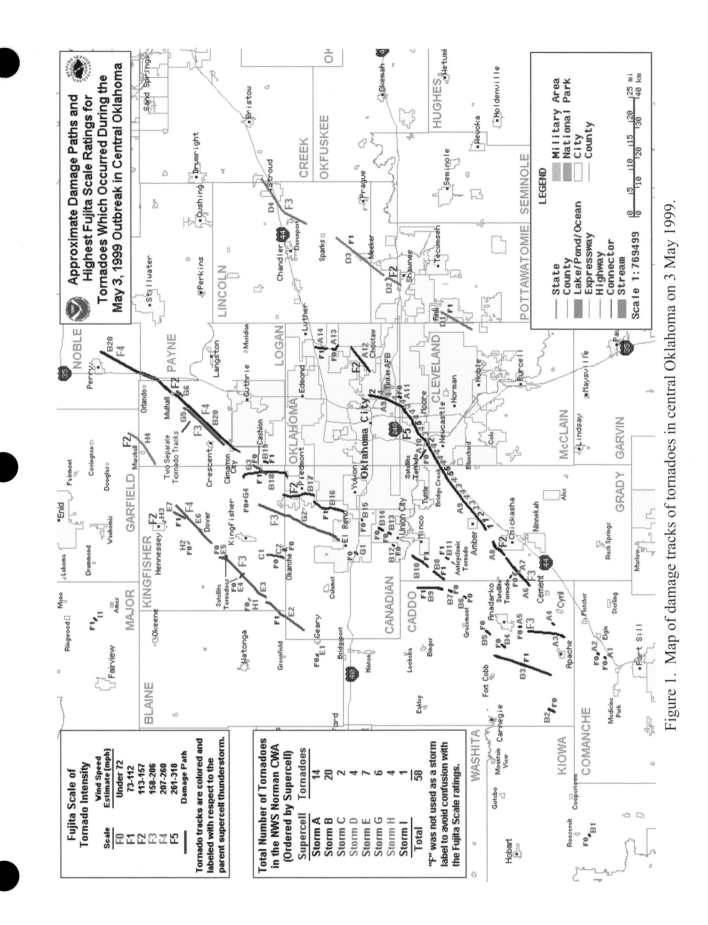

Figure 1. Map of damage tracks of tornadoes in central Oklahoma on 3 May 1999.

its rotational motion, winds relative to the Earth's surface are strongest. On the other side where the tornado's motion across the Earth's surface subtracts from the tornado's spinning motion, winds are not quite as strong. In the Oklahoma City tornado, the strongest winds were likely on the [(*southeast*) (*northwest*)] side of the tornado.

9. Thunderstorm cells that spawn intense tornadoes such as the Oklahoma City tornado typically are associated with the warm sector of a mature extra-tropical cyclone. Considering the circulation surrounding a low-pressure system and the path of the Oklahoma City tornado, it is likely that its parent thunderstorm formed generally to the [(*northwest*) (*southeast*)] of the center of an extra-tropical cyclone.

For further reports of this tornado outbreak and images of the destruction, see:
http://www.srh.noaa.gov/oun/storms/19990503/

As directed by your course instructor, complete this investigation by either:

1. *Going to the Current Weather Studies link on the course website, or*
2. *Continuing to the Applications section for this investigation that immediately follows in this Investigations Manual.*

Investigation 11B: TORNADOES
Applications

An exceptionally large number of tornadoes were reported during early 2007 demonstrating that tornadoes can occur at any time of year. Historically the greatest annual tornado activity in the nation occurs from April to June, when weather systems are particularly vigorous. The 2007 tornado season featured an unusually large number of tornadoes early on. By 9 May 2007, 759 tornadoes had been reported versus a typical 547 through the end of May based on the average of the last 3 years. There had also been 74 deaths (27 in March alone!) versus a typical 24, and there had been 20 "killer" tornadoes (where a death occurred) versus a typical 9 through May. These statistics are compiled by the Storm Prediction Center in Norman, OK, one of NOAA's National Centers for Environmental Prediction.

By comparison, 2006 ended with 1032 tornadoes compared to an annual average over a three-year period (2004-06) of 1366. April was the most active month with 244 and also the deadliest with 37 fatalities. The 2006 year was similar to 2007 in the early onset of tornado occurrences. May 2003 was the most active month of recent times with 41 deaths from 543 tornadoes. For more information on this historic May outbreak, see: *http://www.noaanews .noaa.gov/stories/s1144.htm*.

A persistent weather system in the southern Plains produced several days of frequent severe thunderstorms and tornadoes in early May, 2007. From Friday, 4 May through Sunday, 6 May the central portion of the U.S. experienced 155 tornadoes, 133 cases of damaging winds and 334 hail events. The most heralded case was the devastating tornado that leveled three-quarters of the town of Greensburg, Kansas on Friday killing 9 people and injuring 60. Figure 2 is the map of severe weather occurrences reported to the Storm Prediction Center in Norman, OK for 4 May 2007.

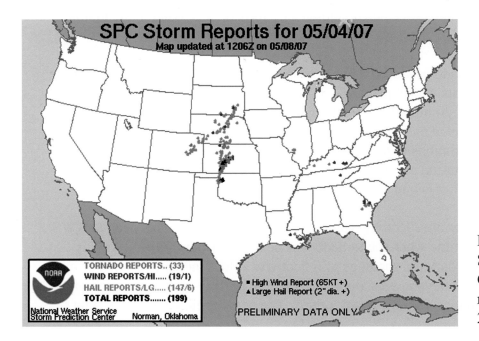

Figure 2. Map of Storm Prediction Center severe weather reports on 4 May 2007.

10. The deadly Greensburg tornado was spawned by a supercell thunderstorm. The concentration of red dots depicting tornado occurrences across central Kansas [(***does***) (***does not***)] suggests that these dangerous twisters may have come from several thunderstorms traveling with the upper-level winds that moved from south-southwest toward the north-northeast.

Extensive analysis of tornado damage along with laboratory studies prompted researchers to update the original estimates of wind speeds corresponding to the number scale developed by Dr. Theodore Fujita in 1971. Current studies have developed an expanded list of damage ratings to many different types of structures including objects such as flagpoles, radio towers and trees. The complete report is at *http://www.wind.ttu.edu/EFScale.pdf*. The enhanced Fujita scale with equivalent winds speeds of 3-second gusts in given in Table 1.

Table 1. EF-Scale Wind Speed Ranges

EF Scale	3-Second Gust Speed (mph)
EF 0	65 - 85
EF 1	86 - 109
EF 2	110 - 137
EF 3	138 - 167
EF 4	168 - 199
EF 5	> 200

11. Evaluation of the damage to structures in Greensburg led National Weather Service experts to label the tornado with an intensity of EF 5 on the new, enhanced Fujita scale. According to the enhanced Fujita scale, an EF 5 category tornado creates damage produced by wind speeds estimated to be _____ miles per hour.

The category of an EF 5 strength tornado is termed "incredible." The last F 5 tornado to occur in the United States was the Oklahoma City tornado discussed in the first part of this investigation.

12. The Greensburg tornado produced damage along a path that was about 22 miles long. The damage track at its widest point was 1.7 miles wide. Reports of this tornado indicated it moved at 20 mph thereby taking 15 to 20 minutes to devastate the town! Many tornadoes travel at even greater forward speeds. High speeds of movement coupled with the limitations of the road network in rural areas [(***would***) (***would not***)] imply that trying to outrun a tornado in a motor vehicle could be a fatal mistake. A sturdy, low-level shelter is one's best protection in such events.

13. Figure 3 is the display of reflectivity (precipitation intensity) from the Wichita NWS Doppler radar at the time when the tornado was near Greensburg (GBD). In this reflectivity view, the dark red shadings of reflectivity values indicate the area of most intense precipitation. Several arcs along the southern portion of the storm cell imply a local internal circulation called a "hook echo". The best developed is to the right of the

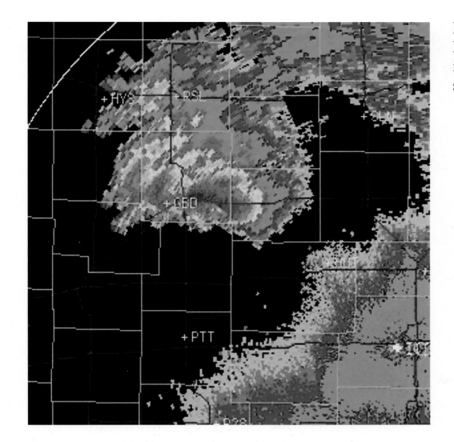

Figure 3. Wichita NWS Doppler radar reflectivity display of Greensburg storm.

"D". A hook echo in that location is often associated with a mesocyclone and tornado formation. The reflectivity image's middle hook location [(**_is_**) (**_is not_**)] consistent with the tornado's path over Greensburg.

14. Figure 4 is the storm relative velocity view from the NWS Dodge City, KS, radar located at the upper left edge of the image just prior to the tornado hitting Greensburg. The velocity shadings show relative motions away from the radar (positive velocities) as shades of red. Motions toward the radar (negatives) are shades of green and blue. Widening radials directed generally southeastward from the Dodge City radar site highlight an area to the right of the center of the image denoted by a yellow arrow.

    The abrupt color shift from green and blue on the northeast to red on the southwest across one of the radials [(**_does_**) (**_does not_**)] indicate an abrupt change of wind flow from strong outward (red) to strong inward (green/blue) over a short distance.

15. The green-to-red color change shows areas where wind directions and speeds change rapidly over distance (intense wind shear). **In the Greensburg shear area indicated by the yellow arrow, draw a short arrow across the small dark red area directed <u>away</u> from the radar and a short arrow across the green/blue area directed <u>toward</u> the radar.** Recall from Investigation 7B, this radial motion pattern [(**_would_**) (**_would not_**)] be consistent with a mesocyclone that could produce a tornado such as occurred at Greensburg.

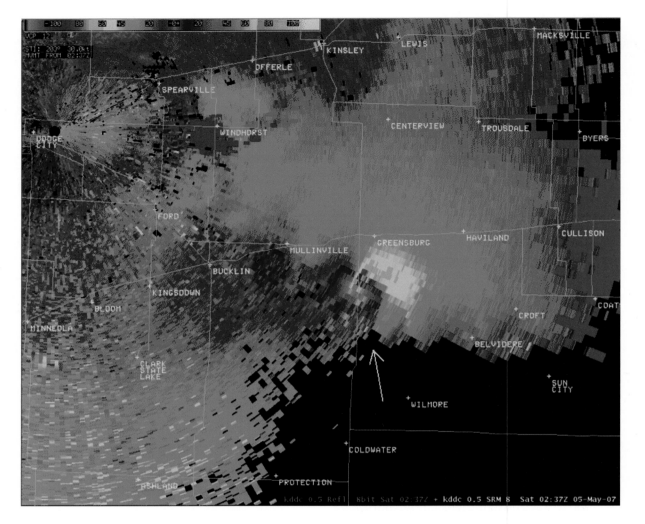

Figure 4. Dodge City NWS Doppler radar relative velocity display of Greensburg storm.

Meteorologists rely on radar-derived information such as the supercell thunderstorm structure and wind patterns to provide tornado warnings for the public to help save lives and minimize property damage. For further information on the Greenburg tornado, see *http://www.noaanews.noaa.gov/stories2007/s2855.htm* or visit the Dodge City NWS site *http://www.crh.noaa.gov/ddc/*. Ironically, another Greensburg resident had a run-in with a tornado in 1928 looking up inside of the twister (*http://www.history.noaa.gov/stories_tales/ inside_tornado.html*).

More information on the newly implemented Enhanced Fujita Scale is available at: *http:// www.spc.noaa.gov/efscale/*.

Additional reports of other tornado episodes containing NWS radar imagery can be accessed at the following links:
• Western Tennessee tornadoes on 2 April 2006 including many photos of property

damage can be found at: *http://www.srh.noaa.gov/meg/events/April2006/index.php*.

- The Evansville tornado of November 2005 can be found at: *http://www.crh.noaa.gov/pah/?n=evansvilletornado-nov.6,2005*. Included are the tornado track, radar images and many damage pictures.
- The central Iowa tornadoes of November 12, 2005: *http://www.crh.noaa.gov/dmx/?n=stratford-woodward-11122005*.
- Donaldsonville, Georgia on March 22, 2005: *http://www.srh.noaa.gov/tlh/Mar22_2005/Mar22_2005.htm*.
- Severe weather in Arkansas on 5-6 April 2006: *http://www.srh.noaa.gov/lzk/html/svr0405.htm* and earlier on 12-13 January: *http://www.srh.noaa.gov/lzk/html/svr0105-nf.htm*.
- Pierce City, MO 4 May 2003 tornado and other 4 May 2003 tornadoes: *http://www.crh.noaa.gov/sgf/Events/2003/may4/*
- LaPlata, MD, Apr. 28, 2003 unusually devastating East Coast tornado: *http://www.erh.noaa.gov/er/lwx/Historic_Events/apr28-2002/laplata.htm*
- Van Wert, Ohio, Nov. 10, 2002: *http://www.crh.noaa.gov/iwx/program_areas/events/2002/11_10_02_tornadoes/index.php*. Additional information about this Nov. 10th outbreak in northern Alabama where additional deaths occurred can be found at: *http://www.srh.noaa.gov/bmx/tornadoes/index.php*.
- The Xenia, OH, September, 2000 tornado that almost repeated 1974, *http://www.erh.noaa.gov/er/iln/92000.htm*.

Your local NOAA NWS office websites may have links to notable severe weather episodes in your area. Finally, for an account of the historic Super Tornado Outbreak of 1974, see: *http://www.publicaffairs.noaa.gov/storms/*. More on the infamous Tri-State Tornado of 1925, see: *http://www.crh.noaa.gov/pah/1925/*.

Last, but not least, a site to answer (almost?) all of your tornado questions: *http://www.spc.noaa.gov/faq/tornado/*.

Suggestions for further activities: Investigate the Internet tornado pages given in this investigation. Examine the types of radar imagery available to forecasters to use in issuing severe weather and tornado warnings. Current radar imagery, including single station views (NEXRAD), is available from the "NWS Radar Page" link on the course website. Selecting a location on the interactive map will allow one to see regional views and select individual station reports. Views of reflectivity in lowest level scan ("base") and greatest intensity of any level ("composite") are available along with base and storm relative velocities and 1-hour and storm total precipitation amounts. These can also be animated.

Investigation 12A: HURRICANES

Objectives:

A hurricane is a tropical cyclone that has maximum sustained surface wind speeds of 119 km per hour (74 mi per hour, 64 knots) or higher. [A knot (kt) is one nautical mile per hour.] A hurricane forms over the warm tropical ocean and derives its energy from latent heat released when water evaporated from the sea condenses in the storm system. A typical hurricane is about one-third the size of an extra-tropical cyclone of middle latitudes, forms in a uniform mass of warm and humid air, and has no fronts or frontal weather. When a hurricane strikes the coast, property damage is caused by a surge of ocean water above flood stage, strong winds, heavy rainfall, and sometimes tornadoes.

Hurricanes that threaten the East and Gulf Coasts of North America usually originate over the tropical North Atlantic off the West African coast, the Caribbean Sea, or the Gulf of Mexico. Most hurricanes initially are steered slowly westward by the trade winds, but eventually curve northwestward, then northward, and finally northeastward around the Bermuda-Azores subtropical High. Precisely where the curvature takes place determines whether the hurricane strikes the Gulf Coast, the East Coast, or turns out to sea. However, a hurricane may depart significantly from this "average" track. In some cases, a hurricane meanders about, even moving in circles or figure-eights. Such behavior greatly complicates the task of hurricane forecasters.

After completing this investigation, you should be able to:

* Describe the track taken by a hurricane that occurred in the western North Atlantic Ocean.
* Indicate the probable position of highest storm surge when a hurricane makes landfall.

Introduction:

The 2005 Hurricane Season in the Atlantic Basin (including the Caribbean and Gulf of Mexico) was a record-breaker. In terms of the number of tropical cyclones, there were 27 named storms (tropical storms or hurricanes) compared to the long-term average of about 10 and the previous record of 21 in 1933. Fifteen of the tropical cyclones reached hurricane intensity which is at least nine above average. And seven of the hurricanes were major systems (Saffir-Simpson category 3 or higher) versus an average of three. The major story, of course, was that four of those hurricanes reached the maximum intensity of category 5 and three made landfall along the U.S. Gulf coast (*Katrina*, *Rita* and *Wilma*).

Responsibility for the forecasting and warning of tropical weather systems in the Atlantic and eastern portion of the Pacific Ocean basins resides with the Tropical Prediction Center/ National Hurricane Center in Miami, FL. The Tropical Prediction Center is a component of NOAA's National Weather Service, National Centers for Environmental Prediction (NCEP). The National Hurricane Center's website: *http://www.nhc.noaa.gov/* contains the latest information on tropical weather systems as well as a wealth of historical and other information regarding hurricanes.

This investigation involves evaluating the forecast track of an intensifying tropical cyclone that began as a tropical depression and quickly reached tropical storm strength. It formed over the southern Bahamas Islands at the beginning of our observation period. This storm was Katrina, the 11th of the 2005 season.

"Katrina was an extraordinarily powerful and deadly hurricane that carved a wide swath of catastrophic damage and inflicted large loss of life. It was the costliest and one of the five deadliest hurricanes to ever strike the United States. . . . Considering the scope of its impacts, Katrina was one of the most devastating natural disasters in United States history." (*Tropical Cyclone Report, Hurricane Katrina, NHC, http://www.nhc.noaa.gov/2005atlan.shtml*).

The following figures are selected from the National Hurricane Center Tropical Cyclone graphical advisories for Katrina (*http://www.nhc.noaa.gov/archive/2005/KATRINA_ graphics.shtml*). Each figure legend shows the stage of development, date and time along with the sequential number of the advisory issued. The center of the circulation is given in latitude and longitude at the time of the advisory and plotted on the map with the dot in an orange circle. Additional information provided is the maximum sustained wind speed, direction and speed of movement of the circulation center. Color coded shadings of land areas in the figures are:

Color	Tropical weather statement	Expected wind speeds
yellow	tropical storm watch	34 - 63 kts (39-73 mph) within 36 hours
blue	tropical storm warning	34 - 63 kts (39-73 mph) within 24 hours
pink	hurricane watch	greater than 64 kts (>74 mph) within 36 hours
red	hurricane warning	greater than 64 kts (>74 mph) within 24 hours

Additionally, large black dots display the forecast position centers with times showing expected tropical storm strength (S) or hurricane (H) and the white cone of forecast uncertainty in position. An approximate distance scale is also displayed along the lower margin of the figure. North latitude values are listed along the left map edge on the horizontal latitude lines while west longitude values are given along the lower edge on the vertical longitude lines.

Figure 1 is the first advisory issued by the National Hurricane Center on this tropical system. It was communicated to emergency managers and the public at 5 PM Eastern Daylight Time on 23 August 2005. At that time the center of the system's circulation was located over the southern Bahamas Islands at 23.2 degrees N and 75.5 degrees W. The maximum sustained wind speed was determined to be 35 miles per hour and the system was moving toward the northwest at 8 mph.

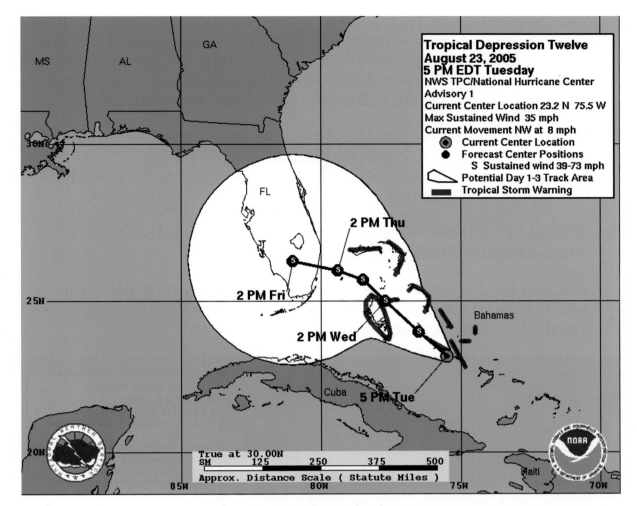

Figure 1. NWS Tropical Prediction Center/National Hurricane Center forecast advisory map for Tropical Depression Twelve, 5 PM EDT 23 AUG 2005.

1. At 5 PM EDT on Tuesday, 23 August, the status of this tropical weather system was a [(***tropical depression***) (***tropical storm***) (***hurricane***)].

2. The forecast path showed the system was expected to travel generally northwestward through the Bahamas and make landfall on the Florida coast at the north edge of the Miami metropolitan area at about midnight on Thursday. At the time of landfall in Florida, the strength of the system was expected to be a [(***tropical depression***) (***tropical storm***) (***hurricane***)].

3. You may note that there are no colored shadings shown along this portion of coastline. As this time of landfall was about 55 hours after the advisory time, would you expect there to be a watch or warning posted for this area at 5 PM on Tuesday? [(***Yes***) (***No***)].

4. If you lived in the threatened region of south Florida, you should expect the highest storm tide surge to occur to the [(***south***) (***north***)] of the point of the center's landfall (intersection of the heavy track line with the coast).

5. While the heavy black line is the forecasters' most probable track of the center of the storm's circulation, there is a distinct probability the center may pass within the cone displayed, in decreasing probability to either side away from the center track. This white cone of potential track location shows in three days (2 PM Friday) the center might possibly be located from [(***Georgia to the Mexican Yucatan Peninsula***) (***north Florida to northern Cuba***)].

6. Figure 2 is the forecast map issued at 5 PM EDT Wednesday, 24 August 2005, 24 hours after the Figure 1 advisory. Plot the approximate Wednesday position of the center in Figure 2 on the Figure 1 map. Did the Wednesday position fall exactly on the forecast track from Tuesday? [(***Yes***) (***No***)].

7. As shown by Figure 2 on Wednesday, the weather system's strength was that of a [(***tropical depression***) (***tropical storm***) (***hurricane***)].

8. Thus, over the 24-hour period from 5 PM EDT on Tuesday to 5 PM Wednesday, the system's strength (in terms of wind speed and therefore terminology) [(***weakened***) (***remained the same***) (***intensified***)].

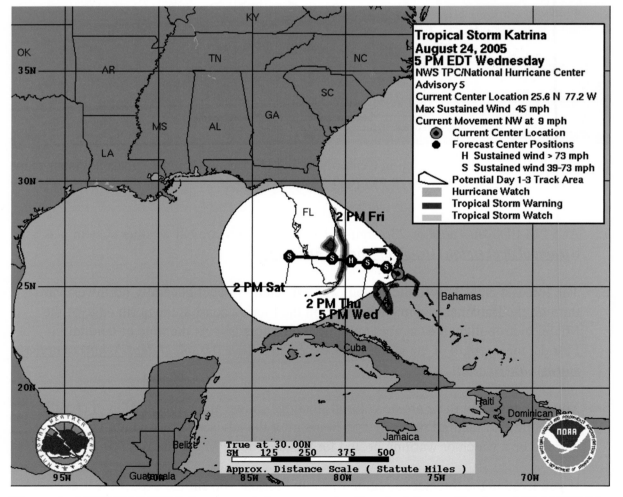

Figure 2. NWS TPC/NHC forecast advisory map for Tropical Storm Katrina, 5 PM EDT 24 AUG 2005.

9. At the time of the Figure 2 advisory, the center of circulation was moving toward the northwest at 9 mph. According to the forecast map, over the next three days, the system was expected to [(***curve toward the north***) (***continue straight toward the northwest***) (***curve toward the west***)].

10. The forecast track projects the system to reach the coast near Miami at about 2 AM EDT on Friday. At this time the storm is expected to be a [(***tropical depression***) (***tropical storm***) (***hurricane***)].

11. Therefore, in its passage from the Bahamas to Florida, the system is expected to [(***weaken***) (***remain the same***) (***strengthen***)].

12. Subsequent to the system's landfall, the passage over the peninsula of Florida shows the strength is projected to be a tropical storm (S). This is less than the strength at landfall. Weakening of the system's circulation should be due to [(***loss of the latent heat source over water***) (***increased friction over land***) (***both of these factors***)].

13. The potential area of location of the center on Saturday remains basically from northern Florida to the coast of Cuba. However, the forecast track is only shown past the west coast of Florida into the eastern Gulf of Mexico. Given that the advisory time is Wednesday, 24 August, and the system is barely a tropical storm still in the Bahamas, would you recommend any specific evacuations or preparations for a location in the Gulf of Mexico area? [(***Yes***) (***No***)].

14. Figure 3 shows now Hurricane Katrina in the Gulf of Mexico at 5 PM EDT on Friday, 26 August 2005, 48 hours following the Figure 2 advisory. Plot the approximate Friday position of the circulation center in Figure 3 on the Figure 2 map. Did the Friday position fall exactly on the forecast track from Wednesday? [(***Yes***) (***No***)].

15. At 5 PM EDT on Friday, the system is a [(***tropical depression***) (***tropical storm***) (***hurricane***)].

16. Below is Table 1 showing the Saffir-Simpson Hurricane Scale. The category of hurricane strength is related to the damage potential and the measured sustained one-minute wind speeds in miles per hour.

Table 1. Saffir-Simpson Hurricane Scale

Category	Damage Potential	Sustained Winds (mph)
1	*Minimal*	74 - 95
2	*Moderate*	96 - 110
3	*Extensive*	111 - 130
4	*Extreme*	131 - 155
5	*Catastrophic*	greater than 155

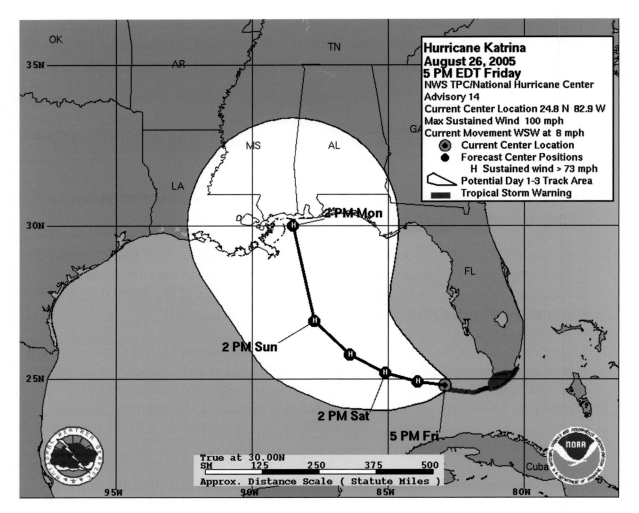

Figure 3. NWS TPC/NHC forecast advisory map for Hurricane Katrina, 5 PM EDT 26 AUG 2005.

At the Figure 3 advisory time, Katrina was a category _____ hurricane.

17. From the actual Figure 3 position compared to its Figure 2 forecast, has the behavior of the system been as anticipated? [(***Yes***) (***No***)]. In fact Katrina was undergoing the first of two periods of rapid strengthening, and by the morning of August 27 it had become a category 3 major hurricane.

18. The forecast track issued at 5 PM EDT Friday, 26 August, projected Katrina to make landfall along the Gulf of Mexico coast near the Mississippi-Alabama border at about _____ PM Monday.

19. Consider the two locations: Mobile Bay, AL (coastal indentation to the right of the final plotted H dot) and New Orleans, LA (to the south of the irregular Lake Ponchatrain oval). Based on the Figure 3 forecast track, one would consider the greater danger due to storm surge from a major landfalling hurricane to be to [(***Mobile***) (***New Orleans***)].

Hurricane Katrina continued intensifying to a category 5 storm with winds of 173 mph before finally weakening to a strong category 3 at landfall near the Louisiana-Mississippi border. The massive size of the storm caused devastating storm surge from Louisiana to the Florida panhandle with a maximum surge of 27.8 feet at Pass Christian, MS. Ironically, category 5 Hurricane Camille in 1969 had a maximum surge of about 32 feet also near Pass Christian.

Of course, a major part of the Katrina story was the death and devastation in New Orleans. Due to Katrina's large size, winds prior to landfall caused water from Lake Pontchartrain to slosh over seawalls and canal banks, undermining and cutting levees, and flooding the city. About 80% of the city flooded, in places to 20 feet deep. The last of the water was not removed until 43 days later. The death toll from Katrina was estimated near 2000, mostly in New Orleans. The total cost was estimated at $81 billion, making Katrina the nation's most costly hurricane ever.

20. Table 2 (from the National Hurricane Center) is a portion of the positions of Katrina across the Gulf of Mexico including and following the Figure 3 map. Plot the positions as dots on the Figure 3 map.

Table 2. Katrina's Final Gulf Track

Position	Date & Time	Latitude (° N)	Longitude (° W)	Wind Speed (knots)	Min. Pressure (mb)
1	26 / 21Z (5 PM)	24.8	82.9	87 (100 mph)	
2	27 / 00Z	24.6	83.3	90	959
3	27 / 12Z	24.4	84.5	100	942
4	28 / 00Z	24.8	85.9	100	941
5	28 / 12Z	25.7	87.7	145	909
6	29 / 00Z	27.2	89.2	140	905
7	29 / 12Z	29.5	89.6	110	923
8	30 / 00Z	32.6	89.1	50	961

Connect these dots with straight line segments to form the actual path taken by Katrina. Based on your plotted points and the Figure 3 track projection, does the anticipated path remain within the cone of potential location through the period until landfall? [(**Yes**) (**No**)]. Given the long lead time and potential threat area highlighted in the Figure 3 advisory, emergency planners would have crucial guidance to enact preparations. Subsequent NHC advisories after Figure 3 provided forecast tracks that were very consistent and accurate to the final path.

Forecasters need to determine which coastal areas should be warned of a possible hurricane landfall and coordinate with state and local emergency managers. Although predicting where landfall might occur can be very challenging with some hurricanes, the necessity to issue forecasts remains because of the system's intensity and potential for loss of life and property damage. Consequently, evacuation of areas greater than might seem necessary after the fact is called for. At the same time, the danger of over-warning the public is a serious issue. If people are warned and nothing happens in their locality, subsequent warnings are taken less seriously. Additionally, the issuance of warnings triggers emergency actions that are economically costly.

The NHC Katrina advisories website provides an animation of the forecast graphics for all advisories issued. The user may adjust the speed or even stop the sequence and zoom in on a particular graph for study.

As directed by your course instructor, complete this investigation by either:

1. *Going to the Current Weather Studies link on the course website, or*
2. *Continuing to the Applications section for this investigation that immediately follows in this Investigations Manual.*

Investigation 12A: HURRICANES
Applications

Figure 4 is the map of the tracks of tropical cyclones in the Atlantic basin for the 2005 hurricane season as issued by the National Hurricane Center. The track of each named system is labeled by number near the beginning and the end of its track. The stage in the development of tropical cyclones (based on sustained wind speed) is color coded in the box at the lower left. Black dots denote the 0000 UTC location of the center of circulation with white dots indicating the 1200 UTC position and date. The original map is found at *http://www.nhc.noaa.gov/tracks/2005atl.gif.*

21. Figure 4 tracks are generally representative of the majority of Atlantic tropical cyclones. At latitudes less than 20 degrees (latitude is plotted along the vertical scale), tropical cyclones in the Atlantic basin tend to track initially towards the [(***west and northwest***) (***east and northeast***)].

22. Once tropical cyclones track north of about 35 degrees latitude, particularly over the open Atlantic Ocean, they tend to move towards the [(***west and northwest***) (***east and northeast***)]. These paths generally follow the prevailing winds in middle latitudes.

23. The plotted tracks indicate that these tropical cyclones [(***do***) (***do not***)] tend to move in a straight-line and therefore, along easily predictable paths. This is especially evident with Ophelia's looping path just offshore along the Atlantic coast!

24. Tropical cyclones originating in the eastern Pacific basin (not shown) also move in the same direction as the Atlantic tropical cyclones at the same latitudes, initially westward. This direction is generally into the Pacific and [(***toward***) (***away from***)] land. A few may travel far enough to affect Hawaii. Also, some do recurve northward or northeastward and may even reach the Mexican or California coasts.

The most costly natural disaster in U.S. history to date has been Hurricane Katrina. Figure 5 from the National Oceanic and Atmospheric Administration (NOAA) shows the track of Hurricane Katrina which made initial Gulf of Mexico landfall near the tip of the Mississippi River delta. On this track map, the path of Katrina's eye is marked by the big red dots with swirls (a hurricane plot symbol) and heavy black curve. The final northern dot is Katrina's position at 1600 (4 PM) CDT on 29 AUG 2005. The inner red circle denotes the extent of hurricane force winds (74 mph or greater), and the outer black circle is tropical storm force winds (39 mph or more). Red squares mark the location of coastal tide stations that take measurements of water level for navigation and other purposes. Some stations also include atmospheric pressure observations. NOAA's Center for Operational Products and Services website, *http://tidesandcurrents.noaa.gov/*, provides current tide levels and predictions.

25. At about the time Katrina crossed the Louisiana coast (near Pilots Station East, SW Pass, LA), it was basically moving towards the [(***west***) (***north***) (***east***)].

26. At this time the greatest height of the storm surge produced by Katrina would have been to the [(***left side***) (***right side***)] of the position of the center of the hurricane as it approached shore.

27. Therefore, the greater storm surge height would be expected at [(***Grand Isle***) (***Pilots Station East***)].

28. Extensive damage from Katrina's storm surge occurred from Waveland, MS eastward to Pensacola, FL. The highest recorded storm surge was 27.8 ft. at Pass Christian, MS (not labeled on map, located near Biloxi, MS). This location [(***is***) (***is not***)] consistent with the expected relationship between hurricane track and height of the storm surge.

    The storm surge accompanying Katrina also traveled up the Mississippi River and across Lake Pontchartrain, leading to high water levels that pressured the levees and canals of New Orleans leading to the breaches and catastrophic flooding.

29. Figure 6 shows the water levels and atmospheric pressure recorded at Pilots Station East from 00Z UTC on 27 August 2005 to 00Z on 31 August 2005. The upper view is the water level in meters relative to Mean Lower Low Water (MLLW). The actual water level is shown in red, while the predicted daily tidal level is shown in blue. The maximum water level was about [(***1.0***) (***2.0***) (***2.3***)] meter(s) above MLLW.

30. This maximum water level value was about [(***0.5***) (***1.0***) (***1.8***)] meter(s) above the normal tide level at that time.

31. Heights of storm surges can vary considerably depending on whether they come ashore during high or low tide. At Pilots Station East, the maximum surge occurred near the time of [(***low***) (***high***)] tide.

32. The lower view is atmospheric pressure in millibars for this same period. The pre- and post-hurricane average pressure (from the ends of the curve) is about [(***1010***) (***1000***) (***990***)] mb.

33. Although not complete, the pressure trace shows the lowest pressure to be about [(***950***) (***920***) (***870***)] mb.

34. This lowest pressure occurred [(***at about the same time as***) (***nearly 12 hours earlier than***)] the time of highest water.

35. The most rapid rise of water (and drop of pressure) occurred over a period of [(***a few hours***) (***at least a day***)]. This time period indicates the great danger to coastal residents who do not evacuate well in advance of hurricane landfall.

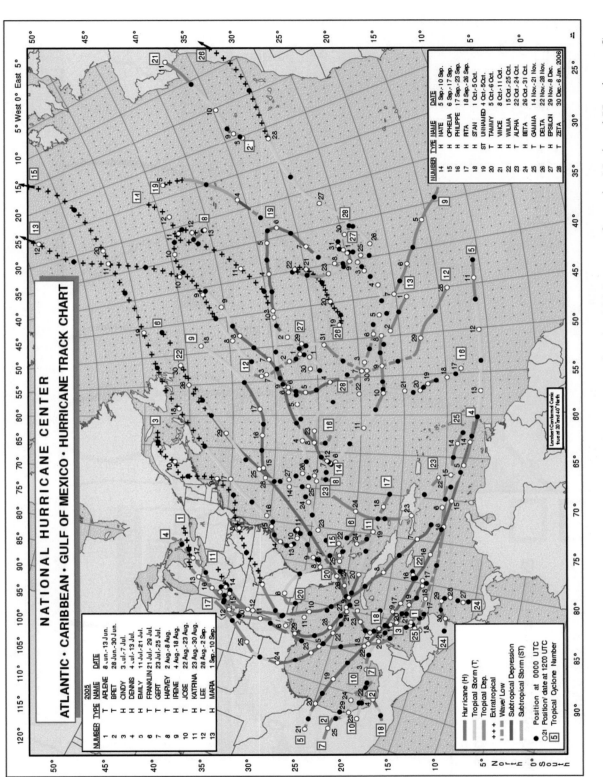

Figure 4. Map of tracks of Atlantic basin tropical weather systems for the 2005 season from the National Hurricane Center.

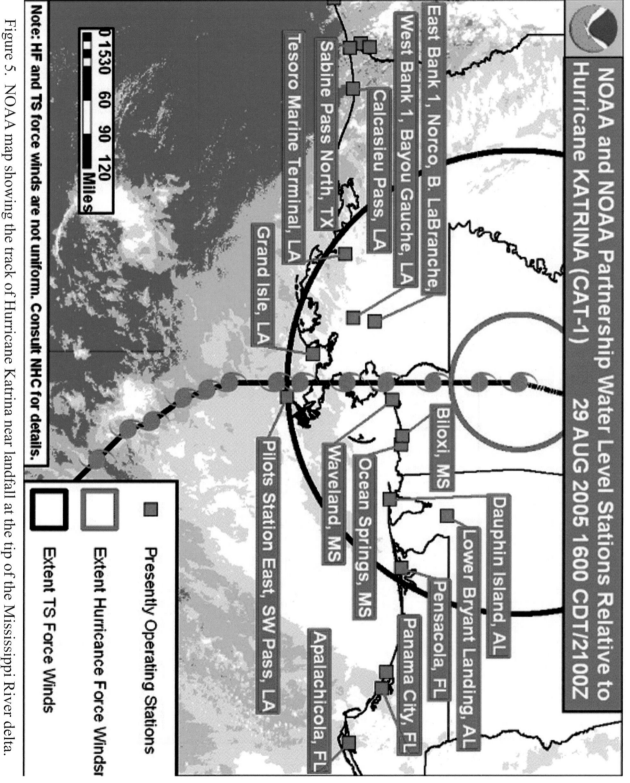

Figure 5. NOAA map showing the track of Hurricane Katrina near landfall at the tip of the Mississippi River delta.

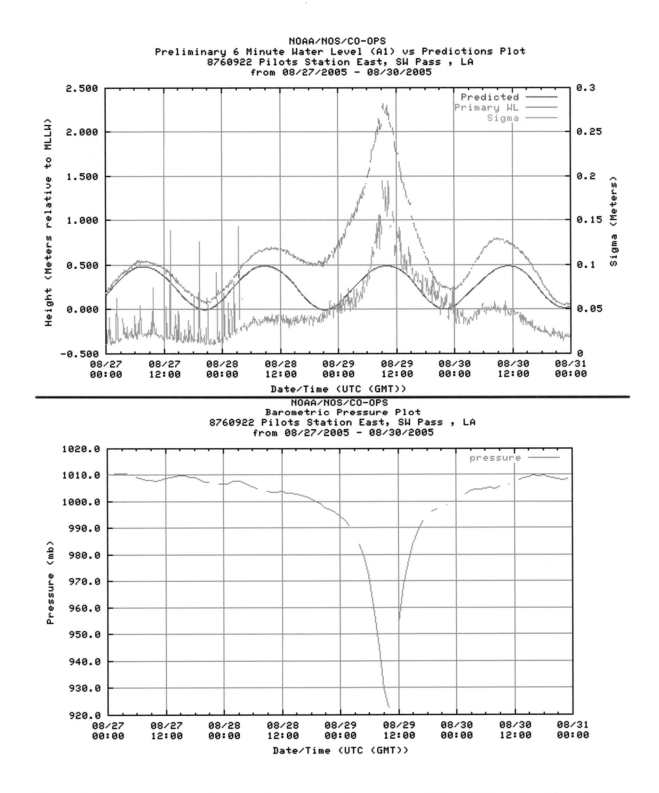

Figure 6. Measured water levels and atmospheric pressure at Pilots Station East from 00Z 27

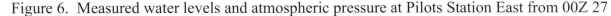

For more information on severe U.S. hurricanes in 2005 whose names were "retired," go to NOAA's website at *http://www.noaanews.noaa.gov/stories2006/s2607.htm.* Several highlighted news stories contain links to additional information on this hurricane season. Also, a discussion of Katrina as well as imagery of damage, radar and satellite views can be found at: *http://www.srh.noaa.gov/mob/0805Katrina/.* Additional Katrina information is at: *http://www.aoml.noaa.gov/hrd/Storm_pages/katrina2005/index.html* and *http://www.srh. noaa.gov/lix/Katrina_overview.html.*

Hurricanes have been called the greatest storms on Earth and are among the greatest natural hazards in terms of their potential for causing loss of life, injuries, and property damage. This investigation demonstrates that the paths of hurricanes can be erratic and difficult to forecast. Upon making landfall the storm's maximum sustained winds usually decrease rapidly although flooding from heavy rainfall may be a bigger threat beyond the coast. This change is a typical occurrence for hurricanes as the system moves away from its warm-water energy source and encounters the greater frictional resistance of the land.

Suggestions for further activities: You may wish to explore other information provided by NOAA's National Hurricane Center's website, particularly if you or your relatives live or visit the Gulf or East Coasts, areas prone to hurricane landfall. For information on tropical cyclones anywhere in the world, any time of the year, check the University of Hawaii website: *http://www.solar.ifa.hawaii.edu/Tropical/tropical.html.*

Investigation 12B: HURRICANE WIND SPEEDS AND PRESSURE CHANGES

Objectives:

Hurricanes are intense tropical cyclones spawned over warm ocean waters. They are fueled primarily by the energy involved in the evaporation of water from the ocean and subsequent condensation of water vapor within the hurricane eyewall and spiral-band cumuliform clouds. As latent heat is released, air is warmed, rises and is replaced by surrounding warm humid air in a seemingly unending spiral. The warm air center of the system exerts a lower pressure than the surrounding ocean regions. The pressure differences drive the air motions that result in hurricane-force winds. Low pressures, high wind speeds, and heavy rains continue until the energy supply to the hurricane is disrupted. Weakening of the system could result from travel over colder ocean waters which limits evaporation, or an encounter with land whose surface roughness (friction) slows the winds as well as limits the supply of water vapor.

After completing this investigation, you should be able to:

- Describe the relationship between the maximum wind speeds and the central pressure in a hurricane.
- Categorize the damage potential of a hurricane based on wind speeds.
- Explain how wind speeds in hurricanes are affected by landfall.

Introduction:

1. Table 1 gives the position, central pressure, and maximum sustained wind speed of the tropical cyclone that evolved into Hurricane Wilma at 6-hourly intervals for the period 17-25 October 2005. The central pressure of the system at 00, 06, 12, and 18 UTC is graphed in Figure 1 following the table using the pressure scale to the left. From Table 1, at what date and time was the central pressure lowest? _____.

2. At this time the central pressure was _____ mb. This most intense condition occurred as Wilma was slowly crossing the warm waters of the Caribbean Sea east of the Yucatán Peninsula.

3. According to the graph, Wilma's central pressure fell steadily from 12 UTC on 17 October (17/12) until [(*18/18*) (*19/12*) (*20/06*)].

4. From 18/18 to 19/12 the total pressure fall was _____ mb.

5. This last pressure fall occurred over a period of 18 hours; this decrease was at a rate of _____ mb/hr.

Table 1. Best track for Hurricane Wilma, 17–25 October 2005.

Date/time	Lat. (°N)	Long. (°W)	Pressure (mb)	Wind speed (kts)
17/1200	16.3	79.7	999	40
17/1800	16.0	79.8	997	45
18/0000	15.8	79.9	988	55
18/0600	15.7	79.9	982	60
18/1200	16.2	80.3	979	65
18/1800	16.6	81.1	975	75
19/0000	16.6	81.8	946	130
19/0600	17.0	82.2	892	150
19/1200	17.3	82.8	882	160
19/1800	17.4	83.4	892	140
20/0000	17.9	84.0	892	135
20/0600	18.1	84.7	901	130
20/1200	18.3	85.2	910	130
20/1800	18.6	85.5	917	130
21/0000	19.1	85.8	924	130
21/0600	19.5	86.1	930	130
21/1200	20.1	86.4	929	125
21/1800	20.3	86.7	926	120
22/0000	20.6	86.8	930	120
22/0600	20.8	87.0	935	110
22/1200	21.0	87.1	947	100
22/1800	21.3	87.1	958	85
23/0000	21.6	87.0	960	85
23/0600	21.8	86.8	962	85
23/1200	22.4	86.1	961	85
23/1800	23.1	85.4	963	90
24/0000	24.0	84.3	958	95
24/0600	25.0	83.1	953	110
24/1200	26.2	81.0	950	95
24/1800	28.0	78.8	955	105
25/0000	30.1	76.0	955	110
25/0600	33.3	72.0	963	100
25/1200	36.8	67.9	970	90
25/1800	40.5	63.5	976	75

From: National Hurricane Center, (*http://www.nhc.noaa.gov/pdf/TCR-AL252005_Wilma.pdf*).

6.   The most rapid "deepening" or intensification of the Wilma's circulation was _____ mb/hr from 19/00 to 19/06.

7.   From 19/12 to 23/06, the central pressure increased by _____ mb, a rate of 0.9 mb/hr.

8.   The rate of pressure change from 19/12 to 23/06 was [(***much less than***) (***about the same as***) (***much greater than***)] the rate for the 18 hours from 18/18 to 19/12.

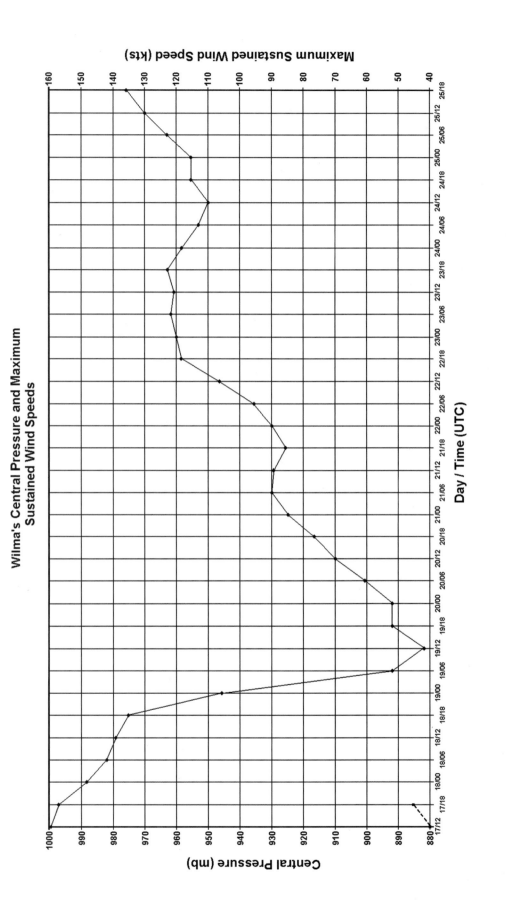

Figure 1. Graph of Wilma's central pressure and maximum sustained wind speeds from 17 - 25 October 2005.

9. Of the two periods, 18/18 to 19/12 (intensifying) and 19/12 to 23/06 (weakening), the greatest rate of change of pressure occurred during Wilma's [(***intensifying***) (***weakening***)] phase.

Using the wind speed values from Table 1, plot the wind speeds every 6 hours, the same times as the plotted pressures, on the graph using the wind speed scale along the <u>right</u> side of the graph. Plot each value with a dot. When completed, connect the dots with a dotted line to make a continuous wind speed time series. The first two dots, at 17/12 and 17/18, have already been plotted.

10. From your completed graph, at what date and time was the wind speed greatest? _____ .

11. This was [(***an earlier***) (***the same***) (***a later***)] time compared to the time of lowest central pressure.

12. Compare the general relationship of the central pressure and wind speed curves as shown by the graph. Generally, the wind speed varies [(***directly***) (***inversely***)] with changes in the central pressure. (That is, two quantities vary *directly* if one increases while the other increases, and *inversely* if one decreases while the other increases.)

13. Hurricane Wilma's center made landfall in crossing the tip of the Yucatán Peninsula in Mexico from about 00 UTC on 22 October to 00 UTC on 23 October. **Place a bracket along the time axis at the bottom of the graph to denote these times and label it with "YP".** This landfall time was for the center of the hurricane, whereas extreme weather conditions associated with the hurricane extended from its eye wall outward several tens of kilometers in all directions. Over the period including landfall, the wind speeds [(***increased***) (***decreased***)] as the hurricane circulation responded to the increased roughness of the underlying land surface.

14. Wilma then moved rapidly northeastward and crossed the coast of southern Florida at 24/1030 (1030 UTC on the 24th). **Place an arrow along the time axis at the bottom of the graph to denote this time and label it with "FL".** In both landfalling cases, in the hours following landfall the central pressure [(***increased***) (***decreased***)] while the sustained wind speed decreased.

The Saffir-Simpson scale is commonly used to assess the damage potential of hurricanes. **Using the scale listed in Investigation 12A, draw horizontal lines on your graph using the wind speed limit values of each category and write the Saffir-Simpson category number and descriptive terminology on the graph between the appropriate boundary lines.**

15. Wilma's category at this time of greatest intensity (lowest central pressure and strongest winds) was _____ .

16. Was Wilma still at hurricane strength when it made landfall in Florida? [(_**Yes**_) (_**No**_)].

As directed by your course instructor, complete this investigation by either:

1. *Going to the Current Weather Studies link on the course website, or*
2. *Continuing to the Applications section for this investigation that immediately follows in this Investigations Manual.*

Investigation 12B: HURRICANE WIND SPEEDS AND PRESSURE CHANGES

Applications

Investigation 12A dealt with the path of Hurricane Katrina and its damaging storm surge. In this investigation we consider Hurricane Wilma's landfall just south of Naples, FL. Hurricane Wilma is notable, in that, while still over the Gulf of Mexico it had the lowest central sea-level air pressure ever measured in an Atlantic basin hurricane.

The prior graph clearly showed how the maximum sustained wind speed was related to the central pressure of the hurricane. We saw from earlier investigations that the pressure gradient force is the principal control of wind speed. The low pressure in the hurricane eye compared to the near-normal sea level pressures surrounding the storm produces a very strong horizontal pressure gradient and, hence, the high wind speeds.

Figure 2 [courtesy of National Oceanic and Atmospheric Administration (NOAA) Weather Service Office in Miami] is a plot of the track of the center of circulation of Wilma along with maximum sustained wind speeds at various times denoted by the squares. (For an animation of the track shown by the NWS Miami radar, see *http://www.srh.noaa.gov/mfl/events/?id=wilma*, and scroll down to Figure 3.)

17. **Center a coin such as a quarter on the Figure 2 printed track in the Gulf of Mexico to represent Hurricane Wilma. As you move the coin northeastward along the hurricane's track, also rotate it counterclockwise to simulate the surface wind directions of the traveling hurricane.** (The motions are not to scale; see the radar animation noted above.) With your coin/hurricane approaching the Florida coast, the wind direction at Naples is generally <u>toward</u> the [(***southeast***) (***northwest***)].

18. After your coin/hurricane passes Naples and over the Florida peninsula, the wind direction at Naples blows generally <u>toward</u> the [(***southeast***) (***northwest***)].

Figure 3 is a plot of the water levels, winds and air pressures at Naples as measured by instruments associated with the NOAA tidal station at Naples harbor. In the middle panel of Figure 3, wind speeds and directions are presented. The time period is from 9:00 a.m. EDT 23 October 2005 to 9:00 a.m. EDT 26 October 2005. The time of the last plotted observation is noted on each panel just preceding the dashed vertical line. Wind speeds are denoted by red dots with directions shown using attached blue arrows. The center of the large circulation of Wilma officially made landfall at 7 a.m. on 24 October a few miles south of Naples at Everglades City. **Draw a vertical line across both the middle wind and lower pressure panels at this time.**

19. In the hours prior to landfall, the wind directions at Naples were generally <u>toward</u> the [(***southeast***) (***west or northwest***)].

20. This direction of air motion [(***was***) (***was not***)] consistent with your coin/hurricane circulation.

21. In the twelve or so hours following landfall, the wind directions at Naples were generally <u>toward</u> the [(***southeast***) (***west or northwest***)].

22. This direction of air motion [(***was***) (***was not***)] consistent with your coin/hurricane circulation.

23. The *maximum* wind speed at Naples, shown by the red dots in the middle panel, was about _____ knots (approx. 85 mph) at 8:00 a.m. on 24 October.

24. The *minimum* air pressure (lower panel) was about [(***962***) (***974***) (***981***)] millibars which occurred an hour earlier.

25. Comparing the middle and lower panels of Figure 3, it can be seen that in general, as pressures were <u>decreasing</u>, wind speeds were [(***decreasing***) (***increasing***)].

26. And as pressures were <u>increasing</u>, wind speeds were [(***decreasing***) (***increasing***)].

27. This wind speed–air pressure relationship [(***was***) (***was not***)] consistent with that found in the Figure 1 graph of this investigation.

28. The top panel of Figure 3 displays the actual water levels above the mean lower low water (MLLW) reference level by a series of red crosses. The predicted tide level is depicted by the smooth blue curve. The highest water level shown was about [(***1***) (***3***) (***5***)] foot (feet). This occurred at about 12 noon on 24 October.

29. This was also the time of predicted [(***low***) (***high***)] tide.

30. Had this storm surge occurred near high tide several hours earlier, the surge would have been about [(***0***) (***2***) (***4***)] feet higher, and therefore more damaging. This contrasts with the Katrina case depicted in Investigation 12A, where the highest surge did occur near the time of high tide.

For more information on Hurricane Wilma, consult the Miami NWS website noted above, or that from the Tampa office (*http://www.srh.noaa.gov/tbw/html/tbw/2005/hurricanes2005. htm*), or Key West (*http://www.srh.noaa.gov/key/HTML/wilma/wilma.html*). The National Hurricane Center website (*http://www.nhc.noaa.gov/*) also contains a summary of the season as well as studies of individual storms.

<u>Suggestions for further activities:</u> Explore other information provided by NOAA's National Hurricane Center's website, particularly if you or your relatives live or visit along the Gulf or East Coasts, areas prone to hurricane landfall. For information on tropical storms anywhere in the world at any time of the year, check the University of Hawaii website: *http://www. solar.ifa.hawaii.edu/Tropical/tropical.html*.

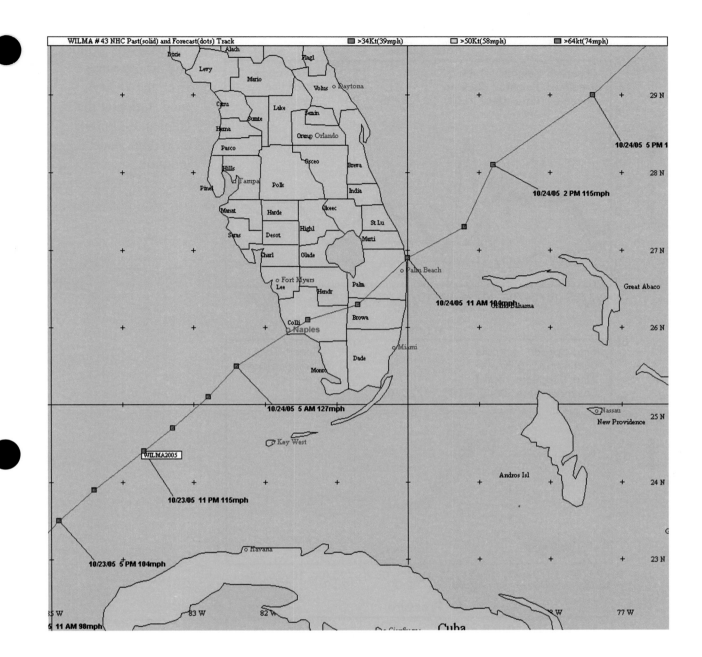

Figure 2. The track of the center of circulation of Wilma as it crossed the Florida area.

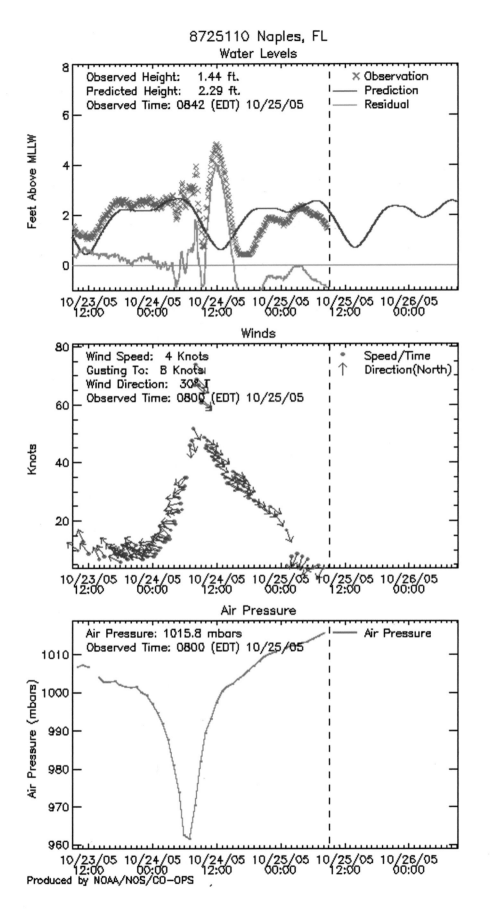

Figure 3. Water levels, winds and air pressures from the NOAA tidal station at the Naples, FL harbor as Wilma made landfall.

Investigation 13A: WEATHER INSTRUMENTS AND OBSERVATIONS

Objectives:

Weather is the state of the atmosphere at a particular place at a given time. We must describe as closely as possible the state of this mixture of gases we call the atmosphere at the time and location where instruments are available. We are interested in knowing for initial descriptive purposes and ultimately for predictive reasons, the atmosphere's heat energy, density, large-scale motions, water vapor concentration, and liquid or solid water in clouds and precipitation. These quantities translate to the more common parameters of: temperature, atmospheric pressure, wind speed and direction, dewpoint (or relative humidity), cloud cover (including height), visibility, precipitation (amount and type), and the general character of the "weather".

Weather observations are taken by international convention at three-hourly intervals each day, at 0000 UTC, 0300 UTC, etc. [Universal Time Coordinated (UTC), also known as Z time or Greenwich Mean Time (GMT), is the time along the prime meridian, 0 degree longitude.] For aviation purposes, weather observations are routinely reported every hour, twenty-four hours a day. In the U.S., most weather observations are taken by the Automated Surface Observing System (ASOS) sensors.

After completing this investigation, you should be able to:

- Describe the Automated Surface Observing System (ASOS) and the data it provides.
- Describe how to access weather observations for the U.S. and the world via the Internet.

Introduction:

Weather observations are a combination of direct measurements by various sensors and determinations made by computer algorithms (programs based on several values). For example, sensors determine the air temperature, dewpoint, pressure, ceiling, precipitation, and wind. The amount of sky cover is determined by the fraction of ceilometer beams that detect cloud or clear air. Visibility is computed from the amount of light scattered back to a sensor from a small volume of air surrounding the sensor. "Weather" type is a combination of temperature, dewpoint, and visibility values and may specify haze, smoke or fog.

1. The ASOS consists of an array of instruments including an electronic thermometer, an electronically chilled mirror and light or absorptive humidity sensor to determine the dewpoint, an anemometer and wind vane or sonic anemometer for wind speed and direction, a vertical pulsed laser ceilometer for cloud height and amount, pulsed laser instruments for detecting scattered light for visibility and weather type, a vibrating column for detecting freezing rain, and a heated tipping bucket or weighing rain gauge for rain and snowfall. (For complete technical details of ASOS sensors, see: *http://www.nws.noaa.gov/asos/*.)

The National Weather Service provides an Internet site that allows you to obtain the latest weather observation from ASOS instruments at any particular location, selected by choosing the state and then the city at: *http://weather.noaa.gov/*. Times are given in Universal Coordinated Time (UTC) with equivalents in local times. Regardless of location, all times are given as Eastern Standard or Daylight, as appropriate with an initial conversion. A sample observation for Nashville International Airport in Tennessee follows:

Current Weather Conditions   Nashville, Nashville International Airport, TN, United States
(KBNA) 36-07-08N 086-41-21W 210M

Conditions at May 05, 2006 (2006.05.05 1453 UTC)

Wind	from the NNW (340 degrees) at 7 MPH (6 KT)
Visibility	10 mile(s)
Sky conditions	overcast
Weather	Light rain
Precipitation last hour	0.01 inches
Temperature	60.1 F (15.6 C)
Dew Point	53.1 F (11.7 C)
Relative Humidity	77%
Pressure (altimeter)	30 in. Hg (1015 hPa)
Pressure tendency	0.00 inches (0.1 hPa) higher than three hours ago
Coded observation	KBNA 051453Z 34006KT 10SM -RA FEW045 SCT070 BKN100 OVC180 16/12 A3000 RMK AO2 SLP156 P0001 60007 T01560117 53001

Notes: Times of observation, taken within 10 minutes of the top of the hour, are ordinarily considered to have been acquired at the top of the hour. The readings above were taken at 1453 UTC, but are considered to be the 1500 UTC readings. The pressure units hectoPascals (hPa) are numerically equivalent to millibars (mb). Standard sea level pressure of 29.92 in. Hg (inches of mercury) = 1013.25 hPa = 1013.25 mb.

Additional information is also available at certain hours. For example, the 1453 UTC (representing 1500 UTC or 15Z) report contains the pressure *tendency*, the amount and direction of the pressure change over the previous three hours. The pressure at 12 UTC would have been [(***30.00***) (***29.98***)] inches of mercury.

2. Another item listed in the report following the current weather conditions is the maximum and minimum temperatures over recent 6- and 24-hour periods. If precipitation had occurred, total precipitation within certain time periods is also listed.

Maximum and Minimum Temperatures

Maximum F (C)	Minimum F (C)	
66.0 (18.9)	57.9 (14.4)	In the 6 hours preceding May 05, 2006 - 07:53 AM EDT / 2006.05.05 1153 UTC
75.0 (23.9)	61.0 (16.1)	In the 24 hours preceding May 05, 2006 - 01:53 AM EDT / 2006.05.05 0553 UTC

The range of temperature (difference between maximum and minimum) over the 24 hours preceding the 0553 UTC 05 May 2006 observation time was _____ F°.

Following the maximum and minimum temperatures and precipitation report (if any) for the particular hour is an hour-by-hour listing (time series) of the weather conditions for the preceding twenty-four hours. In this case:

Date	Time EDT (UTC)	Temperature F (C)	Dew Point F (C)	Pressure Inches (hPa)	Wind MPH	Weather
May 05	11 AM (15)	60.1 (15.6)	53.1 (11.7)	30 (1015)	NNW 7	light rain
	10 AM (14)	57.9 (14.4)	53.1 (11.7)	29.98 (1015)	NNE 6	light rain
	9 AM (13)	57.9 (14.4)	53.1 (11.7)	29.99 (1015)	NNE 7	light rain
	8 AM (12)	57.9 (14.4)	53.1 (11.7)	30 (1015)	NNW 5	light rain
	7 AM (11)	57.9 (14.4)	52.0 (11.1)	29.97 (1014)	N 10	light rain
	6 AM (10)	62.1 (16.7)	53.1 (11.7)	29.95 (1014)	NNW 8	light rain
	5 AM (9)	64.9 (18.3)	52.0 (11.1)	29.93 (1013)	NNW 8	
	4 AM (8)	66.0 (18.9)	57.0 (13.9)	29.93 (1013)	N 8	
	3 AM (7)	66.0 (18.9)	60.1 (15.6)	29.95 (1014)	WNW 9	
	2 AM (6)	66.0 (18.9)	61.0 (16.1)	29.95 (1014)	WNW 8	
	1 AM (5)	66.0 (18.9)	61.0 (16.1)	29.95 (1014)	W 6	
	Midnight (4)	66.9 (19.4)	61.0 (16.1)	29.97 (1014)	W 6	
May 04	11 PM (3)	66.9 (19.4)	61.0 (16.1)	29.97 (1014)	WSW 3	
	10 PM (2)	66.9 (19.4)	60.1 (15.6)	29.94 (1013)	WNW 3	
	9 PM (1)	68.0 (20.0)	60.1 (15.6)	29.93 (1013)	WNW 7	
	8 PM (0)	69.1 (20.6)	59.0 (15.0)	29.93 (1013)	WNW 9	
	7 PM (23)	70.0 (21.1)	60.1 (15.6)	29.95 (1014)	NW 10	
	6 PM (22)	71.1 (21.7)	59.0 (15.0)	29.95 (1014)	W 9	
	5 PM (21)	72.0 (22.2)	59.0 (15.0)	29.96 (1014)	W 13	
	4 PM (20)	73.0 (22.8)	62.1 (16.7)	29.98 (1015)	W 13	
	3 PM (19)	73.9 (23.3)	61.0 (16.1)	29.98 (1015)	WSW 9	
	2 PM (18)	73.0 (22.8)	62.1 (16.7)	29.99 (1015)	SW 6	
	1 PM (17)	71 (22)	62 (17)	29.99 (1015)	W 5	
	Noon (16)	70.0 (21.1)	61.0 (16.1)	30.02 (1016)	Calm	

From the table of hourly observations above, answer the following four questions:

3. The highest temperature during the period was _____ °F.

4. This occurred at _____ EDT (Eastern Daylight Time) on _____ (date).

5. During the period being reported, the minimum pressure was _____ in. This occurred at 8 PM and 9 PM EDT on May 4 and 4 AM and 5 AM on May 5.

6. The weather condition of _____ was reported in one or more of the hourly observations.

7. The following is from the course website and is a partial listing of the State Surface Data - Text for Tennessee (TN) at 15Z (1500 UTC), the same time as the NWS observation given above.

Data for TN

15Z 05 MAY 2006

HH	STN	TMP	DEW	DIR	SPD	GST	CLDL	CLDM	CLDH	ALT	PMSL	PTD	WTHR	PCPN
15	TRI	65	61	21	4		OVC			29.92	1012.2	0.0		0.02
15	CHA	68	62	31	4		BKN			29.93	1012.9	0.1		
15	TYS	69	63	29	5		BKN	OVC		29.91	1011.8	-0.2		
15	CSV	60	58		3		OVC			29.97	1013.5	0.3		T
15	**BNA**	**60**	**53**	**34**	**6**		**SCT**	**BKN**	**OVC**	**30.00**	**1015.6**	**0.1**	**R**	**0.07**
15	MQY	59	55	1	4		BKN			30.00	1015.3	-0.2	R	0.11
15	MEM	62	55	5	11		BKN			30.04	1017.0	1.0		T
15	NQA	57	54	3	5		OVC			30.04				
15	MKL	61	56	1	6		OVC			30.04	1016.9	1.4		T
15	DYR	63	52	2	4		SCT			30.03		0.3		
15	OQT	69	63	0	0		SCT			29.93	1012.4	0.0		
15	CKV	61	51	1	3		OVC			30.01	1016.1	0.8		0.01

In the text listing for TN, the temperature (TMP) and dewpoint (DEW) are in whole degrees Fahrenheit, wind: direction (DIR) in tens of degrees, speed (SPD) and gusts (GST) in knots, and sea level pressure in tenths of hectoPascals (PMSL). The "sky cover" or amount of cloudiness is reported as clear (CLR) - no clouds, scattered (SCT) - less than half covered, broken (BKN) - more than half covered, or overcast (OVC) - completely cloudy for each of the low (CLDL), middle (CLDM) and high (CLDH) levels. Compare the NWS report for Nashville International Airport in item #1 (KBNA) with the same values for Nashville International Airport (BNA) from this question's text listing for TN. Keeping in mind the units used, the reported elements are [(***the same***) (***different***)].

8. The course website delivers national and regional maps on which surface weather data are plotted. The data on these maps are updated hourly. Figure 1 is a sample national map (U.S. - Data) which displays data collected at 14Z (10 am Eastern Daylight Time, 9 am CDT, etc.) on 4 May 2006. (The station identifiers for the reporting stations can be found by calling up the "Available Surface Stations" map on the course website. The identifiers shown on that map do not include a "K" that is the first letter of all coterminous United States station identifications.) Surface weather data are plotted on the national map in, on, and around a circle representing the station. Temperature, in Fahrenheit degrees, is plotted at the "11 o'clock" position relative to the station circle. The temperature at Nashville, Tennessee, at Figure 1 map time was _____ ° F.

9. The national map displays surface observational data from a sufficient number of stations to determine large-scale weather patterns and features. Temperatures reported on the Figure 1 map show that the area of the nation where the lowest temperatures prevail is over the [(***Northern Plains***) (***Southwest***) (***Southeast***) (***Northeast***)].

10. Figure 2 is a sample regional map, one of nine including Alaska and Hawaii, provided via the course website. This map is labeled [(***Southern Plains - Data***) (***Southeast - Data***)]. This map is for the same time as the national map, Figure 1.

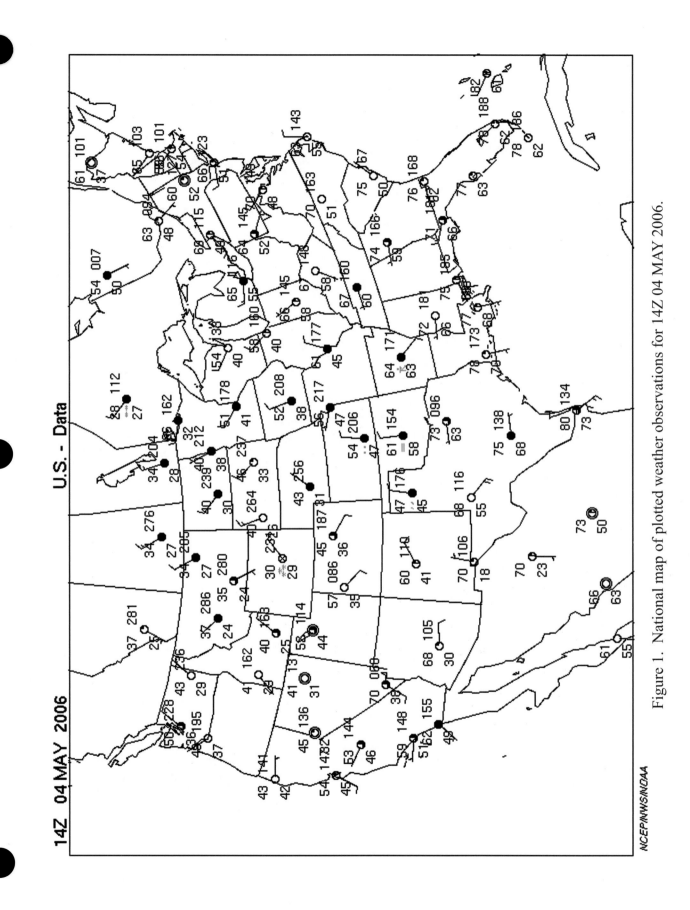

Figure 1. National map of plotted weather observations for 14Z 04 MAY 2006.

U.S. - Data

14Z 04 MAY 2006

NCEP/NWS/NOAA

13A - 5

Weather Studies: Investigations Manual 2007-2008

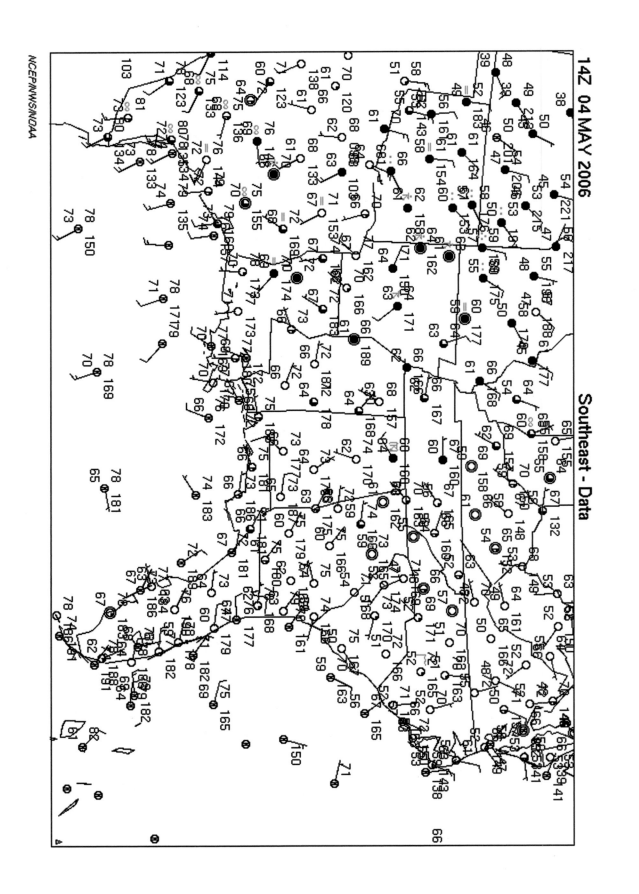

11. The regional maps display many more stations, allowing for more detailed weather analysis. For a comparison of the station densities on the two maps, the national map has one station plotted in Tennessee whereas the number of stations on the regional map (including the two along the southern border of TN) is _____.

As directed by your course instructor, complete this investigation by either:

1. ***Going to the Current Weather Studies link on the course website, or***
2. ***Continuing to the Applications section for this investigation that immediately follows in this Investigations Manual.***

Investigation 13A: WEATHER INSTRUMENTS AND OBSERVATIONS

Applications

From the course website, under the **Surface** section, click on "Meteograms for Selected Cities". From the meteograms page, select your nearest city from the map or table listing. Print that page.

12. The meteogram portrays [(**6**) (**12**) (**25**)] hourly observations over the time period shown.

Go to *http://www.weather.gov/view/national.php?map=on* and click on the state of your meteogram station. [This may also be found from the course website section **Extras**, link of "Additional Links", and then first choice of *NWS "Weather Page"*.] Select the same city or station identifier letters as your meteogram. (The station codes used by the NWS website have a leading "K" with the specific 3 station letters. For example, Cape Hatteras, NC is *K*HSE.)

Compare the course website's meteogram with the NWS "Weather Page" data for the same station. Times are given in UTC along the horizontal axis labeled at the bottom of the meteogram increasing from left to right. Time for the tabular 24-hour summary observations from the NWS website is in Eastern time (or selectable local time) with the UTC in parenthesis. Note that the listing starts with the most recent at the top. Choose several hours that are common to both the meteogram plot and the NWS data table. Draw vertical lines across the meteogram at those hours. Compare the temperature, dewpoint and wind speed and wind direction for those common UTC hours as shown on the meteogram to those reported in the table.

13. The observation values for the same time as shown on the meteogram and listed in the table are [(***the same***) (***different***)].

Current weather observations can be found on the Internet in a variety of formats from the course website, National Weather Service websites and others. Investigate these sources and their displays.

Suggestions for further activities:

For those in the lower 48 states - Regional maps are made available on the course website so that you can track changes in weather and weather features, such as cold fronts, as they progress across the country. Call up the regional map that best fits your location. Mark your present location on the regional map and on the national map (Figure 1). You can check the three-letter identifier of the nearest station to your location by selecting the "Available Surface Stations" map on the website – click on the map for a full listing of stations.

For those in Alaska, Hawaii/Pacific or Puerto Rico/Caribbean areas - Regional maps for the coterminous U.S. are available to provide a detailed track of changeable weather and weather features. For areas outside of the "Lower 48" on the course website, scroll down to the area with Alaska/Hawaii and Pacific/Puerto Rico and Caribbean links and click on your region's link. For Alaska and Hawaii - Eastern Pacific, select "Surface map: state" under your region's heading and mark your location on this regional map. For Puerto Rico - Caribbean, select "Surface: area observations," then mark your present location on this regional map and click on the red dot closest to your location for station information.

You may wish to see what stations report hourly observations to the National Weather Service. Go to http://www.weather.gov/view/national.php?map=on. Click on your state (or one of interest). The state map shown lists those stations providing observations. Clicking on a city name brings up the NWS website with the current weather observation and those of the past 24 hours.

Investigation 13B: WEATHER FORECASTS

Objectives:

Modern weather forecasting is based on a process termed *numerical weather prediction* (NWP). In a computer (or numerical) model of the atmosphere the physical laws that govern fluid motions (Newton's laws of motion, the first law of thermodynamics, conservation of mass, etc.) are put into computational forms for computer calculation. Supercomputers distribute an initial set of data throughout a three-dimensional grid that represents the atmosphere from the surface to the upper stratosphere. The relationships between variables (*e.g.* temperature, pressure, winds, water vapor) are used to take the initial values of these quantities a short step forward in time. Those new values are then used to step ahead once more at all the grid points.

The starting point for these calculations is weather observations. By international convention, weather observations are taken at 0000Z and 1200Z at both the surface and in the upper atmosphere, worldwide. These observational data are exchanged and collected at national weather centers. The U.S. National Centers for Environmental Prediction, National Oceanic and Atmospheric Administration (NCEP/NOAA), collects these data and inputs them to the computer forecast process. After running the computer program to simulate times into the future of 6, 12, 18, 24 hours, or longer, the predicted values throughout the atmosphere are related to the surface temperatures, dewpoints, cloud cover, wind, and precipitation probabilities that are familiar components of weathercasts. This computer-generated information is distributed to local NOAA/National Weather Service (NWS) forecast offices.

The final step is taken by NWS meteorologists at local forecast offices. They use their experience and knowledge of local influences on the weather to adjust the computer information to the final forecasts that are provided to the public.

After completing this investigation, you should be able to:

- Describe the general elements of a weather forecast.
- Compare the course website forecasts with those made available to the public by NWS forecast offices.

Introduction:

Forecasts of weather conditions are provided for many cities around the coterminous US via maps similar to those from the course website (Forecasts). Forecast maps are provided for 12, 24, 36, and 48 hours after either 0000 UTC (00Z) or 1200 UTC (12Z) when observations of the surface and upper atmospheric conditions are made. These maps give predicted conditions at selected cities for a certain future (*valid*) time, specified in the upper left margin of each map, by way of a "forecast station model."

FORECAST STATION MODEL LEGEND

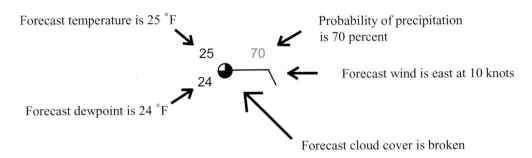

Forecast temperature is 25 °F

Probability of precipitation is 70 percent

25   70

24

Forecast wind is east at 10 knots

Forecast dewpoint is 24 °F

Forecast cloud cover is broken

The meaning of the weather symbols used for weather forecasts and cloud coverage are given in the **Weather Map Symbols** file under **Extras** from the course website.

Figure 1 is the 36-Hour Forecast map for 00Z 31 MAR 2006 (6 PM CST). The latest data utilized to make the forecast were observed at 12Z 29 MAR. **From Figure 1, decode the forecast station model for St. Louis, Missouri (highlighted station)**. Note that the southern two-thirds of the western Missouri border parallels a north-south oriented longitude line. The forecast conditions for 6 PM were:

1. temperature: _____ °F with dewpoint 54 °F.
2. wind direction: [(***west-southwest***) (***south-southeast***)]
3. wind speed: _____ kts
4. cloud cover: _____
5. probability of precipitation: _____ %

Forecast maps show the results of numerical weather prediction output. Meteorologists at National Weather Service offices around the country use this computer guidance information to develop local forecasts of expected weather conditions that take into account the effects of local conditions (topography, bodies of water, surrounding surface conditions) that may affect general weather patterns. For example, one obvious effect is higher temperatures in urban areas compared to surrounding rural areas.

NWS offices issue detailed forecasts ("short-term forecast period") for segments of the next two days and more general forecasts ("extended forecast period") for the following several days. Following Figure 1 is a forecast for St. Louis issued by the local NWS forecast office for a period that included the time of the Numerical Weather Prediction (NWP) forecast shown in Figure 1.

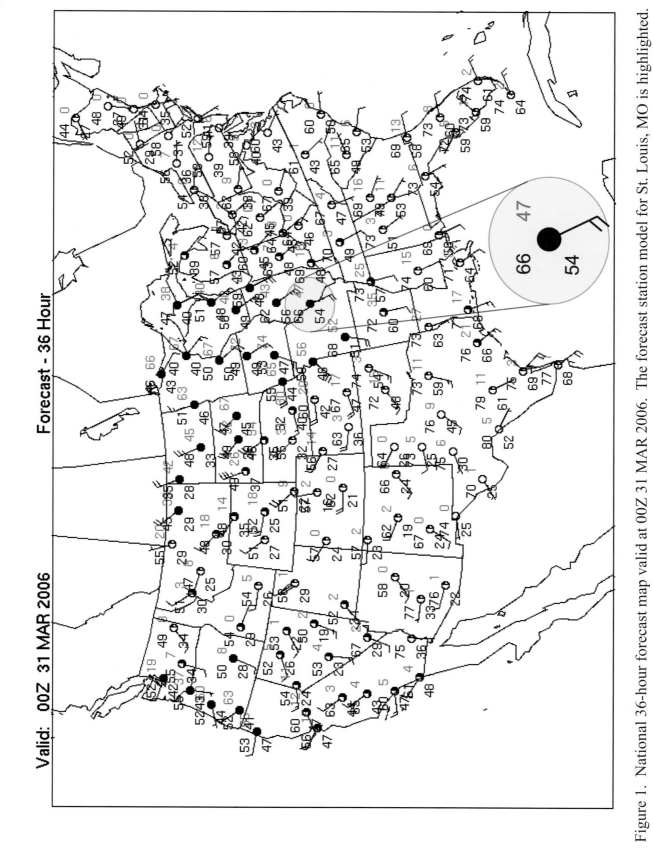

Figure 1. National 36-hour forecast map valid at 00Z 31 MAR 2006. The forecast station model for St. Louis, MO is highlighted.

NATIONAL WEATHER SERVICE ST LOUIS MO
111 PM CST WED MAR 29 2006

JEFFERSON-MADISON IL-MONROE IL-ST. CHARLES-ST. CLAIR IL-ST. LOUIS-ST. LOUIS
CITY- INCLUDING THE CITIES OF...BELLEVILLE...EDWARDSVILLE...ST CHARLES...ST
LOUIS
111 PM CST WED MAR 29 2006

THIS AFTERNOON
MOSTLY SUNNY. HIGH AROUND 60. SOUTHEAST WIND AROUND 10 MPH.

TONIGHT
PARTLY CLOUDY UNTIL EARLY MORNING THEN BECOMING MOSTLY CLOUDY. LOW IN
THE MID 40S. SOUTHEAST WIND AROUND 10 MPH.

THURSDAY
BREEZY. MOSTLY CLOUDY. CHANCE OF SHOWERS AND THUNDERSTORMS IN THE
MORNING...THEN CHANCE OF THUNDERSTORMS IN THE AFTERNOON. HIGH IN THE
UPPER 60S. SOUTH WIND 10 TO 20 MPH. GUSTS UP TO 30 MPH IN THE AFTERNOON.
CHANCE OF RAIN 40 PERCENT.

THURSDAY NIGHT
BREEZY. OCCASIONAL THUNDERSTORMS IN THE EVENING...THEN CHANCE OF
THUNDERSTORMS AFTER MIDNIGHT. STORMS MAY BE SEVERE WITH DAMAGING WINDS
AND LARGE HAIL IN THE EVENING. LOW IN THE MID 50S. SOUTH WIND 15 TO 20 MPH
WITH GUSTS TO AROUND 30 MPH. CHANCE OF RAIN 80 PERCENT.

FRIDAY
BREEZY. MOSTLY CLOUDY. HIGH IN THE MID 60S. WEST WIND AROUND 15 MPH WITH
GUSTS TO AROUND 30 MPH.

FRIDAY NIGHT
COLDER. PARTLY CLOUDY. LOW IN THE LOWER 40S.

SATURDAY
PARTLY CLOUDY. HIGH IN THE LOWER 60S.

SATURDAY NIGHT
PARTLY CLOUDY. LOW IN THE MID 40S.

SUNDAY
PARTLY SUNNY WITH A 30 PERCENT CHANCE OF SHOWERS AND THUNDERSTORMS.
HIGH AROUND 70.

SUNDAY NIGHT
MOSTLY CLOUDY WITH A 30 PERCENT CHANCE OF SHOWERS AND THUNDERSTORMS.
LOW AROUND 50.

MONDAY THROUGH TUESDAY
PARTLY CLOUDY. HIGH IN THE UPPER 60S. LOW IN THE MID 40S.

The forecast was issued by the St. Louis NWS office at 1:11 PM CST (1811Z) on Wednesday.

6. The total forecast period covers approximately the next [(***day***) (***three days***) (***week***)].

7. The first several days of the forecast period are divided into [(***morning and afternoon***) (***day and night***)] segments.

8. During the first three days of the forecast period, the weather elements described are: [(***temperature***) (***wind***) (***precipitation probability***) (***sky conditions***) (***all of these***)].

9. For the remaining portion of the forecast period, the following weather parameter is <u>not</u> given: [(***temperature***) (***wind***) (***sky conditions and weather***)].

From the written forecast above, indicate the probable weather during Thursday afternoon about 6 PM (00Z). Keep in mind that the late afternoon temperature might be slightly lower than the day's high temperature. Other late afternoon values can be estimated by using the conditions given for the day with some change toward evening conditions.

10. temperature: about [(***70***) (***65***)] °F
11. cloud cover: [(***partly cloudy***) (***overcast***)]
12. probability of precipitation: [(***50***) (***20***)] %
13. wind: [(***west about 5 mph***) (***south about 15 mph***)]

14. Compare the forecast conditions from the forecast map segment (Figure 1) with those you determined from the text forecast (item 7) for the same time. The forecasts were [(***less than***) (***more than***)] 5 degrees different on the temperature.

15. Both of the forecasts [(***contain***) (***do not contain***)] cloud cover as a forecast element.

16. The probabilities of precipitation were [(***reasonably close***) (***very far apart***)].

17. In general, these are [(***consistent***) (***widely differing***)] forecasts.

18. On Thursday, 30 MAR 2006, at 6 PM CST (00Z), the following weather conditions were actually observed at St. Louis, Missouri:

    Weather Conditions: temperature 73 F, dewpoint 54 F, wind south at 20 kts (23 mph), sky overcast [rain was occurring to the west and later at St. Louis]

    Comparing the actually observed conditions at 6 PM CST 30 MAR (00Z 31 MAR 2006) with those forecast from data 36 hours previous show that most people would probably consider the forecast to have been [(***useful***) (***very misleading***)].

As directed by your course instructor, complete this investigation by either:

1. *Going to the Current Weather Studies link on the course website, or*
2. *Continuing to the Applications section for this investigation that immediately follows in this Investigations Manual.*

Investigation 13B: WEATHER FORECASTS
Applications

"The National Weather Service (NWS) provides weather, hydrologic, and climate forecasts and warnings for the United States, its territories, adjacent waters and ocean areas, for the protection of life and property and the enhancement of the national economy. NWS data and products form a national information database and infrastructure which can be used by other governmental agencies, the private sector, the public, and the global community." (NOAA/ NWS Mission Statement)

The gathering of weather information is therefore a process that is conducted primarily so the NWS can fulfill its forecasting and warning mission. The Internet now forms an exceptional vehicle to disseminate those forecasts, warnings, and other weather and climate information to the public in text and graphic formats. The following Internet address: *http://www.weather.gov/* is the location for the latest official watches and warnings from the National Weather Service. The areas on this U.S. map that currently have active warnings, watches, advisories, and/or special weather statements are colored according to the legend below the map. Figure 2 is the watches and warnings map for 28 March 2007 as an example.

19. Find your location on the National Weather Service interactive map and click on it. The resulting webpage shows the local NWS Forecast Office's (location at the top of the page) area of responsibility for issuing weather warnings and forecasts. From the regional map, click on your approximate location. Examine the forecast products that are displayed. Under the pictorial forecasts of the next few days are detailed forecasts. These detailed descriptive forecasts are presented out to [(**_3_**) (**_5_**) (**_7_**)] days.

20. Scroll down the page and click on the National Digital Forecast Database maps. (If your NWS Forecast Office page does not have the National Digital Forecast Database listing, go back and choose another page that does.) The "Daily View" maps for most of the weather elements (e.g., temperature) are available at [(**_3-_**) (**_6-_**) (**_12-_**)] hour intervals. Some products are for longer periods and there are tabs for choosing a Weekly View or for Loops.

A ***warning*** is a statement issued by the National Weather Service indicating that a specified hazardous weather or hydrologic event is imminent or actually occurring. The intention of these warnings is to urge the public to take immediate appropriate action for personal safety. Warnings may be issued for flash floods, hurricanes, severe thunderstorms, tornadoes, or winter storms. Often these warnings are carried by television stations interrupting broadcasts or as text and graphics on-screen or via radio. Special NOAA Weather Radio receivers can be triggered by the local NWS office to signal the issuance of a warning and alert the public.

All weather warnings, watches, advisories, and statements are posted on the maps you have been examining. Browse the national map (*http://www.weather.gov/*) and check on several watches and warnings to familiarize yourself with these products.

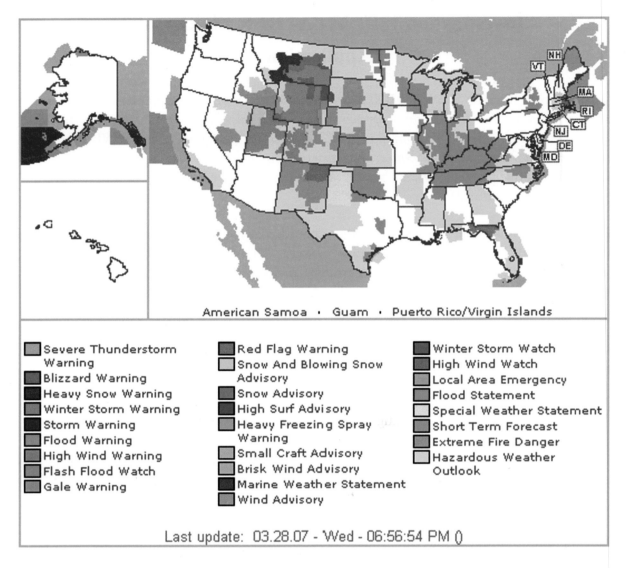

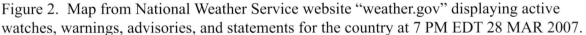

Figure 2. Map from National Weather Service website "weather.gov" displaying active watches, warnings, advisories, and statements for the country at 7 PM EDT 28 MAR 2007.

Official NWS forecasts are updated several times daily and made available to private meteorological companies and the media. Whether you receive your weather forecast from radio, TV, newspapers or the Internet, the original source for the information is your local NWS office.

Suggestions for further activities: You may wish to call up the website of your local NWS Office. Go to *http://www.wrh.noaa.gov/wrh/forecastoffice_tab.php* to find your nearest NWS Office. Click on the station. From the regional map showing each office's area of responsibility, you can click at your location to obtain the specific forecast for you. Take some time to explore the types of forecast products available.

Investigation 14A: ATMOSPHERIC OPTICAL PHENOMENA

Objectives:

Solar radiation, consisting of a range of wavelengths, interacts with matter in many ways. The wavelengths from about 0.4 to 0.7 micrometers (μm) are known as visible light because we sense them with our eyes. Visible light also interacts with the air, cloud and precipitation particles, and aerosols in several ways including scattering, reflection, and refraction. These *optical effects* can produce spectacular displays of light and color. These phenomena also give evidence of processes taking place in the atmosphere that may be harbingers of future weather.

After completing this investigation, you should be able to:

- Explain how light interacts with atmospheric water droplets and ice crystals to form rainbows and halos.
- Describe the implications of these optical phenomena for the state of the atmosphere.

Introduction:

When a light ray crosses an interface from one transparent medium to another (such as from air to water), the speed of light changes. If the angle of the light ray is other than perpendicular to the interface, the direction of motion in the new medium is also altered. This change of direction is described by *Snell's law* which states that when a light ray passes into a medium in which the speed of light is slower, the light ray is bent <u>toward</u> the line perpendicular to the interface (Figure 1). If light speeds up when it enters the second medium, a light ray bends <u>away from</u> the perpendicular. Refraction is the bending of a light ray.

For light passing from air (higher speed) into a hexagonal ice crystal (lower speed), the light ray is bent towards the crystal interior. In exiting from the crystal, it is refracted once more, but in reverse fashion. A hexagonal crystal has six rectangular sides, each of which adjoins adjacent sides at a 120-degree angle, and two ends (hexagonal in shape) which are positioned at a 90-degree angle to the sides. A refracted light ray follows one of two paths through a hexagonal ice crystal: through two sides, or a side and an end. The deflection angle of a ray passing through two sides is 22° from its original direction while that through a side and an end is 46° from its original direction.

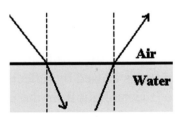

Figure 1. Refraction of a light ray crossing an air-water interface.

Figure 2 approximates the orientation of ice crystals that would interact with light rays to form halos of 22° and 46° relative to the observer. The angle is measured where straight lines drawn from the center of the sun (or moon) and from the halo meet in the observer's eye. Because ice crystals are more or less randomly oriented, the combination of all the rays

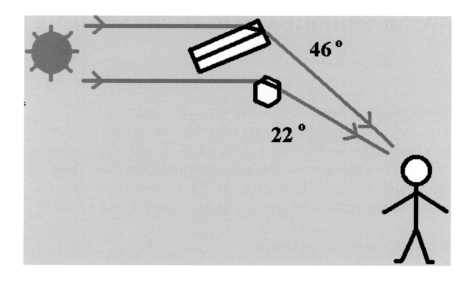

Figure 2. Refraction of sunlight by ice crystals to form a halo (not to scale).

would appear as a circle about the light source. The 22° halo is seen when the light passes in and out of rectangular sides of the ice crystal. The similar process occurs for the 46° halo except the light passes through one side and one end of the crystal. Because there are six sides and only two ends to an ice crystal, probability favors seeing more 22° halos than the 46° kind. The 22° halo is also brighter.

1. As shown in Figure 2, the observer would need to look in the direction [(***towards***) (***away from***)] the sun to see a halo. (Caution: never look directly at the sun! Sky observations near the sun need eye protection or blockage of the sun's direct rays, such as with your hand.)

2. Halos indicate clouds that are composed of [(***ice crystals***) (***liquid droplets***)].

Figure 3 shows, from the perspective of the observer, the circular 22° and 46° halos about the sun position along with a sun pillar and parhelia (sundogs). A sun pillar is a bright column seen above and below the sun position. The pillar is caused by reflection of the sunlight from the upper and lower surfaces of ice crystals with surfaces oriented horizontally, much like looking at a streetlight through partially opened horizontal venetian blinds. This is best seen near sunrise or sunset when the atmosphere is stable and the larger surfaces of the crystals are horizontally oriented.

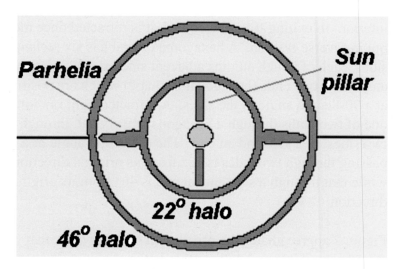

Figure 3. Common halo phenomena about central solar disk (not to scale).

3. *Parhelia*, commonly called sundogs or mock suns, are bright spots sometimes seen at and just outside the 22° halo circle at the same level as the sun. The distance of parhelia from the sun increases with increasing solar altitude; at solar altitudes greater than about 60 degrees, parhelia cannot be observed. They also are primarily formed by the refraction of light from crystals with their rectangular sides oriented vertically. Parhelia and 22° halos, have some coloration caused by refraction of light through the crystals. The term "sundogs" refer to the dogs that followed the mythological chariot of Mercury, the sun god. It [(***would***) (***would not***)] be likely for a sun pillar to be observed during unstable atmospheric conditions.

4. Figure 4 suggests the orientation that raindrops would have to the sun's rays and the observer's location for the formation of a rainbow. The color separation in the primary and secondary rainbows is formed from refraction of the ray both on entering and on leaving a drop. The longer wavelength red light is refracted less than the shorter wavelength violet, resulting in the color separation. The primary rainbow has a single internal reflection of the ray whereas the secondary bow results from [(***one***) (***two***) (***three***)] reflections of the ray inside the drop.

5. Rainbows would be seen by looking generally [(***toward***) (***away from***)] the sun.

6. Observing a rainbow can provide weather forecasting hints. A rainbow seen in the morning would be produced by rain falling generally to the [(***east***) (***west***)] of the observer.

7. Because weather systems generally move from west to east, this bow-producing rainshower would move [(***toward***) (***away from***)] the observer.

8. In a similar way, a rainbow seen in the afternoon is a harbinger of [(***stormy***) (***clearing***)] weather to follow.

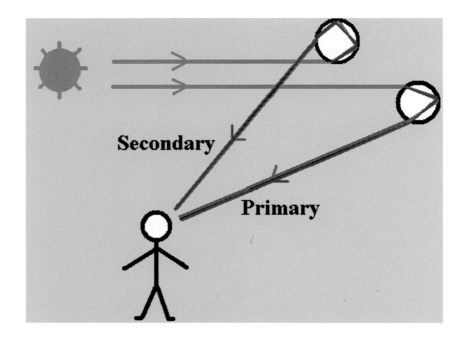

Figure 4. Refraction and reflection of sunlight by water drops to form a rainbow (not to scale).

9. Because raindrops have curved surfaces, one [(**_would_**) (**_would not_**)] expect to see sun pillars or other surface reflection phenomena from raindrops.

10. Rays from drops produce rainbows in circular arcs about the *antisolar* point, the point opposite the sun along a line from the sun through the observer's eyes. The angle measured where straight lines from the antisolar point and from a point on the primary rainbow meet in the observer's eye is about 42°. It is about 50° for the secondary bow. Someone claiming to have seen a rainbow ringing the sun [(**_would be wrong_**) (**_could be right_**)]. Maybe it was a 22° halo which may appear reddish on its inner side.

11. Many raindrops must be involved in order for an observer to see a rainbow. A raindrop must be oriented at an angular width of slightly more than 42° to deliver red to the observer's eye while another drop must at slightly less than 41° to deliver violet. Consequently, red is the [(**_outer_**) (**_inner_**)] color in the arc of a primary rainbow. Millions of raindrops fill in the colors to form the bow that can form a circular arc that sometimes stretches from horizon to horizon.

As directed by your course instructor, complete this investigation by either:

1. ***Going to the Current Weather Studies link on the course website, or***
2. ***Continuing to the Applications section for this investigation that immediately follows in this Investigations Manual.***

Investigation 14A: ATMOSPHERIC OPTICAL PHENOMENA
Applications

Rainbows are produced from light interacting with water drops in the atmosphere. See Figure 5 to view a portion of a rainbow. For other views of rainbows, you can go to the Internet site *http://www.atoptics.co.uk/bows.htm* and click on "A's Dark Band" on the left side bar of the page.

12. The anti-solar point, the point opposite the sun along the line from the sun through the observer's eyes, is to the lower right corner, off the photo in Figure 5. The rainbow forms a circular arc about that point. With the sun in the sky, the anti-solar point is below the horizon so that only a portion of the circle would be seen. Here the arc of the primary rainbow separates the part of the image with the lighter background from the part with the darker background. From the inside of the arc outwards, the colors in the primary rainbow range from [(***red to violet***) (***violet to red***)].

Figure 5: A double rainbow.

13. The primary rainbow is formed from the sun's rays being refracted upon entering a drop, then reflected within the drop, and then refracted again upon leaving the drop. A secondary rainbow would be formed with an additional reflection inside the drop. A faint portion of the secondary rainbow can be seen across the left side of the image. The color sequence in the secondary rainbow is reversed from the primary bow, with reddish hues appearing on the [(***inside***) (***outside***)] of the secondary rainbow arc.

A faint reddish-purple coloration sometimes seen inside the primary bow is called a supernumerary bow. This can be seen in Figure 5. If you go to the Internet site mentioned above, select "Supernumeraries" on the left side bar of the page for a close-up view of a supernumerary bow. It is formed as a diffraction pattern from the primary bow light rays. The darker area between the primary and secondary bows, known as Alexander's dark band, is produced by the absence of rays being directed in those angles by the reflections. More about this phenomenon can be seen by returning to the "A's Dark Band" page.

14. As described earlier in this investigation, light rays may also be reflected and refracted by ice crystals in the atmosphere. Ice crystals interact with light to form halos. Click on the "Ice Halos" to the left and then click on "22° halo" under the image. The ring centering on the sun is a 22-degree halo. The halo is formed by light being refracted through the ice crystals to the observer while the observer looks in the general direction [(***away from***) (***toward***)] the light source.

The atmosphere itself may also refract light to form dramatic optical effects. One may recall the impression that the sun at sunrise or sunset or the moon rising or setting seems particularly large. This view is enhanced by the oval shape imparted to the sun or moon near the horizon. Rays from the bottom and the top of the disk are refracted by differing amounts leaving the oval impression. Figure 6 is a view of a moonrise showing this ovoid shape.

Figure 6. Photograph showing atmospheric refraction of lunar disk near the horizon.

15. The image shows the moon just above the horizon distorted from a circular disc. This departure from a circle results from the moon's rays traveling through layers of air of varying densities near the Earth's surface. For the moon lower on the horizon, the refraction by air should [(***increase***) (***decrease***)]. As the moon rises higher into the sky and consequently is seen through air of more uniform density, the moon's disk appears more circular.

Also of note in the figure is the reddish color of the moon. Light reaching the observer is coming through a relatively long path of atmosphere where the blues and greens of the reflected solar light are absorbed, leaving red. This coloration is from the same process that is responsible for red sunsets and sunrises.

Suggestions for further activities: To view images of rainbows, halos, and other optical phenomena, go to *http://www.atoptics.co.uk/* and *http://www.meteoros.de/indexe.htm.* (Figures 5 and 6 are from NOAA's NWS Forecast Office page at Sullivan, WI.)

Investigation 14B: ATMOSPHERIC REFRACTION

Objectives:

Light does not always travel in straight lines (even though our minds always assume that the light entering our eyes did just that)! Air may be transparent, but it slows the speed of light passing through it slightly compared to light's speed in a vacuum. The greater the number of air molecules encountered, the more the light is slowed. When the sun is close to the horizon, particularly near sunrise or sunset, the sun's rays entering the atmosphere at a low angle must travel through a relatively long air path. Light rays approaching Earth's surface are progressively slowed as they pass through the higher altitude, less dense air into lower altitude, more dense air. Associated with the slowing is a downward "bending" (refraction) of the light ray. You have observed the effects of this when you have viewed sunsets or sunrises.

After completing this investigation, you should be able to:

- Describe how refraction of light varies with solar altitude.
- Explain how solar refraction affects length of daylight.

Introduction:

You can observe the refraction of light passing from a less dense medium into a more dense medium using an opaque cup, a coin, and water. Place the coin at the bottom of the empty cup and look into the cup at an angle such that you cannot quite see the coin over the edge of the cup (Figure 1a). Slowly pour water into the cup, making sure the coin remains in the same position. The coin in the water should appear "magically," as shown in Figure 1b. Reflected light from the coin is refracted when it passes from water to air as shown by the solid-line path.

The total path of air through which a light ray from the sun must pass to an observer varies with the observer's latitude and the time of day. For someone on the equator at local noon on an equinox, the sun is directly overhead at the zenith and its *solar altitude* is 90 degrees. The rays of the sun come straight down and pass through the minimum atmospheric path length.

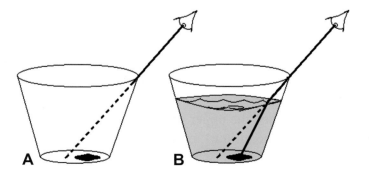

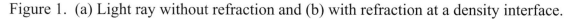

Figure 1. (a) Light ray without refraction and (b) with refraction at a density interface.

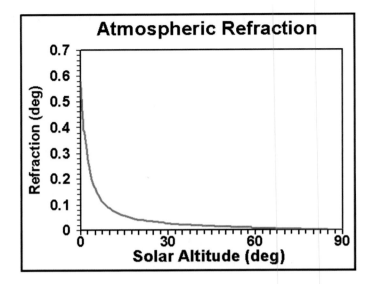

Figure 2. Amount of angular refraction of sunlight as a function of solar altitude.

At sunrise or sunset (solar altitude of 0 degrees), the atmospheric path is maximum in length. The amount of refraction or bending of light rays from the sun due to atmospheric effects can be calculated for the sun's solar altitude angle. Figure 2 shows the amount of refraction that occurs (in degrees) for a clear sky at various solar altitudes.

1. Figure 2 shows that the atmospheric refraction of light [(*increases*) (*decreases*)] as the solar altitude decreases.

2. The maximum amount of atmospheric refraction of a solar ray is [(*less than one degree*) (*several degrees*)] when the sun is on the horizon (solar altitude of 0 degrees).

3. At sunset (or sunrise), the refraction of a sun's ray is 0.58 degrees. The mean angular diameter of the sun's visible disk is approximately 0.53 degrees. (Angular diameter is the angle formed at the observer's eye by two lines drawn from opposite edges of the sun's disk.) Thus, the sun's position may be distorted by the bending of its rays by slightly more than its own diameter. When very near the horizon, the apparent sun (the one we see) is approximately [(*0.5*) (*3*)] degree(s) higher than it would be in the absence of atmospheric refraction. In other words, the sun can be below the horizon when the bent rays give its appearance as being fully above the horizon!

4. Refer to Figure 3 of Investigation 3B. A spherical Earth would be half sunlit at all latitudes on an equinox, except at the poles. Without an atmosphere, the period of daylight at any latitude on Earth (except at the poles) would be [(*11*) (*12*) (*13*)] hours and 0 minutes on that first day of spring or fall.

5. Sunrise or sunset occurs when the upper limb of the sun's visible disk is first or last seen under average atmospheric conditions, on a water horizon.

    As shown in Figure 6 of Investigation 3B, the daily path of the sun through the sky varies at different latitudes on Earth. At the equator, the daily path of the sun is always perpendicular to the horizon. As the latitude increases, the angle between the sun's path through the daytime sky and the horizon [(***increases***) (***decreases***)] until it is nearly parallel to the local horizon at the North and South Poles. Thus, the time it takes the sun to change solar altitude (measured vertically from the horizon) while actually moving steadily along its inclined path will increase with increasing latitude.

In Table 1 that follows, sunrise and sunset times are given for Kampala, Uganda (0.05 degrees N, 32.4 degrees E), Salem, Oregon (44.9 degrees N, 123.0 degrees W), and Alert, Northwest Territories, Canada (82.5 degrees N, 62.3 degrees W) for 21 March (representative of the first day of spring). For each city calculate the total length of daylight for 21 March and the minutes beyond 12 hours due to atmospheric refraction. [Table values were obtained from the US Naval Observatory website: *http://www.usno.navy.mil/*].

Table 1: Sunrise/Sunset Times - 21 March

City	Latitude	Sunrise	Sunset
Kampala	0.1° N	6:54 a.m.	7:01 p.m.
Salem	44.9° N	6:12	6:27
Alert	82.5° N	4:40	5:59

Note: due to the city's location within its time zone and other astronomical factors, the daylight period is not symmetrical about noon.

6. Kampala's hours and minutes of daylight: _____ hrs _____ min.

7. Salem's hours and minutes of daylight: _____ hrs _____ min.

8. Alert's hours and minutes of daylight: _____ hrs _____ min.

9. Kampala's minutes of daylight beyond 12 hours: _____ min.

10. Salem 's minutes of daylight beyond 12 hours: _____ min.

11. Alert 's minutes of daylight beyond 12 hours: _____ min.

12. The number of minutes of daylight beyond twelve hours on 21 March [(***increases***) (***decreases***)] with increasing latitude. The additional daylight time is due to the combination of two factors, the orientation of the sun's path and atmospheric refraction. The smaller the angle of the sun's path to the horizon, the greater the effect of refraction in lengthening the period of daylight.

As directed by your course instructor, complete this investigation by either:

1. ***Going to the Current Weather Studies link on the course website, or***
2. ***Continuing to the Applications section for this investigation that immediately follows in this Investigations Manual.***

Investigation 14B: ATMOSPHERIC REFRACTION
Applications

13. The sunrise/sunset data appearing in Table 1 were taken from tables similar to the example shown in Figure 3 of this investigation. Figure 3 displays "Rise and Set for the Sun for 2007" for Beaver, Alaska, located at 66.4 degrees N. The sunrise and sunset times are given in local Standard Time on a 24-hour clock; for example, 1836 means 6:36 p.m., local Standard Time. The table indicates that on 21 March the sun rises at _____ a.m. and sets at _____ p.m., local Standard Time.

14. The period of sunlight on 21 March is 12 hours and _____ minutes.

15. The number of minutes of daylight beyond 12 hours on 21 March at Beaver [(*fits*) (*does not fit*)] the pattern of change in the length of daylight with increasing latitude shown in Table 1.

Beaver (66.4 degrees N) is located almost exactly on the Arctic Circle (66.5 degrees N). From astronomical considerations based on straight and parallel rays of sunlight striking the Earth, the Arctic Circle (or the Antarctic Circle) should be the lowest latitude at which there would be one continuous 24-hour period of daylight and one continuous 24-hour period of darkness each year.

16. According to the table, the longest continuous daylight period at Beaver is _____ days in length.

17. The shortest period of daylight occurs on or about 21 December (the first day of winter) and is _____ hours and _____ minutes long.

18. Does Beaver fit its Arctic Circle location as described above in terms of periods of daylight and darkness over the period of a year? [(*yes*) (*no*)]

19. Atmospheric refraction is the primary cause of the differences between the periods of daylight that might be expected with straight rays of sunlight striking the Earth's surface and the daylight periods calculated by the U.S. Naval Observatory. It was shown earlier in this investigation that when near the horizon the apparent sun (the one we see) is [(*higher*) (*lower*)] than it would be if there were no atmospheric refraction. Thus, the sun at the Arctic Circle stays continuously above the horizon for considerably more than one day and it never actually goes below the horizon for a continuous 24-hour day.

Suggestions for further activities: The U.S. Naval Observatory provides sunrise and sunset tables for over 22,000 locations in the United States. Go to the following Internet address: *http://aa.usno.navy.mil/data/docs/RS_OneYear.html*. Scroll down to "Form A - Cities or Towns in the U.S." For the current year, specify "sunrise/sunset" table and select the state or territory for your hometown. Type in your hometown or where you live in the U.S., and click on the "Compute Table" button. A table should appear. If the message: *"Unable to find location in our file. Try another location."* is returned, check your spelling or select a nearby larger community.

Print out the table. To print the full 12-month table (you may wish to include it with your study materials for possible future reference), you must use **landscape** orientation and **8-point** type. Your Internet browser contains options (often called "preferences") that allow you to select the font style and size to use for text files such as this ("fixed font"). If you cannot vary these options yourself, contact your instructor or computer resource person. [Note: Be sure to change your font, size, and orientation back to your original settings after printing out the table.]

Astronomical Applications Dept.
U. S. Naval Observatory
Washington, DC 20392-5420

BEAVER, ALASKA
Rise and Set for the Sun for 2006

Alaska Standard Time

Location: W147 23, N66 22

Day	Jan.		Feb.		Mar.		Apr.		May		June		July		Aug.		Sept.		Oct.		Nov.		Dec.	
	Rise	Set	Rise	Set	Rise	Set	Rise	Set	Rise	Set	Rise	Set	Rise	Set	Rise	Set	Rise	Set	Rise	Set	Rise	Set	Rise	Set
	h m	h m	h m	h m	h m	h m	h m	h m	h m	h m	h m	h m	h m	h m	h m	h m	h m	h m	h m	h m	h m	h m	h m	h m
01	1126	1421	0948	1619	0803	1803	0602	1947	0403	2133	0148	2352	****	****	0331	2217	0524	2013	0701	1815	0848	1617	1044	1433
02	1124	1424	0945	1623	0759	1806	0558	1950	0359	2137	0143	2358	****	****	0335	2213	0527	2009	0704	1812	0852	1613	1048	1430
03	1122	1427	0941	1627	0755	1809	0554	1953	0355	2141	0137		****	****	0339	2209	0531	2005	0708	1808	0856	1610	1052	1427
04	1119	1430	0937	1631	0751	1813	0550	1957	0351	2145	0131	0005	0107	0042	0343	2205	0534	2001	0711	1804	0859	1606	1055	1424
05	1117	1434	0934	1635	0747	1816	0546	2000	0347	2149	0124	0012	0120	0029	0347	2201	0537	1957	0714	1800	0903	1602	1059	1421
06	1114	1437	0930	1639	0743	1820	0543	2004	0343	2153	0116	0020	0129	0021	0351	2157	0540	1953	0718	1756	0907	1558	1102	1419
07	1112	1441	0926	1643	0740	1823	0539	2007	0339	2157	0105	0032	0136	0013	0355	2153	0544	1949	0721	1752	0911	1555	1106	1416
08	1109	1445	0922	1646	0736	1826	0535	2010	0334	2201	****	****	0143	0007	0359	2149	0547	1945	0724	1748	0915	1551	1109	1414
09	1106	1448	0919	1650	0732	1830	0531	2014	0330	2205	****	****	0149	0001	0402	2145	0550	1941	0727	1745	0918	1547	1112	1412
10	1103	1452	0915	1654	0728	1833	0527	2017	0326	2209	****	****		2356	0406	2141	0553	1937	0731	1741	0922	1544	1115	1410
11	1100	1456	0911	1658	0724	1837	0523	2021	0322	2213	****	****	0155	2350	0410	2137	0557	1933	0734	1737	0926	1540	1118	1408
12	1057	1500	0907	1701	0720	1840	0519	2024	0318	2217	****	****	0200	2345	0414	2133	0600	1930	0738	1733	0930	1537	1121	1406
13	1054	1503	0904	1705	0716	1843	0515	2028	0314	2221	****	****	0206	2340	0417	2129	0603	1926	0741	1729	0934	1533	1123	1404
14	1051	1507	0900	1709	0712	1847	0511	2031	0310	2226	****	****	0211	2336	0421	2124	0606	1922	0744	1725	0938	1529	1126	1403
15	1048	1511	0856	1712	0709	1850	0507	2035	0305	2230	****	****	0216	2331	0425	2120	0610	1918	0748	1721	0942	1526	1128	1402
16	1044	1515	0852	1716	0705	1853	0503	2038	0301	2234	****	****	0221	2326	0428	2116	0613	1914	0751	1718	0946	1522	1130	1401
17	1041	1519	0849	1720	0701	1857	0459	2042	0257	2238	****	****	0226	2322	0432	2112	0616	1910	0755	1714	0950	1519	1131	1400
18	1038	1523	0845	1723	0657	1900	0455	2045	0253	2243	****	****	0231	2317	0436	2108	0619	1906	0758	1710	0954	1515	1133	1400
19	1034	1527	0841	1727	0653	1903	0451	2049	0248	2247	****	****	0235	2313	0439	2104	0622	1902	0801	1706	0958	1512	1134	1400
20	1031	1531	0837	1731	0649	1907	0447	2052	0244	2252	****	****	0240	2308	0443	2100	0626	1858	0805	1702	1001	1508	1135	1400
21	1027	1535	0833	1734	0645	1910	0443	2056	0240	2256	****	****	0244	2304	0446	2056	0629	1854	0808	1659	1005	1505	1136	1400
22	1024	1539	0830	1738	0641	1913	0439	2100	0235	2301	****	****	0249	2259	0450	2053	0632	1850	0812	1655	1009	1501	1136	1401
23	1020	1543	0826	1741	0637	1917	0435	2103	0231	2305	****	****	0253	2255	0453	2049	0635	1847	0815	1651	1013	1458	1136	1401
24	1017	1547	0822	1745	0634	1920	0431	2107	0227	2310	****	****	0258	2251	0457	2045	0639	1843	0819	1647	1017	1455	1136	1403
25	1013	1551	0818	1749	0630	1923	0427	2111	0222	2315	****	****	0302	2247	0500	2041	0642	1839	0823	1643	1021	1451	1136	1404
26	1010	1555	0814	1752	0626	1927	0423	2114	0217	2320	****	****	0306	2242	0504	2037	0645	1835	0826	1640	1025	1448	1135	1406
27	1006	1559	0810	1756	0622	1930	0419	2118	0213	2325	****	****	0311	2238	0507	2033	0648	1831	0830	1636	1029	1445	1134	1408
28	1003	1603	0807	1759	0618	1933	0415	2122	0208	2330	****	****	0315	2234	0510	2029	0652	1827	0833	1632	1033	1442	1133	1410
29	0959	1607			0614	1937	0411	2126	0203	2335	****	****	0319	2230	0514	2025	0655	1823	0837	1628	1037	1439	1132	1412
30	0956	1611			0610	1940	0407	2129	0158	2341	****	****	0323	2226	0517	2021	0658	1819	0841	1624	1041	1436	1130	1415
31	0952	1615			0606	1943			0153	2346			0327	2221	0521	2017			0844	1621			1128	1417

Add one hour for daylight time, if and when in use.

(**** object continuously above horizon)

(---- object continuously below horizon)

Figure 3. Daily sunrise and sunset times for Beaver, Alaska (66 degrees, 22 minutes N).

Investigation 15A: VISUALIZING CLIMATE

Objectives:

Climate is the synthesis of weather conditions, both the average of parameters, generally temperature and precipitation, over a period of time and the extremes in weather. For this reason, much of the information on climate is given in statistical terms. For greater ease of interpretation, these statistical values are often shown in graphs, typically as the magnitude of the average value (or extremes) versus the months of the year. One form of display that shows the relationships between temperature and precipitation during the yearly cycle is the *climograph*.

After completing this investigation, you should be able to:

- Portray the statistical climate values of mean monthly temperature and average monthly precipitation in the graphical form called the climograph.
- Compare temperature and precipitation distributions on climographs from different locations noting similarities and differences.
- Explain how certain climograph patterns can be explained by various climate controls.
- Relate certain patterns of temperature and precipitation to particular climate classification types.

Introduction:

Every place on Earth has climate characteristics that distinguish it from other places. It is desirable to systematically describe these characteristics so that the climates of various locations can be compared. This investigation focuses on climate as described by averages alone. It is important to remember that by using averages, only a generalized picture of the climate remains. A *climograph* is a commonly used tool to describe the climate of a given place and compare climates in various places. A climograph can be drawn to show monthly mean temperatures and average precipitation totals for a single station through the year on the same graph. Figures 2 - 7 are climographs for six locations in the United States which give examples of major climate types discussed in the Climate Classification, provided in pages 15A-8 to 15A-12.

A climograph can provide at a glance the magnitudes and ranges of monthly mean temperatures and average monthly precipitation throughout the year. These statistics are genetically tied to various climate-controlling factors which vary systematically from place to place. It is possible to relate distributions of temperature and precipitation to specific controls to gain a more comprehensive understanding of the causes of the climate in a specific area. Because these controls and the climates which result have significant impact on other elements of the Earth system (vegetation, soils, weathering rates of rocks, etc.), such an understanding has widespread applications. It is also desirable to have a shorthand classification for the major types of recurrent temperature and precipitation patterns so one may be able to generalize about climates up to the global scale.

1. By convention, climographs are usually constructed with time of year displayed horizontally across the base of the graph. The initial letter of the month is listed at mid-month along the bottom, with the precipitation scale along the left side and mean temperature scale on the right side. Mean monthly precipitation totals (rain plus melted snow) are presented as a bar graph. The mean temperature values are plotted as points connected by a curve. In the U.S., climate data are prepared with precipitation in inches and temperatures in degrees Fahrenheit. **Use the data and grid in Figure 1 below to make a climograph for Boston, MA. Mark a short horizontal line at mid-month to note the position of the mean total precipitation value of that month and fill in the space below to create a bar. (Use Figures 2 - 7 as a guide.) Place a dot at mid-month at the level denoting the mean monthly temperature value. When all the months are plotted, connect the dots with curved line segments to represent the march of average monthly temperature.**

    Your completed climograph for Boston, MA (Figure 1) shows that the mean monthly temperature rises from near freezing during the winter months (Dec., Jan., and Feb.) to means around 70 °F during the summer months (June, Jul, and Aug) and then falls as winter approaches. The observed temperatures from which the means are computed result mainly from the seasonal swing of solar heating, which in turn is largely determined by latitude. As a general rule, the higher the latitude the lower the winter season temperatures. The lowest mean monthly temperature in Boston occurs in [(*__January__*) (*__December__*)].

2. This minimum monthly temperature [(*__is__*) (*__is not__*)] within a month or so of the time of minimum solar heating in a mid-latitude, Northern Hemisphere location.

3. Where solar heating varies significantly from the winter to summer solstices, the range of temperatures, indicated by the amplitude of the temperature curve on a climograph, is relatively great. Where the amplitude is relatively small, the seasonal temperature contrast is also small. Examine the temperature curve on the climograph for Hilo, HI (Figure 2). The range of mean monthly temperatures for Hilo is about [(*__20__*) (*__5__*) (*__30__*)] Fahrenheit degrees.

4. From the shape of the curve and range of temperature, it is evident that Hilo experiences relatively [(*__little__*) (*__significant__*)] variation in solar heating through the course of a year.

5. The highest mean monthly temperature in Hilo occurs in August. This temperature is about [(*__76__*) (*__86__*)] °F.

6. The lowest mean monthly temperature is about [(*__71__*) (*__81__*)] °F. in both January and February.

Month	Temp.(F)	Precip.(in)
J	29.3	3.92
F	31.5	3.30
M	38.9	3.85
A	48.3	3.60
M	58.5	3.24
J	68.0	3.22
J	73.9	3.06
A	72.3	3.37
S	64.7	3.47
O	54.1	3.79
N	44.9	3.98
D	34.8	3.73

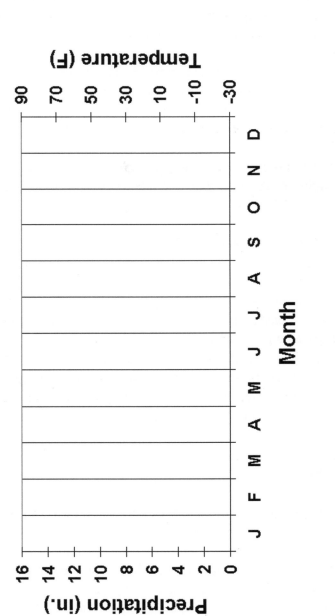

Boston (42 N, 71 W)

Figure 1. Humid Continental Climate (Dfa) - Boston.

7. These temperatures suggest that Hilo is a [(***high***) (***low***)] latitude location.

8. The month of occurrence of the highest mean temperature suggests that Hilo is located in the [(***Northern***) (***Southern***)] Hemisphere.

9. Temperature and temperature range can also be influenced by large bodies of water (ocean or large lake). Generally speaking, a maritime influence will moderate temperatures in places that would normally be colder in winter and warmer in summer based on latitude alone. The seasonal range in temperatures is likely to be less due to a maritime influence; that is, the temperature curve on the climograph will exhibit less amplitude. In continental locations or locations downwind of large land masses temperatures tend to be higher in summer and lower in winter. As a result, the seasonal temperature range will be far greater than for places surrounded by or downwind of a large water body. It is likely that Hilo's relatively low annual temperature range [(***is***) (***is not***)] also moderated by the surrounding Pacific Ocean.

10. Examine the climograph for Fairbanks, AK (Figure 6). The highest mean monthly temperature is [(***62***) (***82***)] °F.

11. The lowest monthly mean temperature for Fairbanks is [(***-10***) (***10***)] °F.

12. These temperatures suggest that Fairbanks is a [(***high***) (***low***)] latitude location.
13. The average monthly temperatures in Fairbanks cover a range of about [(***70***) (***50***) (***30***)] Fahrenheit degrees.

14. This range of temperatures suggests that Fairbanks has a [(***continental***) (***maritime***)] climate.

15. Compare the annual temperature range for Boston, on the Atlantic coast, (Figure 1) and Seattle, WA, near the Pacific coast, (Figure 5). Seattle's annual temperature range is [(***greater than***) (***less than***)] that of Boston.

16. These cities are at approximately the same latitude and both are located near the coast. The climate control causing the difference in annual temperature range is the influence of the prevailing westerly wind at both locations. For Seattle, the temperature range is influenced mainly by the [(***ocean***) (***continent***)] which is upwind and in Boston by winds blowing from the continent.

17. Climate classification systems allow climate differences and similarities to be expressed in a "shorthand" form. The broad-scale climate boundaries in the *Köppen* climate classification system (see Climate Classification on pages 15A-9 to 15A-13) are based on patterns in annual and monthly mean temperature and precipitation, which closely correspond to the limits of vegetative communities. The major classifications of *Tropical Humid* (A), *Subtropical* (C), *Snow Forest* (D), and *Polar* (E) are based on temperature; the group *Dry* (B) is based on precipitation; and the group *Highland* (H) applies to

Hilo (19 N, 155 W)

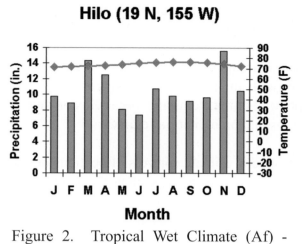

Figure 2. Tropical Wet Climate (Af) - Hilo.

Tucson (32 N, 111 W)

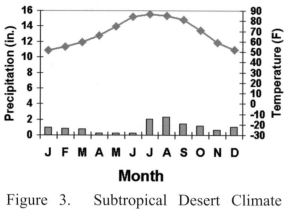

Figure 3. Subtropical Desert Climate (BWh) - Tucson.

Atlanta (33 N, 84 W)

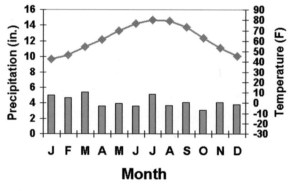

Figure 4. Subtropical Humid Climate (Cfa) - Atlanta.

Seattle (47 N, 122 W)

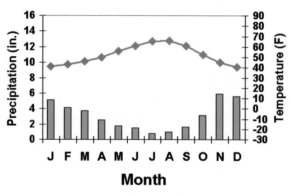

Figure 5. Marine West Coast Climate (Cfb) - Seattle.

Fairbanks (64 N, 147 W)

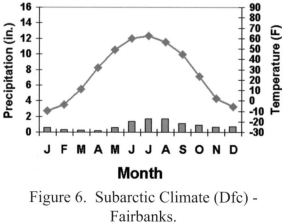

Figure 6. Subarctic Climate (Dfc) - Fairbanks.

Barrow (71 N, 156 W)

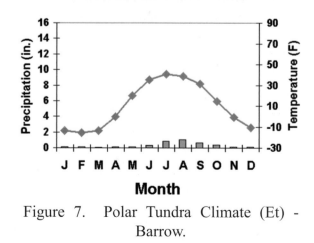

Figure 7. Polar Tundra Climate (Et) - Barrow.

mountainous regions. Temperatures for both Fairbanks and Boston place them in the [(***Tropical Humid (A)***) (***Subtropical (C)***) (***Snow Forest (D)***) (***Polar (E)***)] classification.

18. The second letter of the Boston (Figure 1) and Fairbanks (Figure 6) classification corresponds to seasonal precipitation regimes with an "f" signifying year-round precipitation. According to their climographs and climate classifications, Boston and Fairbanks have [(***similar***) (***very different***)] seasonal precipitation regimes.

19. Arid and Semiarid climates can be caused by several climate controls. Locations on the eastern side of planetary-scale, persistent high pressure systems, such as those occurring around 30 degrees N in the Atlantic and Pacific, experience subsiding air, which inhibits cloud formation and precipitation. The west side of such systems, by contrast, tend to be humid. The cause of dryness in Tucson AZ, for example, is due mainly to its position [(***east***) (***west***)] of a subtropical high pressure system which persists off the southwest U.S. coast in the Pacific.

20. Atlanta, GA at about the same latitude as Tucson, but in the southeastern United States, is humid because it is located [(***east***) (***west***)] of such a high pressure system in the Atlantic.

21. Dry or wet conditions can also be caused by location upwind or downwind of a mountain range. Areas to the lee of high mountains tend to be dry because of the "wringing out" of moisture on the wet, windward slopes (due to orographic lifting, cooling and condensation) and the compressional warming of air which occurs as the air descends on the leeward slopes. The atmospheric stability caused by cold ocean currents offshore can also prevent precipitation by stabilizing the air and inhibiting convection. Instability can occur if ocean currents are warm. The dryness of Tucson, which is downwind of the Coastal Ranges and the cold California Current, is [(***probably***) (***not likely***)] drier because of the influence of mountains and ocean currents.

As directed by your course instructor, complete this investigation by either:

1. *Going to the Current Weather Studies link on the course website, or*
2. *Continuing to the Applications section for this investigation that immediately follows in this Investigations Manual.*

Investigation 15A: VISUALIZING CLIMATE
Applications

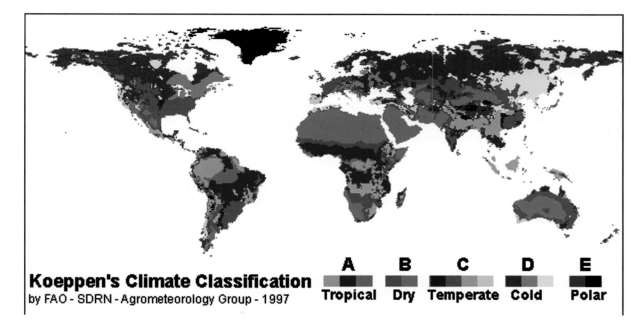

Figure 8. Koeppen's Climate classification. (Adapted from UN Food and Agriculture Organization, Sustainable Development website.)

22. The Figure 8 world map showing the Koeppen (or Köppen) climate classification demonstrates the actual application of climatic controls. For example, on this Mercator projection map, horizontal lines are constant latitudes. Therefore, at similar latitudes across the Eurasian land mass, Europe to the west is shown in purple, indicating a temperate climate while eastern Asia is in yellow indicating a cold type climate. The climate control primarily at work in these local climate types is the prevailing wind circulation in relation to [(***elevation***) (***proximity to large bodies of water***) (***Earth's surface characteristics***)].

23. The region of Tibet in south central Asia is shown in the greenish-brown of a polar type climate although it is surrounded by dry or temperate climates. This classification is most likely the result of Tibet's [(***elevation***) (***proximity to large bodies of water***) (***Earth's surface characteristics***)]

Suggestions for further activities: You can make your own climographs with monthly average temperatures and precipitation totals from *http://www.worldclimate.com*. Monthly and annual values are provided in both English and metric units. By inputting data to spreadsheet software, graphing can be easily accomplished allowing comparisons among stations.

CLIMATE CLASSIFICATION

- Tropical Humid Climates
- Dry Climates
- Subtropical Climates
- Snow Forest Climates
- Polar Climates
- Highland Climates

One of the most widely used climate classification systems was designed by German climatologist and plant geographer Wladimir Köppen (1846-1940) and subsequently modified by his students R. Geiger and W. Pohl. The Köppen system is an empirical approach to organizing Earth's myriad of climate types. Recognizing that indigenous vegetation is a natural indicator of regional climate, Köppen and his students looked for patterns in annual and monthly mean temperature and precipitation, which closely correspond to the limits of vegetative communities thereby revealing broad-scale climatic boundaries throughout the world. Records of annual and monthly mean temperature and precipitation are sufficiently long and reliable in many parts of the world that they serve as a good first approximation of climate. Since its introduction in the early 1900s, Köppen's climate classification has undergone numerous and substantial revisions by Köppen himself and by other climatologists and has had a variety of applications.

As shown in the Table below, the Köppen climate classification system identifies six main climate groups; four are based on temperature, one is based on precipitation, and one applies to mountainous regions. Köppen's scheme uses letters to symbolize major climatic groups: (A) Tropical Humid, (B) Dry, (C) Subtropical (Mesothermal), (D) Snow Forest (Microthermal), (E) Polar, and (H) Highland. Additional letters further differentiate climate types.

Tropical Humid Climates

Tropical humid climates (A) constitute a discontinuous belt straddling the equator and extending poleward to near the Tropic of Cancer in the Northern Hemisphere and the Tropic of Capricorn in the Southern Hemisphere. Mean monthly temperatures are high and exhibit little variability throughout the year. The mean temperature of the coolest month is no lower than 18 °C (64 °F), and there is no frost. The temperature contrast between the warmest and coolest month is typically less than 10 Celsius degrees (18 Fahrenheit degrees). In fact, the diurnal (day-to-night) temperature range generally exceeds the annual temperature range. This monotonous air temperature regime is the consequence of consistently intense incoming solar radiation associated with a high maximum solar altitude and little variation in the period of daylight throughout the year.

Although tropical humid climate types are not readily distinguishable on the basis of temperature, important differences occur in precipitation regime. Tropical humid climates are subdivided into tropical wet (Af), tropical monsoon (Am), and tropical wet-and-dry (Aw). Although these climate types generally feature abundant annual rainfall, more than 100 cm (40 in.) on average, their rainy seasons differ in length and, in the case of Am and Aw, there is a pronounced dry season and wet season. In tropical wet climates, the yearly average rainfall of 175 to 250 cm (70 to 100 in.) supports the world's most luxurious vegetation. Tropical rainforests occupy the Amazon Basin of Brazil, the Congo Basin of Africa, and the islands of Micronesia. For the most part, rainfall is distributed uniformly throughout the year, although some areas experience a brief (one or two month) dry season. Rainfall occurs as heavy downpours in frequent thunderstorms triggered by local convection and the intertropical convergence zone (ITCZ). Convection is largely controlled by solar radiation and rainfall typically peaks in midafternoon, the warmest time of day. Because the water vapor concentration is very high, even the slightest cooling at night leads to saturated air and the formation of dew or radiation fog, giving these regions a sultry, steamy appearance.

TABLE
Köppen-Based Climate Classification

Tropical humid (A)
    Af   tropical wet
    Am   tropical monsoon
    Aw   tropical wet-and-dry

Dry (B)
    BS   steppe or semiarid (BSh, BSk)
    BW   arid or desert (BWh, BWk)
    BWn foggy desert

Subtropical (C)
    Cs   subtropical dry summer (Csa, Csb)
    Cw   subtropical dry winter
    Cf   subtropical humid (Cfa, Cfb, Cfc)

Snow forest (D)
    Dw   dry winter (Dwa, Dwb, Dwc, Dwd)
    Df   year-round precip. (Dfa, Dfb, Dfc, Dfd)
    Ds   dry summer

Polar (E)
    Et   tundra
    Ef   ice cap

Highland (H)

Tropical monsoon (Am) climates feature a seasonal rainfall regime with extremely heavy rainfall during several months and a lengthy dry season. The principal control for these climates involves seasonal shifts in wind from land to sea, typified by the Asian monsoon. During the low-sun season, high air pressure over the Asian continent causes dry air to flow southward into parts of Southeast Asia and India. During the high-sun season, low air pressure covers the Tibetan Plateau and the winds reverse direction, advecting moisture inland from over the Indian Ocean. Local convection, orographic lifting, and shifts of the ITCZ combine to deluge the land with torrential rains. Am climates also occur in western Africa and northeastern Brazil.

For the most part, tropical wet-and-dry climates (Aw) border tropical wet climates (Af) and are transitional to subtropical dry climates in a poleward direction. Aw climates support the savanna, tropical grasslands with scattered deciduous trees. Summers are wet and winters are dry, with the dry season lengthening poleward. This marked seasonality of rainfall is linked to shifts of the intertropical convergence zone (ITCZ) and semipermanent subtropical anticyclones, which follow the seasonal excursions of the sun. In summer (*high-sun* season), surges of the ITCZ trigger convective rainfall; in winter (*low-sun* season), the dry eastern flank of the subtropical anticyclones dominates the weather.

The annual mean temperature in Aw climates is only slightly lower, and the seasonal temperature range is only slightly greater, than in the tropical wet climates (Af). The diurnal temperature range varies seasonally, however. In summer, frequent cloudy skies and high humidity suppress the diurnal temperature range by reducing both solar heating during the day and radiational cooling at night. In winter, on the other hand, persistent fair skies have the opposite effect on radiational heating and cooling and increase the diurnal temperature range. Cloudy, rainy summers plus dry winters also mean that the year's highest temperatures typically occur toward the close of the dry season in late spring.

Dry Climates

Dry climates (B) characterize those regions where average annual potential evaporation exceeds average annual precipitation. *Potential evaporation* is the quantity of water that would vaporize into the atmosphere from a surface of fresh water during long-term average weather conditions. Air temperature largely governs the rate of evaporation so it is not possible to specify some maximum rainfall amount as the criterion for dry climates. Rainfall is not only limited in B climates but also highly variable and unreliable. As a general rule, the lower the mean annual rainfall, the greater is its variability from one year to the next.

Earth's dry climates encompass a larger land area than any other single climate grouping. Perhaps 30% of the planet's land surface, stretching from the tropics into midlatitudes, experience a moisture deficit of varying degree. These are the climates of the world's deserts and steppes, where vegetation is sparse and equipped with special adaptations that permit survival under conditions of severe moisture stress. Based on the degree of dryness, we distinguish between two dry climate types: steppe or semiarid (BS) and arid or desert (BW). Steppe or semiarid climates are transitional between more humid climates and arid or desert climates. Mean annual temperature is latitude dependent, as is the range in variation of mean monthly temperatures through the year. Hence, a distinction is made between warm dry climates of tropical latitudes (BSh and BWh) and cold, dry climates of higher latitudes (BSk and BWk).

Dryness is the consequence of subtropical anticyclones, cold surface ocean currents, or the rain shadow effect of high mountain ranges. Subsiding stable air on the eastern flanks of subtropical anticyclones gives rise to tropical dry climates (BSh and BWh). These huge semipermanent pressure systems, centered over the ocean basins, dominate the weather year-round near the Tropics of Cancer and Capricorn. Consequently, dry climates characterize North Africa eastward to northwest India, the southwestern United States and northern Mexico, coastal Chile and Peru, southwest Africa, and much of the interior of Australia.

Although persistent and abundant sunshine is generally the rule in dry tropical climates, there are some important exceptions. Where cold ocean waters border a coastal desert, a shallow layer of stable marine air drifts inland. The desert air thus features high relative humidity, persistent low stratus clouds and fog, and considerable dew formation. Examples are the Atacama Desert of Peru and Chile, the Namib Desert of southwest Africa, and portions of the coastal Sonoran Desert of Baja California and stretches of the coastal Sahara Desert of northwest Africa. These anomalous foggy desert climates are designated BWn.

Cold, dry climates of higher latitudes (BWk and BSk) are situated in the rain shadows of great mountain ranges. They occur primarily in the Northern Hemisphere, to the lee of the Sierra Nevada and Cascade ranges in North America and the Himalayan chain in Asia. Because these dry climates are at higher latitudes than their tropical counterparts, mean annual temperatures are lower and the seasonal temperature contrast is greater. Anticyclones dominate winter, bringing cold and dry conditions, whereas summers are hot and generally dry. Scattered convective showers, mostly in summer, produce relatively meager precipitation.

Subtropical Climates

Subtropical climates are located just poleward of the Tropics of Cancer and Capricorn and are dominated by seasonal shifts of subtropical anticyclones. There are three basic climate types: subtropical dry summer (or *Mediterranean*) (Cs), subtropical dry winter (Cw), and subtropical humid (Cf), which receive precipitation throughout the year.

Mediterranean climates occur on the western side of continents between about 30 and 45 degrees latitude. In North America, mountain ranges confine this climate to a narrow coastal strip of California. Elsewhere, Cs climates rim the Mediterranean Sea and occur in portions of extreme southern Australia. Summers are dry because at that time of year Cs regions are under the influence of stable subsiding air on the eastern flanks of the semi-permanent subtropical highs. Equatorward shift of subtropical highs in autumn allows extra-tropical cyclones to migrate inland, bringing moderate winter rainfall. Mean annual precipitation varies greatly-ranging from 30 to 300 cm (12 to 80 in.) with the wettest winter month typically receiving at least three times the precipitation of the driest summer month.

Although Mediterranean climates exhibit a pronounced seasonality in precipitation (dry summers and wet winters), the temperature regime is quite variable. In coastal areas, cool onshore breezes prevail, lowering the mean annual temperature and reducing seasonal temperature contrasts. Well inland, however, away from the ocean's moderating influence, summers are considerably warmer; hence, inland mean annual temperatures are higher and seasonal temperature contrasts are greater than in coastal Cs localities. Climatic records of coastal San Francisco and inland Sacramento, CA illustrate the contrast in temperature regime within Cs regions. Although the two cities are separated by only about 145 km (90 mi.), the climate of Sacramento is much more continental (much warmer summers and somewhat cooler winters) than that of San Francisco. The warm climate subtype is designated Csa and the cooler subtype is Csb.

Subtropical dry winter climates (Cw) are transitional between Aw and BS climates and located in South America and Africa between 20 and 30 degrees S. Cw climates also occur between the Aw and H climates of the Himalayas and Tibetan plateau and between the BS and Cfa climates of Southeast and East Asia. Northward shift of the subtropical high pressure systems is responsible for the dry winter in South America and Africa. The narrowness of the two continents between 20 and 30 degrees S means a relatively strong maritime influence and dictates against extreme dryness. In spring, subtropical highs shift southward and rains return. In Asia, winter dryness is caused by winds radiating outward from the massive cold Siberian high. As the continent warms in spring, the Siberian high weakens and eventually is replaced by low pressure. Moist winds then flow inland bringing summer rains. Mean annual precipitation in Cw climates is in the range of 75 to 150 cm (30 to 60 in.).

Subtropical humid climates (Cf) occur on the eastern side of continents between about 25 and 40 degrees latitude (and even more poleward where the maritime influence is strong). Cfa climates are the most important of the Cf climate subtypes in terms of land area and number of people impacted. Cfa climates are situated primarily in the southeastern United States, a portion of southeastern South America, eastern China, southern Japan, on the extreme southeastern coast of South Africa, and along much of the east coast of Australia. These climates feature abundant precipitation (75 to 200 cm, or 30 to 80 in., on average annually), which is distributed throughout the year. In summer, Cfa regions are dominated by a flow of sultry maritime tropical air on the western flanks of the subtropical anticyclones. Consequently, summers are hot and humid with frequent thunderstorms, which can produce brief periods of substantial rainfall. Hurricanes and tropical storms contribute significant rainfall (up to 15% to 20% of the annual total) to some North American and Asian Cfa regions, especially from summer through autumn. In winter, after the subtropical highs shift toward the equator, Cfa regions come under the influence of migrating extratropical cyclones and anticyclones.

In Cfa localities, summers are hot and winters are mild. Mean temperatures of the warmest month are typically in the range of 24 to 27 °C (75 to 81 °F). Average temperatures for the coolest months typically range from 4 to 13 °C (39 to 55 °F). Subfreezing temperatures and snowfalls are infrequent.

A strong maritime influence is responsible for the cool summers and mild winters of Cfb climates. These climates occur over much of Northwest Europe, New Zealand, and portions of southeastern South America, southern Africa, and Australia. The coldest subtype, the Cfc, is relegated to coastal areas of southern Alaska, Norway, and the southern half of Iceland. Cfb and Cfc climates are relatively humid with mean annual precipitation ranging between 100 and 200 cm (40 and 80 in.).

Snow Forest Climates

Snow forest climates (D) occur in the interior and to the leeward sides of large continents. The name emphasizes the link between biogeography and the Köppen climate classification system. These climates feature cold snowy winters (except for the Dw subtype in which the winter is dry) and occur only in the Northern Hemisphere. Snow forest climates are subdivided according to seasonal precipitation regimes with Df climates experiencing year-round precipitation whereas Dw climates have a dry winter. D climates with dry summers (Ds) are rare and small in extent. Additional distinction is made between warmer subtypes (Dwa, Dfa, Dwb, and Dfb) and colder subtypes (Dwc, Dfc, Dwd, Dfd).

The warmer subtypes, sometimes termed *temperate continental*, have warm summers (mean temperature of the warmest month greater than 22 °C or 71 °F) and cold winters. They are located in Eurasia, the northeastern third of the United States, southern Canada, and extreme eastern Asia. Continentality increases inland with maximum temperature contrasts between the coldest and warmest months as great as 25 to 35 Celsius degrees (45 to 63 Fahrenheit degrees). The southerly Dfa climates have cool winters and warm summers and the more northerly Dfb climates have cold winters and mild summers. The freeze-free period varies in length from 7 months in the south to only 3 months in the north. The weather in these regions is very changeable and dynamic because these areas are swept by extra-tropical cyclones and anticyclones and by surges of contrasting air masses. Polar front cyclones dominate winter, bringing episodes of light to moderate frontal precipitation. These storms are followed by incursions of dry polar and arctic air masses. In summer, cyclones are weak and infrequent as the principal storm track shifts poleward. Summer rainfall is mostly convective, and locally amounts can be very heavy in severe thunderstorms and mesoscale convective complexes (MCCs). Although precipitation is distributed rather uniformly throughout the year, most places experience a summer maximum.

In northern portions, winter snowfall becomes an important factor in the climate. Mean annual snowfall and the persistence of a snow cover increase northward. Because of its high albedo for solar radiation and its efficient emission of infrared, a snow cover chills and stabilizes the overlying air. For these reasons, a snow cover tends to be self-sustaining; once established in early winter, an extensive snow cover tends to persist.

Moving poleward, summers get colder and winters are bitterly cold. These so-called *boreal climates* (Dfc, Dfd, Dwc, Dwd) occur only in the Northern Hemisphere as an east-west band between 50 to 55 degrees N and 65 degrees N. It is a region of extreme continentality and very low mean annual temperature. Summers are short and cool, and winters are long and bitterly cold. Because midsummer freezes are possible, the growing season is precariously short. Both continental polar (cP) and arctic (A) air masses originate here, and this area is the site of an extensive coniferous (boreal) forest. In summer, the mean position of the leading edge of arctic air (the arctic front) is located along the northern border of the boreal forest. In winter, the mean position of the arctic front is situated along the southern border of the boreal forest.

Weak cyclonic activity occurs throughout the year and yields meager annual precipitation (typically less than 50 cm, or 20 in.). Convective activity is rare. A summer precipitation maximum is due to the winter dominance of cold, dry air masses. Snow cover persists throughout the winter and the range in mean temperature between winter and summer is among the greatest in the world.

Polar Climates

Polar climates (E) occur poleward of the Arctic and Antarctic circles. These boundaries correspond roughly to localities where the mean temperature for the warmest month is 10 °C (50 °F). These limits also approximate the tree line, the poleward limit of tree growth. Poleward are tundra and the Greenland and Antarctic ice sheets. A distinction is made between tundra (Et) and ice cap (Ef) climates, with the dividing criterion being 0 °C (32 °F) for the mean temperature of the warmest month. Vegetation is sparse in Et regions and almost nonexistent in Ef areas.

Polar climates are characterized by extreme cold and slight precipitation, which falls mostly in the form of snow (less than 25 cm, or 10 in., melted, per year). Greenland and Antarctica could be considered deserts for lack of significant precipitation, despite the presence of large ice sheets. Although summers are cold, the winters are so extremely cold that polar climates feature a marked seasonal temperature contrast. Mean annual temperatures are the lowest of any place in the world.

Highland Climates

Highland Climates (H) encompass a wide variety of climate types that characterize mountainous terrain. Altitude, latitude, and exposure are among the factors that shape a complexity of climate types. For example, temperature decreases rapidly with increasing altitude and windward slopes tend to be wetter than leeward slopes. Climate-ecological zones are telescoped in mountainous terrain. That is, in ascending several thousand meters of altitude, we encounter the same bioclimatic zones that we would experience in traveling several thousand kilometers of latitude. As a general rule, every 300 m (980 ft) of elevation corresponds roughly to a northward advance of 500 km (310 mi).

Investigation 15B: LOCAL CLIMATE DATA

Objectives:

Climate data are extremely useful for many purposes. Farmers use their knowledge of weather and climate over a long period to determine what crops to plant and for guidance on when to plant and harvest. Utilities use climate data for planning production and distribution of energy supplies and the reallocation among types of such supplies. The building industry uses climate data in the design of structures, including their necessary strength, and the associated building codes that regulate them. These are just a few of the multitude of uses for climate data.

In the U.S., weather data are gathered by NOAA's National Weather Service offices and other organizations and compiled at state, regional, and national centers for distribution to users. NOAA's National Climatic Data Center in Asheville, NC is responsible for compiling U.S. data as well as being a depository for much worldwide data on weather and the environment. This information, in turn, is made available to users in print, CD-ROM, and online electronic formats.

After completing this investigation, you should be able to:

- Interpret information appearing in *Local Climatic Data, Annual Summary with Comparative Data* based on weather data collected at a local National Weather Service office.
- Determine how to access archived climate data from National Climatic Data Center (NCDC).

Introduction:

A basic publication of the National Climatic Data Center based on weather data from local National Weather Service (NWS) offices is the *Local Climatological Data* (LCD). It is published in monthly and annual summaries. LCDs are published for about 275 NWS observing sites. Portions of the *LCD, Annual Summary with Comparative Data*, for Grand Island, Nebraska (GRI) for the year 2005 are used in this investigation. Grand Island is located near the geographic center of the coterminous United States.

1. **Examine the temperature graph appearing on the report's front page (Figure 1)**. Daily temperature ranges are plotted as vertical lines on the graph. The top end of each line signifies the maximum daily temperature and the bottom end reports the day's minimum temperature. Assuming that frost occurs if the temperature falls to 32 °F or lower, the approximate date of the last spring frost in 2005 was about [(*3*) (*16*) (*25*)] May.

2. The date of the year's first fall frost was about [(*2*) (*15*) (*30*)] September.

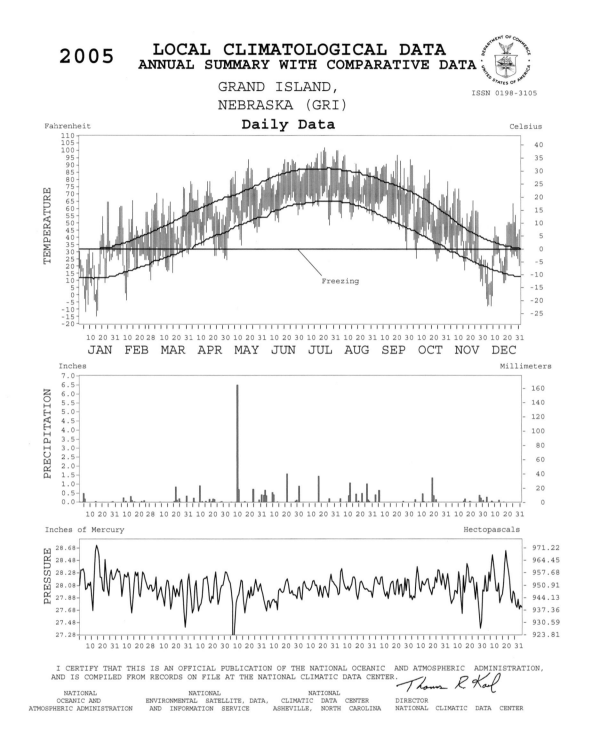

2005 **LOCAL CLIMATOLOGICAL DATA**
ANNUAL SUMMARY WITH COMPARATIVE DATA

GRAND ISLAND,
NEBRASKA (GRI)

ISSN 0198-3105

Daily Data

I CERTIFY THAT THIS IS AN OFFICIAL PUBLICATION OF THE NATIONAL OCEANIC AND ATMOSPHERIC ADMINISTRATION,
AND IS COMPILED FROM RECORDS ON FILE AT THE NATIONAL CLIMATIC DATA CENTER.

NATIONAL	NATIONAL	NATIONAL	
OCEANIC AND	ENVIRONMENTAL SATELLITE, DATA,	CLIMATIC DATA CENTER	DIRECTOR
ATMOSPHERIC ADMINISTRATION	AND INFORMATION SERVICE	ASHEVILLE, NORTH CAROLINA	NATIONAL CLIMATIC DATA CENTER

Figure 1. Local Climatological Data, Annual Summary, Grand Island, NE 2005, cover.

Examine page 2 (Figure 2) of the *LCD, Annual Summary* entitled, "METEOROLOGICAL DATA FOR 2005" and answer the following questions:

3. What month had the lowest average temperature ("Average Dry Bulb")? _____.

4. What was the average temperature that month? _____°F.

5. What month had the highest average temperature? _____

6. What was that temperature? _____°F.

7. How many days in the year had temperatures of 90 °F or higher? _____.

8. How many had temperatures of 0 °F or lower? _____.

9. On how many days in the year were thunderstorms reported? _____.

10. The strongest gust of wind, as reported in the Maximum 5-Second Wind category was a speed of _____ mph.

11. This occurred on _____ and _____ (dates).

12. The total precipitation for the year (Water Equivalent: Total) was _____ in.

13. The total number of days when there was at least a trace of precipitation (equal to or greater than 0.01 in.) was _____.

14. The greatest 24-hour snowfall during the year was _____ in.

15. This occurred on _____ (date).

METEOROLOGICAL DATA FOR 2005
GRAND ISLAND, NE (GRI)

LATITUDE: 40° 57' 30" N	LONGITUDE: 98° 18' 45" W	ELEVATION (FT): GRND: 1841 BARO: 1844	TIME ZONE: CENTRAL (UTC + 6)	WBAN: 14935

	ELEMENT	JAN	FEB	MAR	APR	MAY	JUN	JUL	AUG	SEP	OCT	NOV	DEC	YEAR
TEMPERATURE °F	MEAN DAILY MAXIMUM	29.4	45.4	54.4	63.7	73.5	83.5	89.4	84.6	83.2	68.2	54.1	35.3	63.7
	HIGHEST DAILY MAXIMUM	65	66	75	79	94	94	102	100	97	94	79	64	102
	DATE OF OCCURRENCE	25+	14	28	19+	21	26+	23	03+	21	02	02	26	JUL 23
	MEAN DAILY MINIMUM	13.7	23.6	27.4	40.0	48.8	61.8	65.3	63.0	56.2	41.9	29.7	17.5	40.7
	LOWEST DAILY MINIMUM	-14	-3	11	28	25	51	49	53	32	24	10	-7	-14
	DATE OF OCCURRENCE	15	09	01	24+	03	15	27	14	29	24	29	08+	JAN 15
	AVERAGE DRY BULB	21.6	34.5	40.9	51.9	61.2	72.7	77.4	73.8	69.7	55.1	41.9	26.4	52.3
	MEAN WET BULB	20.0	30.5	35.0	46.4	53.8	65.6	67.8	66.7	60.8	47.4	35.9		
	MEAN DEW POINT	16.6	25.4	26.3	40.3	47.5	61.6	62.7	63.1	55.3	41.4	28.9		
	NUMBER OF DAYS WITH:													
	MAXIMUM ≥ 90°	0	0	0	0	1	9	14	7	5	3	0	0	39
	MAXIMUM ≤ 32°	19	2	0	0	0	0	0	0	0	0	4	14	39
	MINIMUM ≤ 32°	31	25	25	5	3	0	0	0	1	7	19	29	145
	MINIMUM ≤ 0°	7	1	0	0	0	0	0	0	0	0	0	5	13
H/C	HEATING DEGREE DAYS	1340	845	739	391	177	4	4	1	39	349	685	1186	5760
	COOLING DEGREE DAYS	0	0	0	2	66	240	393	282	185	46	0	0	1214
RH	MEAN (PERCENT)	83	74	61	68	64	70	63	74	64	66	65	77	69
	HOUR 00 LST	86	78	69	76	77	78	74	85	74	76	72	82	77
	HOUR 06 LST	85	86	80	86	83	86	81	91	84	86	78	84	84
	HOUR 12 LST	78	65	50	57	51	60	49	58	49	51	54	68	58
	HOUR 18 LST	83	65	44	52	48	55	50	59	47	54	60	76	58
S	PERCENT POSSIBLE SUNSHINE													
W/O	NUMBER OF DAYS WITH:													
	HEAVY FOG(VISBY ≤ 1/4 MI)	5	5	0	0	0	1	0	2	0	2	2	0	17
	THUNDERSTORMS	0	0	0	2	6	5	2	6	2	1	0	0	24
CLOUDINESS	SUNRISE-SUNSET: (OKTAS)													
	CEILOMETER (≤ 12,000 FT.)													
	SATELLITE (> 12,000 FT.)													
	MIDNIGHT-MIDNIGHT: (OKTAS)													
	CEILOMETER (≤ 12,000 FT.)													
	SATELLITE (> 12,000 FT.)													
	NUMBER OF DAYS WITH:													
	CLEAR													
	PARTLY CLOUDY													
	CLOUDY													
PR	MEAN STATION PRESS. (IN.)	28.21	28.12	27.95	27.98		27.91	28.04	28.05	28.06	28.10	27.98	28.06	
	MEAN SEA-LEVEL PRESS. (IN.)	30.26	30.13	29.93	29.93		29.95	29.97	29.98	30.06	29.96			
WINDS	RESULTANT SPEED (MPH)	1.4	1.9	2.4	1.7	2.1	2.9	1.5	3.1	6.5	3.3	4.9	5.9	1.4
	RES. DIR. (TENS OF DEGS.)	32	26	31	32	19	17	11	14	17	17	28	28	22
	MEAN SPEED (MPH)	10.5	10.1	11.8	12.8	12.4	11.4	10.6	8.2	11.7	11.1	13.3	11.2	11.3
	PREVAIL.DIR.(TENS OF DEGS.)	17	17	32	15	17	16	17	16	16	16	32	29	16
	MAXIMUM 2-MINUTE WIND:													
	SPEED (MPH)	41	35	48	38	45	49	43	30	36	40	55	41	55
	DIR. (TENS OF DEGS.)	32	33	33	34	06	31	34	29	35	28	32	32	32
	DATE OF OCCURRENCE	22+	28	10	22	11+	21	01	26+	28	05	28	15	NOV 28
	MAXIMUM 5-SECOND WIND:													
	SPEED (MPH)	52	41	60	45	62	56	48	37	44	46	62	52	62
	DIR. (TENS OF DEGS.)	32	33	31	34	29	32	33	21	35	27	32	33	32
	DATE OF OCCURRENCE	22	28	10	22	10	21	01	17	28	05	28	15	NOV 28
PRECIPITATION	WATER EQUIVALENT:													
	TOTAL (IN.)	0.76	0.86	1.54	1.76	8.51	4.11	2.51	3.77	1.10	2.49	0.99	0.47	28.87
	GREATEST 24-HOUR (IN.)	0.52	0.41	0.85	0.91	7.21	1.57	1.44	1.06	0.65	1.71	0.51	0.28	7.21
	DATE OF OCCURRENCE	04-05	12-13	21-22	10	11-12	21	17	12	05	19-20	27-28	03	MAY 11-12
	NUMBER OF DAYS WITH:													
	PRECIPITATION ≥ 0.01	7	7	7	11	8	9	3	10	3	7	7	5	84
	PRECIPITATION ≥ 0.10	2	3	4	5	5	7	3	7	2	5	4	2	49
	PRECIPITATION ≥ 1.00	0	0	0	0	1	1	1	2	0	1	0	0	6
SNOWFALL	SNOW,ICE PELLETS,HAIL:													
	TOTAL (IN.)	10.7	4.6	0.5	T	0.0	0.0	0.0	0.0	0.0	T	2.8	5.0	23.6
	GREATEST 24-HOUR (IN.)	5.6	2.1	0.3	T	0.0	0.0	0.0	0.0	0.0	T	2.0	4.0	5.6
	DATE OF OCCURRENCE	04	06	22	30+						22	28	03	JAN 04
	MAXIMUM SNOW DEPTH (IN.)	7	3	T	0	0	0	0	0	0	0	3	7	7
	DATE OF OCCURRENCE	18+	10+	26								29	10+	DEC 10+
	NUMBER OF DAYS WITH:													
	SNOWFALL ≥ 1.0	3	3	0	0	0	0	0	0	0	0	1	1	8

published by: NCDC Asheville, NC   2

Figure 2. Grand Island LCD Meteorological Data for 2005.

Examine page 3 (Figure 3) of the *LCD, Annual Summary* entitled "NORMALS, MEANS, AND EXTREMES". "Normals" are averages of individual weather elements over a fixed period of time, usually 30 years. Normals for this *LCD* were based on 1971-2000. "Mean" values are averages for the entire period of record of the weather element. Respond to the following:

16. The normal monthly temperatures (Normal Dry Bulb) range from a low of 22.4 °F in January to a high of _____ °F in the month of _____ in Grand Island, NE.

17. The Highest Daily Maximum temperature ever recorded at Grand Island was _____ °F in August 1983.

18. The mean number of days per year with thunderstorms is _____.

19. Over the year the mean wind speed is _____ mph from a direction coded as *18* (tens of degrees measured clockwise from north), meaning from the south.

20. The normal yearly total precipitation is _____ inches.

21. This is [(***less than***) (***equal to***) (***more than***)] the total for 2005 (Figure 2).

22. By way of notable events, the Maximum in 24 Hours of <u>Precipitation</u> was _____ (in.) that occurred in May 2005.

23. The normal number of days with <u>Snowfall</u> of one inch or greater is _____.

24. Also included as part of the *LCD, Annual Summary* is a brief narrative describing the location and climatic aspects of the area surrounding the local NWS office. According to the Grand Island description in Figure 4, its climate is described as primarily "_____" in nature.

25. Incursions of maritime tropical air from the Gulf of Mexico [(***do***) (***do not***)] make it to Grand Island.

26. Grand Island's east-west upslope terrain produces episodes of _____ when winds are from the east.

27. Meanwhile warm and dry winds from the _____, called a _____, may occasionally bring dust storms.

As directed by your course instructor, complete this investigation by either:

1. *Going to the Current Weather Studies link on the course website, or*
2. *Continuing to the Applications section for this investigation that immediately follows in this Investigations Manual.*